THEN
SINGS
MY SOUL

300 *of the* WORLD'S GREATEST
HYMN STORIES

THEN
SINGS
MY SOUL

THOMAS NELSON
Since 1798

NASHVILLE DALLAS MEXICO CITY RIO DE JANEIRO BEIJING

© 2006 Robert J. Morgan

Published in Nashville, Tennessee, by Thomas Nelson, Inc.

Thomas Nelson, Inc. titles may be purchased in bulk for educational, business, fund-raising, or sales promotional use. For information, please e-mail SpecialMarkets@thomasnelson.com.

ISBN 978-0-8499-2042-4

Printed in China

Library of Congress Cataloging-in-Publication-Data is available.

To Corinna

Table of Contents

xii

INDICES

From the Publisher...

The volume in front of you brings together the entire contents of *Then Sings My Soul, Volumes 1* and *2,* in a new, easy-to-read, lay-flat binding. We expect it to become a permanent fixture on music stands and piano benches all over the world.

This is another way of saying that—as well-received as both earlier volumes were—this one might find its way into even more homes and places of worship.

But why? Granted, because this version will stay open by itself, those who want to play the music as they work their way through will find both hands free. Yet that doesn't explain how we got to this point in the first place, with a book just begging to be re-issued in a larger, more user-friendly format. What was it about the originals that resonated so powerfully with so many people?

It wouldn't be hard to make a case for Rob Morgan, the author. His writing talent, his keen sensitivity to the great music of the church, and the care he took in pulling the pieces together all contribute to an immensely readable, engaging work.

We might also make a case for the 300 hymns themselves. Powerful music of praise, quiet music of devotion, deeply moving music of worship—somehow these all help us communicate with God in ways that words alone can neither equal nor explain.

On the other hand, when finally we *do* communicate directly with Him, sometimes we give ourselves too much credit. Is it not God Himself who speaks to us in great music? God Himself who speaks to us in mighty words of praise and exhortation? God Himself who speaks to us through the stories of His own people, ancient and modern, flawed and failing and profoundly unworthy yet able, somehow, to bring about His will?

Music, lyrics, words of explanation—to do His work they must carry with them a tiny portion of God Himself. Yet even the tiniest bit of His presence is sufficient to raise our eyes and open our hearts to behold Him in our midst, smiling and listening and blessing us for reaching toward Him in all the ways He has given us.

Maybe that is what these great hymns are all about.

Preface to the New Edition

I recently received a delightful letter from a woman in Minnesota who wrote, "My mother tells me that when she was nursing me (back in 1959, when breast-feeding was not the norm), she sang all the way through the Lutheran hymnal, start to finish. I've grown up very fond of the Lutheran hymnody, sang in church and church-college choir all the way through, am now a member of our small but strong adult choir at church, and direct the youth choir for our congregation."

Not many children are raised on the great hymns anymore, but there's a heartening resurgence in Christian hymnody and I'm praying that this volume of hymns and hymn stories will find its way into many homes and hearts.

The great hymns of the Christian faith communicate the truths of Scripture in singable form. They take the infallible assertions of God, convert them to verses, and drop them into our hearts like internal symphonies. The great hymns are an assorted collection of dearest friends who enter our homes as live-in guests to comfort us in trial, strengthen us in temptation, and enrapture us in praise.

These hymns remind us of God's promises when we're too weary to open our Bibles, and they relax our hearts when we're too worried to sleep. They frame our praise, word our prayers, express our faith, and harmonize our hearts. They reinforce our faith with the bracing timbers of God's Word while repelling the attacks of the enemy.

I agree with Amy Carmichael, the renowned missionary to India, who wrote a friend, saying, "I wonder if you feel as I do about the heavenliness of song. I believe truly that Satan cannot endure it, and so slips out of the room—more or less!—when there is true song."*

When I rise in the morning in a grumpy mood, I can usually adjust my attitude with a verse or two of "When Morning Gilds the Skies." When I'm troubled at night, I comfort myself with ""What a Friend We Have in Jesus." When I'm uncertain of a decision I've made, I find reassurance in "All the Way My Savior Leads Me." When I'm washing the supper dishes, I can turn the kitchen sink into a chapel with just a verse of "How Great Thou Art!"

. . . or perhaps "El Shaddai" or "Lord, I Life Your Name on High." We can make room for the new songs without abandoning the old hymns. One man sent me a note saying he loves the old hymns but can't stand modern praise and worship music. I wrote back reminding him that if we ever raise a generation of believers which doesn't write its own music, Christianity is dead. Every era needs to compose its own songs to God, and the music of the younger generation will seldom sound like that of the

---

*Quoted by Frank L. Houghton, *Amy Carmichael of Dohnavur* (Fort Washington, PA: Christian Literature Crusade, 1953), p. 354.

older one. Just ask Isaac Watts, the father of English hymnody, whose elders railed against his new-fangled hymns.

I love today's new-fangled praise music; I just don't want to lose the old-fashioned hymns! They're a short-cut to our heritage and one of the greatest legacies of our Christian history. How tragic if all our hymns suddenly disappeared (as they have in some churches).

I still want to crown Him with many crowns, to stand on the promises and lean on the everlasting arms, to rescue the perishing and care for the dying, and to turn my eyes upon Jesus. I still need a fountain filled with blood, grace greater than all my sins, the old rugged cross, and a little talk with Jesus.

Hymns like these don't belong in our museums; they belong in our mouths. So sing to the Lord a new song, but don't forget the old ones. They enable us to "rejoice, give thanks, and sing, and triumph evermore."

Lift up your heart, lift up your voice,
Rejoice, again I say, rejoice!

THEN
SINGS
MY SOUL

The Lord Bless You and Keep You

Numbers 6:24–26

Peter C. Lutkin

The Lord Bless You and Keep You

FOURTEENTH CENTURY BC

The LORD bless you and keep you; the LORD make His face shine upon you, and be gracious to you; the LORD lift up His countenance upon you, and give you peace.
Numbers 6:24–26

T he Dead Sea Scrolls were, until recently, our oldest copies of biblical text. But in 1979, Villanova professor, Judith Hadley, was assisting archaeologist, Gabriel Barkay, in excavating a site in Jerusalem's Hinnom Valley. In a burial cave, she saw something resembling the metal cap of a pencil. It was a sensational find, a tiny silver scroll of great antiquity. Another was found nearby. These tiny amulets, dating to the Hebrew monarchy seven centuries before Christ, were so small and fragile they took several years to painstakingly clean and open.

When scientists finally unrolled them, they found the world's oldest extant copy of a biblical text, the words of Numbers 6:24–26: *The LORD bless you and keep you; The LORD make His face shine upon you, and be gracious to you; the LORD lift up His countenance upon you, and give you peace.*

While the amulets date from the seventh century BC, the original words are far older, coming 1,400 years before Christ. As the Israelites wandered in the wilderness, the Lord commanded the priests to bless the people with this three-fold blessing.

These ancient lyrics have been set to music many times, but never more beautifully than by Peter Christian Lutkin in his classic tune BENEDICTION. During the Fanny Crosby/Ira Sankey era of gospel music, when so much was written for easy congregational singing, Lutkin wrote more elaborate melodies with a classical flare.

Lutkin was born in Wisconsin in 1888, and devoted his life to church music, studying the masters in Europe, excelling on the organ, and founding the School of Music at Northwestern Illinois. He helped start the American Guild of Organists. He died in 1931 and was buried in Rosehill Cemetery in Chicago.

In his *Notes from My Bible*, D. L. Moody said about the priestly blessing of Numbers 6: "Here is a benediction that can give all the time without being impoverished. Every heart may utter it, every letter may conclude with it, every day may begin with it, every night may be sanctified by it. Here is blessing—keeping—shining—the uplifting upon our poor life of all heaven's glad morning. It is the Lord Himself who (gives us) this bar of music from heaven's infinite anthem."

The LORD bless you and keep you;
The LORD make His face shine upon you, and be gracious to you;
The LORD lift up His countenance upon you, and give you peace.

Be Thou My Vision

Irish Hymn, c. 8th Century

Irish Folk Melody

1. Be thou my Vi - sion, O Lord of my heart;
2. Be thou my Wis-dom, and thou my true Word;
3. Rich - es I heed not, nor man's emp - ty praise;
4. High King of heav - en, my vic - to - ry won,

Naught be all else to me, save that thou art;
I ev - er with thee and thou with me, Lord;
Thou mine in - her - i - tance, now and al - ways;
May I reach heav - en's joys, O bright heaven's Sun!

Thou my best thought, by day or by night,
Thou my great Fa - ther, and I thy true son,
Thou and thou on - ly, first in my heart,
Heart of my own heart, what - ev - er be - fall,

Wak - ing or sleep - ing, thy pres - ence my light.
Thou in my dwell - ing, and I with thee one.
High King of heav - en, my trea - sure thou art.
Still be my Vi - sion, O Rul - er of all.

Be Thou My Vision

EIGHTH CENTURY

Go therefore and make disciples of all the nations, baptizing them in the name of the Father and of the Son and of the Holy Spirit. Matthew 28:19

Only one missionary is honored with a global holiday, and only one is known by his own distinct color of green—St. Patrick, of course, missionary to Ireland.

Patrick was born in AD 373, along the banks of the River Clyde in what is now called Scotland. His father was a deacon, and his grandfather a priest. When Patrick was about 16, raiders descended on his little town and torched his home. When one of the pirates spotted him in the bushes, he was seized, hauled aboard ship, and taken to Ireland as a slave. There he gave his life to the Lord Jesus.

"The Lord opened my mind to an awareness of my unbelief," he later wrote, "in order that I might remember my transgressions and turn with all my heart to the Lord my God."

Patrick eventually escaped and returned home. His overjoyed family begged him to never leave again. But one night, in a dream reminiscent of Paul's vision of the Macedonian Man in Acts 16, Patrick saw an Irishman pleading with him to come evangelize Ireland.

It wasn't an easy decision, but Patrick, about 30, returned to his former captors with only one book, the Latin Bible, in his hand. As he evangelized the countryside, multitudes came to listen. The superstitious Druids opposed him and sought his death. But his preaching was powerful, and Patrick became one of the most fruitful evangelists of all time, planting about 200 churches and baptizing 100,000 converts.

His work endured, and several centuries later, the Irish church was still producing hymns, prayers, sermons, and songs of worship. In the eighth century, an unknown poet wrote a prayer asking God to be his Vision, his Wisdom, and his Best Thought by day or night.

In 1905, Mary Elizabeth Byrne, a scholar in Dublin, Ireland, translated this ancient Irish poem into English. Another scholar, Eleanor Hull of Manchester, England, took Byrne's translation and crafted it into verses with rhyme and meter. Shortly thereafter it was set to a traditional Irish folk song, "Slane," named for an area in Ireland where Patrick reportedly challenged local Druids with the gospel.

It is one of our oldest and most moving hymns:

> *Be Thou my vision, O Lord of my heart,*
> *Naught be all else to me save that Thou art.*
> *Thou my best thought by day or by night,*
> *Waking or sleeping, Thy presence my light.*

All Glory, Laud, and Honor

Theodulph of Orleans

Melchior Teschner

1. All glory, laud, and hon-or To Thee, Re-deem-er, King.
2. The com-pa-ny of an-gels Are prais-ing Thee on high,
3. To Thee, be-fore Thy pas-sion, They sang their hymns of praise;

To whom the lips of chil-dren Made sweet ho-san-nas ring.
And mor-tal men and all things Cre-a-ted make re-ply.
To Thee, now high ex-alt-ed, Our mel-o-dy we raise.

Thou art the King of Is-ra-el, Thou Da-vid's roy-al Son,
The peo-ple of the He-brews With palms be-fore Thee went;
Thou didst ac-cept their prais-es; Ac-cept the praise we bring,

Who in the Lord's name com-est, The King and Bless-ed One.
Our praise and prayer and an-thems Be-fore Thee we pre-sent.
Who in all good de-light-est, Thou good and gra-cious King.

All Glory, Laud, and Honor

AD 820

Behold, your King is coming to you; He is just and having salvation, lowly and riding on a donkey, a colt, the foal of a donkey. Zechariah 9:9

The mighty Charlemagne (742–814), King of the Franks, united most of western Europe under his crown. He was a visionary who advanced education and reformed the laws, economy, and culture of Europe.

When Charlemagne died, his son, Louis I, assumed the throne. At first, all went well. But in 817, he began dividing the empire among his nephew and his four sons, causing no end of problems. Twice he was deposed by his sons, and, though he regained his throne both times, he was never again able to rest securely.

Caught in the middle of this epic family conflict was Theodulph, Bishop of Orleans, a city south of Paris. Theodulph, born in Spain about 750, had gone to France as a church leader at Charlemagne's request. He was a brilliant man who worked hard to reform the clergy. He established schools and advanced education. He advocated high morals, built churches, and composed hymns of praise to God.

But during the political intrigues of Louis' reign, Theodulph was accused (falsely, it seems) of conspiring with King Bernard of Italy; and on Easter Sunday, 818, he was imprisoned in the monastery of Angers, a city southwest of Paris.

There, as he meditated on our Lord's triumphal entry into Jerusalem prior to His Crucifixion and Resurrection, Theodulph wrote the great Palm Sunday hymn, "All Glory, Laud, and Honor."

According to a tradition that can be neither confirmed nor denied, when King Louis later visited Angers, he momentarily halted by the monastery where Theodulph was held, and the bishop appeared at the window, singing "All Glory, Laud and Honor." The king was reportedly so moved that he ordered the bishop's release.

For whatever reason, we know Theodulph *was* released in 821, but he died on his way back to Orleans, or shortly after his return there.

Originally there were 78 verses (39 couplets) to this hymn! Theodulph had lots of time in his prison-monastery. The first several are the ones we commonly sing today. One stanza that has fallen by the wayside is this quaint verse:

> *Be Thou, O Lord, the Rider,*
> *And we the little ass,*
> *That to God's holy city*
> *Together we may pass.*

Jesus, the Very Thought of Thee

Att. to Bernard of Clairvaux

John B. Dykes

1. Je - sus, the ver - y thought of Thee
2. No voice can sing, no heart can frame,
3. O hope of ev - ery con - trite heart,
4. Je - sus, our on - ly joy be Thou,

With sweet - ness fills my breast;
Nor can the mem - 'ry find
O joy of all the meek,
As Thou our prize wilt be;

But sweet - er far Thy face to see
A sweet - er sound than Thy blest name,
To those who fall, how kind Thou art!
Je - sus, be Thou our glo - ry now

And in Thy pres - ence rest.
O Sav - ior of man - kind.
How good to those who seek.
And thro' e - ter - ni - ty.

Jesus, the Very Thought of Thee

TWELFTH CENTURY

These things I have spoken to you, that in Me you may have peace. In the world you will have tribulation; but be of good cheer, I have overcome the world. John 16:33

When Bernard (c. 1090–1153), a sickly youth in Dijon, France, was unable to fulfill military service, he became a monk. So successful was he that he eventually founded the famous monastery in nearby Clairvaux; in time almost 170 other monasteries sprang from Bernard's leadership. He became the most powerful preacher of his era, and is remembered as a pious man, a deeply contemplative mystic, the "honey-tongued doctor." Martin Luther called Bernard "the best monk that ever lived, whom I admire beyond all the rest put together."

He wasn't a perfect man, as seen in his support for the Second Crusade to liberate the Holy Land from Muslim control. But for 800 years, his words have been read and sung, and his good work has continued.

If you've never read Bernard, here are some excerpts from his writings and sermons:

- How do we know that Christ has really overcome death? Precisely in that he, who did not deserve it, underwent it . . . . But what kind of justice is this, you may say, that the innocent should die for the guilty? It is not justice, but mercy.
- I was made a sinner by deriving my being from Adam; I am made righteous by being washed in the blood of Christ.
- You will never have real mercy for the failings of another until you know and realize that you have the same failings in your soul.
- Thank you, Lord Jesus, for your kindness in uniting us to the church you so dearly love, not merely that we may be endowed with the gift of faith, but that, like brides, we may be one with you . . . , beholding with unveiled faces that glory which is yours in union with the Father and the Holy Spirit forever and ever. Amen.
- You wish me to tell you why and how God should be loved. My answer is that God Himself is the reason He is to be loved.

Several well-known hymns are attributed to St. Bernard: "Jesus, the Very Thought of Thee," "O Sacred Head Now Wounded," and a lesser-known hymn entitled "Open Wide are Thine Hands," the second verse of which says:

Lord, I am sad and poor, but boundless is Thy grace;
Give me the soul transforming joy for which I seek Thy face.

O Sacred Head, Now Wounded

Based on Medieval Latin poem
Ascribed to Bernard of Clairvaux

Hans Leo Hassler
Harm. by J.S. Bach

1. O   sa - cred Head now wound - ed, With   grief and shame weighed down,
2. What Thou, my Lord hast suf - fered Was   all   for sin - ners' gain:
3. What lan - guage shall I   bor - row To   thank thee, dear - est Friend,

Now   scorn - ful - ly   sur - round - ed With thorns, Thine on - ly crown;
Mine,   mine was the   trans - gres - sion, But Thine the dead - ly pain;
For   this thy dy - ing   sor - row, Thy   pit - y   with - out end?

How   pale thou art with   an - guish, with   sore a - buse and scorn!
Lo,   here I fall, my   Sav - ior! 'Tis   I   de - serve Thy place;
O   make me thine for - ev - er, And   should I faint - ing be,

How   does that vis - age   lan - guish Which once was bright as   morn!
Look   on me with Thy   fa - vor, Vouch - safe to me Thy   grace.
Lord,   let me nev - er,   nev - er Out - live my love to   thee.

O Sacred Head, Now Wounded

1153

Oh, give thanks to the LORD, for He is good! For His mercy endures forever. Psalm 118:1

Bernard was born into a knight's family in a French castle in 1090. He was educated in the fashion of medieval aristocracy, but he later felt the Lord calling him to the monastic ministry. Being a born leader, he arrived at the monastery of Cîteaux with thirty other young men whom he had persuaded to join him.

Three years later, Bernard, twenty-five, founded his own monastery at Clairvaux, a town near the Swiss border. Here he would remain the rest of his life. He was a brilliant monk, and in time he advised kings and popes from his monastic cell. Historian Harold O. J. Brown wrote, "The ability of one man without political office or power to change history solely by his teaching and example is without parallel until the sixteenth century when Martin Luther would once again transform Europe from his pulpit and professor's chair in a small town in Saxony."

Bernard fought heresy and helped preserve the doctrine of the Trinity. Yet he also supported Christian military orders such as the Knights Templar—soldiers living under monastic discipline who fought to preserve European Christianity and fight Muslims in the Holy Land. He advocated a militant faith that depended on both sword and Spirit.

This man, then, is a paradox to us. We don't know whether to claim him or disdain him. Perhaps it's best to leave that judgment to God and to appreciate him for his songs, such as this pensive hymn on the sufferings of Christ, "O Sacred Head, Now Wounded."

Here are two lesser-known verses of this hymn. Transport yourself to Bernard's cloister, and hear these words echoing through the dimly lit corridors of the monastery. Consider what the Lord did for you during His six hours on Zion's cross.

> *Now from Thy cheeks has vanished their color once so fair;*
> *From Thy red lips is banished the splendor that was there.*
> *Grim death, with cruel rigor, hath robbed Thee of Thy life;*
> *Thus Thou hast lost Thy vigor, Thy strength in this sad strife.*

> *My burden in Thy Passion, Lord, Thou hast borne for me,*
> *For it was my transgression which brought this woe on Thee.*
> *I cast me down before Thee, wrath were my rightful lot;*
> *Have mercy, I implore Thee; Redeemer, spurn me not!*

All Creatures of Our God and King

St. Francis of Assisi

Geistliche Kirchengesänge Cologne

1. All crea-tures of our God and King, Lift up your voice and with us
2. Let all things their Cre - a - tor bless, And wor-ship Him in hum-ble-

sing, Al -le - lu - ia! Al -le - lu - ia! Thou burn-ing sun with
ness. O praise Him! Al -le - lu - ia! Praise, praise the Fa - ther,

gold - en beam, Thou sil - ver moon with soft - er gleam, O praise Him
praise the Son, And praise the spir - it, Three in One! O praise Him

O praise Him! Al -le - lu - ia! Al -le - lu - ia! Al -le - lu - ia!

All Creatures of Our God and King

1225

I tell you that if these should keep silent, the stones would immediately cry out.
Luke 19:40

So many stories have arisen around St. Francis of Assisi that it's difficult to separate truth from fiction. We know he was born in 1182 in central Italy, son of a rich merchant. After a scanty education, Francis joined the army and was captured in war. He came to Christ shortly after his release, renounced his wealth, and began traveling about the countryside, preaching the gospel, living simply, seeking to make Christ real to everyone he met.

Francis loved nature, and many stories spotlight his interaction with animals. Once as he hiked through Italy's Spoleto Valley, he came upon a flock of birds. When they didn't fly away, he decided to preach them a little sermon: "My brother and sister birds," he reportedly said, "you should praise your Creator and always love Him. He gave you feathers for clothes, wings to fly, and all other things you need. It is God who made your home in thin, pure air. Without sowing or reaping, you receive God's guidance and protection."

The flock, it is said, then flew off rejoicing.

That perspective is reflected in a hymn Francis composed just before his death in 1225, called, "Cantico di fratre sole"—"Song of Brother Sun." It exhorts all creation to worship God. The sun and moon. All the birds. All the clouds. Wind and fire. All men of tender heart. All creatures of our God and King.

Though written in 1225, an English version didn't appear until 1919, when Rev. William H. Draper decided to use it for a children's worship festival in Leeds, England.

But is it sound theology to exhort birds and billowing clouds to lift their voices in praise? Yes! "All Creatures of our God and King" simply restates an older hymn—Psalm 148—which says:

Praise Him, sun and moon; / Praise Him, all you stars of light . . . . /
You great sea creatures and all the depths; / Fire and hail, snow and clouds; /
Stormy wind, fulfilling His word; / Mountains and all hills; /
Fruitful trees and all cedars; / Beasts and all cattle; /
Creeping things and flying fowl . . . / Let them praise the name of the LORD, /
For His name alone is exalted . . . / Praise the LORD!

The God of Abraham Praise

Thomas Olivers

Traditional Hebrew Melody

1. The God of A-br'ham praise, Who reigns en-throned a-bove,
2. He by Him-self hath sworn; We on His oath de-pend.
3. The God who reigns on high The great arch-an-gels sing,
4. The whole tri-um-phant host Give thanks to God on high;

The An-cient of e-ter-nal days And God of love.
We shall, on ea-gles' wings up-borne, To heav'n as-cend.
And "Ho-ly, ho-ly, ho-ly," cry, "Al-might-y King!"
"Hail, Fa-ther, Son and Ho-ly Ghost!" They ev-er cry.

Je-ho-vah, great I AM, By earth and heav'n con-fessed:
We shall be-hold His face; We shall His pow'r a-dore
Who was and is the same And ev-er-more shall be;
Hail, A-br'ham's God and mine! With heav'n our songs we raise:

We bow and bless the sa-cred name For-ev-er blest.
And sing the won-ders of His grace For-ev-er-more.
E-ter-nal Fa-ther, great I AM, We wor-ship Thee.
All might and maj-es-ty are Thine And end-less praise.

The God of Abraham Praise

1404/1770

I am the God of your father—the God of Abraham . . . Exodus 3:6

The God of Abraham Praise" is perhaps the most Jewish of all Christian hymns, and its writing covers many centuries. Its roots go back to the medieval Jewish scholar Moses Maimonides (1135–1204), who wrote a confession of faith containing thirteen creeds.

Centuries later, in 1404, another Jewish scholar, Daniel ben Judah, a judge and liturgical poet in Rome, deeply impressed with Maimonides' creed, composed the *Yigdal*, a doxology of thirteen stanzas widely sung in Jewish synagogues to this day.

Centuries later, in 1770, an opera vocalist named Meyer Lyon sang the *Yigdal* in London's Great Synagogue, Duke's Place. In the audience that night was Thomas Olivers.

Thomas (1725–1799) had been born in Tregynon, Wales, and orphaned about age four. He studied the craft of shoemaking, but he learned the art of sinning better, "the worst boy known in Tregynon for thirty years."

When he was eighteen, Thomas was thrown out of town, and he wandered down to Bristol, England, where evangelist George Whitefield happened to be preaching from Zechariah 3:2: "Is not this a brand plucked out of the fire?"

"When that sermon began," Thomas recalled, "I was one of the most abandoned and profligate young men living; before it ended I was a new creature. The world had changed for Tom Olivers." He became a traveling evangelist and passionate Christian worker.

On that Sabbath evening in 1770, when Thomas heard Meyer Lyon sing the *Yigdal*, he was so moved that he later approached Lyon, acquired the music, and adapted the Jewish Doxology into a Christian hymn of thirteen stanzas, beginning, "The God of Abraham Praise."

"Look at this," he told a friend, "I have rendered it from the Hebrew, giving it, as far as I could, a Christian character." Thomas annotated his hymn with footnotes, citing Scripture references for almost every line, the first being Exodus 3:6: "I am the God of thy Father, the God of Abraham." It appeared in 1785 in John Wesley's *Pocket Hymnbook*.

Modern congregations don't have the patience to sing all thirteen stanzas, so here is one of the lesser-known verses for you to ponder:

The God Who reigns on high the great archangels sing,
And "Holy, holy, holy!" cry, "Almighty King!"
Who was, and is, the same, and evermore shall be:
Jehovah, Lord, the great I AM, we worship Thee!

A Mighty Fortress Is Our God

Martin Luther   Martin Luther

1. A might-y for-tress is our God. A bul-wark nev-er fail - ing;
2. Did we in our own strength con-fide, Our striv-ing wouldbe los - ing,
3. And though this world with dev - ils filled, Should threat-en to un-do us,
4. That word a-bove all earth - ly powers, No thanks to them, a-bid - eth;

Our helper He a-mid the flood Of mor-tal ills pre - vail - ing.
Were not the right man on our side, The man of God's own choos - ing.
We will not fear, for God hath willed, His truth to tri - umph through us.
The Spir-it and the gifts are ours Through Him who with us sid - eth.

For still our an-cient foe Doth seek to work us woe- His craft and power are
Dost ask who that may be? Christ Je-sus, it is He- Lord Sab - a - oth His
The prince of dark-ness grim, We trem-ble not for him- His rage we can en-
Let goods and kin-dred go, This mor-tal life al - so- The bo - dy they may

great, And, armed with cru - el hate, On earth is not His e - qual.
name, From age to age the same, And He must win the bat - tle.
dure, For lo, his doom is sure: One lit - tle word shall fell him.
kill; God's truth a - bid-eth still: His king-dom is for-ev - er.

A Mighty Fortress Is Our God

1529

God is our refuge and strength, a very present help in trouble. Psalm 46:1

W e think of Martin Luther as a great reformer, Bible translator, political leader, fiery preacher, and theologian. But he was also a musician, having been born in an area of Germany known for its music. There in his little Thuringian village, young Martin grew up listening to his mother sing. He joined a boys' choir that sang at weddings and funerals. He became proficient with the flute (recorder), and his volcanic emotions often erupted in song.

When the Protestant Reformation began, Luther determined to restore worship to the German Church. He worked with skilled musicians to create new music for Christians, to be sung in the vernacular. He helped revive congregational singing and wrote a number of hymns.

Often he "borrowed" popular secular melodies for his hymns, though occasionally a tune brought criticism and he was "compelled to let the devil have it back again" because it was too closely associated with bars and taverns.

In the forward of a book, Luther once wrote: "Next to the Word of God, the noble art of music is the greatest treasure in the world. It controls our thoughts, minds, hearts, and spirits . . . . A person who . . . does not regard music as a marvelous creation of God . . . does not deserve to be called a human being; he should be permitted to hear nothing but the braying of asses and the grunting of hogs."

Luther's most famous hymn is "Ein' feste Burg ist unser Gott,"—"A Mighty Fortress Is Our God." Based on Psalm 46, it reflects Luther's awareness of our intense struggle with Satan. In difficulty and danger, Luther would often resort to this song, saying to his associate, "Come, Philipp, let us sing the 46th Psalm."

This is a difficult hymn to translate because the original German is so vivid. At least 80 English versions are available. The most popular in America was done by Frederic Henry Hodge. But an older version appeared in the Pennsylvania Lutheran Church Book of 1868:

A mighty fortress is our God, | A trusty Shield and Weapon; |
He helps us free from every need, | That hath us now o'ertaken.

The British version of "A Mighty Fortress" is Thomas Carlyle's translation:

A safe stronghold our God is still, | A trusty shield and weapon; |
He'll help us clear from all the ill | That hath us now o'ertaken.

From Heaven Above to Earth I Come

Martin Luther, translated by Catherine Windworth

Attr. to Martin Luther

1. From heav'n a - bove to earth I come, to bear good news to ev - ery home; glad tid - ings of great joy I bring, Where - of I now will say and sing.

2. To you, this night, is born a Child Of Mar - y, chos - en moth - er mild; This ten - der Child of low - ly birth, Shall be the joy of all your earth.

3. 'Tis Christ our God, who far on high Had heard your sad and bit - ter cry; Him - self will your Sal - va - tion be, Him - self from sin will make you free.

4. These are the to - kens ye shall mark, The swad - dling clothes and man - ger dark; There shall ye find the young Child laid, By Whom the heav'ns and earth were made.

From Heaven Above to Earth I Come

1531

Then God blessed them, and God said to them, "Be fruitful and multiply; fill the earth and subdue it . . ." Genesis 1:28

Martin Luther never expected to marry, for he had taken a vow of celibacy as an Augustinian monk. Even after discovering the great Reformation truths of *Scripture Alone, Faith Alone*, he still intended to keep his vow. As the Reformation picked up steam and other monks began to marry, he exclaimed, "Good heavens! They won't give me a wife."

It wasn't just monks who were renouncing their celibacy, however; it was nuns, too. When Luther heard that a group of nuns from a nearby cloister wanted to escape their situation (which amounted to virtual captivity) he agreed to help them, though doing so was a serious violation of the law. Enlisting the aid of a local merchant named Leonard Kopp, sixty, Luther arranged for the nuns to be smuggled out in the empty barrels used to deliver herring to the nunnery. It was a fishy plan if ever there was one, but it worked.

Having liberated these women, Luther now felt responsible for placing them in homes. He managed to find husbands for all but one—Katharina Von Bora. Two years passed, and Luther was deeply troubled by his failure to find her a husband. She was now twenty-six years old, brilliant and effervescent, but still unclaimed.

In a visit to his parents, Luther, forty-two, joked that he might have to marry Katharina himself. His dad heartily endorsed the idea, and, to make a long story short, the two were married on June 27, 1525.

By autumn, Katharina informed Martin that she was pregnant, and Luther cheerfully announced, "My Katharina is fulfilling Genesis 1:28"—the verse about being fruitful and multiplying.

"There's about to be born a child of a monk and a nun," he bragged to friends. Accordingly, little Hans was born on June 7, 1526.

Luther was devoted to his son, and five years later he wrote this Christmas carol for him. Luther called it "a Christmas child's song concerning the child Jesus," and it was sung each year during the Christmas Eve festivities at Luther's massive home—a former Augustinian monastery—on the upper end of Wittenberg's main street.

For over five hundred years it has been one of Lutheranism's greatest carols, delighting children today just as it thrilled little Hans in the sixteenth century.

All People That on Earth Do Dwell

William Kethe

Genevan Psalter

1. All peo - ple that on earth do dwell,
2. The Lord, ye know, is God in - deed,
3. O, en - ter then His gates with praise,
4. For why? The Lord our God is good,

Sing to the Lord with cheer - ful voice;
With - out our aid He did us make;
Ap - proach with joy His courts un - to;
His mer - cy is for - ev - er sure;

Him serve with mirth His praise forth tell,
We are His flock, He doth us feed,
Praise laud and bless His Name al - ways,
His truth at all times firm - ly stood,

Come ye be - fore Him and re - joice.
And for His sheep He doth us take.
For it is seem - ly so to do.
And shall from age to age en - dure.

All People That on Earth Do Dwell

1561

Serve the LORD *with gladness; Come before His presence with singing.* Psalm 100:2

Disagreements about church music are nothing new. When the Reformation swept across Europe in the 1500s, there was a division among Protestants concerning congregational singing. Some of the Reformers, like Martin Luther of Germany, advocated singing hymns and carols. Others, like John Calvin of Geneva, thought that only the Psalms of David should be sung.

Calvin had been born in Noyon, France, in 1509, and educated at the University of Paris. In 1533, he experienced a "sudden conversion" that changed the course of his life. Joining a group of Protestants in Paris, his brilliance and preaching skills elevated him to leadership in the French Protestant movement. That same year, anti-Reformation riots drove him from Paris and he eventually settled in Geneva, Switzerland, which became a center of Reformation life through his ministry.

Calvin was a fierce advocate for the use of metrical versions of the Psalms. He felt that church worship should be simple, consisting of prayer, preaching, and the singing of the Psalms. Like Augustine, he believed that a person cannot "sing things worthy of God unless he has received them from Him," and that there are "no better songs nor more appropriate to the purpose than the Psalms of David which the Holy Spirit made and spoke through him."

In 1551, a hymnbook of Psalms was published in Geneva. In it, Psalm 134 was set to a majestic and beautiful melody composed (or adapted) by a man named Louis Bourgeois.

Ten years later another edition of the Psalter was published, and this time the same majestic, stirring tune was used with the words to Psalm 100 as versified by Rev. William Kethe, who had fled his native Scotland during the persecutions of Queen Mary.

Ever since the publication of the 1561 hymnal, this tune has been called "The Old 100th," because of its association with Psalm 100. Christians today know it as the melody to which the Doxology is typically sung ("Praise God from whom all blessings flow"), but for five hundred years, it has been more closely associated with William Kethe's rendition of Psalm 100.

"All People That on Earth Do Dwell" is known as "Calvin's Reformation Hymn." If you know the melody of the Doxology, take time to sing this old hymn and make a joyful noise unto the Lord.

We Gather Together

Anonymous Dutch Hymn

Dutch Folk Song

1. We gath-er to-geth-er to ask the Lord's bless-ing;
2. Be-side us to guide us, our God with us join-ing,
3. We all do ex-tol Thee, Thou Lead-er tri-um-phant,

He chas-tens and has-tens His will to make known;
Or-dain-ing, main-tain-ing His king-dom di-vine;
And pray that Thou still our De-fend-er wilt be.

The wick-ed op-press-ing now cease from dis-tress-ing,
So from the be-gin-ning the fight we were win-ning:
Let Thy con-gre-ga-tion es-cape tri-bu-la-tion:

Sing prais-es to His name: He for-gets not His own.
Thou, Lord, wast at our side, all glo-ry be Thine!
Thy Name be ev-er praised! O Lord, make us free!

We Gather Together

1597

So the nations shall fear the name of the LORD, And all the kings of the earth Your glory. Psalm 102:15

Those who have visited the Netherlands with its picturesque dikes and windmills may be unaware of the terrific struggle for religious freedom that took place there in the sixteenth and seventeenth centuries. In 1555, the Low Country was given to King Philip II of Spain by his father, Emperor Charles V of Germany. Philip was an arch-Catholic, but the winds of Calvinistic Reformation had reached the Netherlands. Roman Catholic churches were plundered, and the authority of Spain was resisted.

In 1557, King Philip sent the dreaded Duke of Alba (Fernando Alvarez de Toledo) to bring the Netherlands back into the Pope's fold. He established a reign of terror during which ten thousand people were executed and another forty thousand exiled. His ruling counsel was called the "Council of Troubles," but it's better known to history as the "Blood Council." The bodies of thousands of people were hung in the streets and on the doorposts of houses. Alva didn't hesitate to massacre whole cities. An attack on Leiden was stopped only by cutting the dikes and flooding the countryside.

On January 6, 1579, the Catholic southern regions of the Netherlands (modern Belgium) declared their allegiance to Philip; but three weeks later the northern part (modern Holland) refused to submit to the Catholic rule of Spain. In 1581, Holland declared its independence, led by the courageous William of Orange. Holland was devastated by warfare, and in the process William was cut down by an assassin's dagger. But the brave nation would not be denied, and eventually Spain lost its hold on the Dutch Republic.

This hymn, "We Gather Together," which Americans associate with their Thanksgiving holiday, was actually written sometime in 1597 to celebrate Holland's freedom from Spain. Its author, an unknown Dutchman, was full of thanksgiving that his people were finally free from Spanish tyranny and free to worship as they chose. Notice how he expressed this theme in these three beautiful verses:

The wicked oppressing now cease from distressing . . .

. . . so from the beginning the fight we were winning;
Thou, Lord, wast at our side, all glory be Thine!

We all do extol Thee, Thou Leader triumphant,
And pray that Thou still our Defender wilt be.
Let Thy congregation escape tribulation:
Thy Name be ever praised! O Lord, make us free!

Now Thank We All Our God

Martin Rinkart

Johann Crüger

1. Now thank we all our God, With heart and hands and voic - es,
2. O may this boun-teous God Through all our life be near us,
3. All praise and thanks to God The Fa - ther now be giv - en,

Who won-drous things hath done, In whom this world re - joic - es;
With ev - er joy - ful hearts And bless - ed peace to cheer us;
The Son, and Him who reigns With them in high-est heav - en,

Who, from our moth-ers' arms, Hath blessed us on our way
And keep us in His grace, And guide us when per - plexed,
The one e - ter - nal God, Whom earth and heav'n a - dore;

With count-less gifts of love, And still is ours to - day.
And free us from all ills In this world and the next.
For thus it was, is now, And shall be ev - er - more.

Now Thank We All Our God

1636

In everything give thanks; for this is the will of God in Christ Jesus for you.
1 Thessalonians 5:18

An old English preacher once said, "A grateful mind is a great mind," and the Bible agrees. There are 138 passages of Scripture on the subject of thanksgiving, and some of them are powerfully worded. Colossians 3:17 says: "And whatever you do in word or deed, do all in the name of the Lord Jesus, giving thanks to God the Father through Him." 1 Thessalonians 5:18 adds, "In everything give thanks; for this is the will of God in Christ Jesus for you."

Unfortunately, few hymns are devoted exclusively to thanking God. Among the small, rich handful we *do* have is "Now Thank We All Our God." The German Christians sing this hymn like American believers sing the "Doxology," yet it's loved on both sides of the Atlantic and around the world.

It was written by Martin Rinkart (1586–1649), a Lutheran pastor in the little village of Eilenberg, Saxony. He grew up as the son of a poor coppersmith, felt called to the ministry, and after his theological training began his pastoral work just as the Thirty Years' War was raging through Germany.

Floods of refugees streamed into the walled city of Eilenberg. It was the most desperate of times. The Swedish army encompassed the city gates, and inside the walls there was nothing but plague, famine, and fear. Eight hundred homes were destroyed, and people began dying in increasing numbers. There was a tremendous strain on the pastors, who expended all their strength in preaching the gospel, caring for the sick and dying, and burying the dead. One after another, the pastors themselves took ill and perished until at last only Martin Rinkart was left. Some days he conducted as many as fifty funerals.

Finally the Swedes demanded a huge ransom. It was Martin Rinkart who left the safety of the city walls to negotiate with the enemy, and he did it with such courage and faith that there was soon a conclusion of hostilities, and the period of suffering ended.

Rinkart, knowing there is no healing without thanksgiving, composed this hymn for the survivors of Eilenberg. It has been sung around the world ever since.

Now thank we all our God, with heart and hands and voices,
Who wondrous things has done, in Whom this world rejoices

If Thou But Suffer God to Guide Thee

Georg Neumark

Georg Neumark

1. If thou but suf - fer God to guide thee, and hope in
2. On - ly be still, and wait His lei - sure in cheer - ful
3. Sing, pray, and keep his ways un - swerv - ing, so do thine

Him through all thy ways, He'll give thee strength, what - e'er be - tide thee,
hope, with heart con - tent To take what - e'er Thy Fa - ther's plea - sure
own part faith - ful - ly; And trust His Word, though un - de - serv - ing,

and bear thee through the e - vil days; Who trusts in God's un -
and all - dis - cern - ing love hath sent; Nor doubt our in - most
thou yet shall find it true for thee; God nev - er yet for -

chang - ing love builds on the Rock that naught can move.
wants are known to Him who chose us for His own.
sook at need the soul that trust - ed Him in - deed.

If Thou But Suffer God to Guide Thee

1641

For this is God, Our God forever and ever; He will be our guide Even to death.
Psalm 48:14

The newer hymnbooks list this as "If You Will Only Let God Guide You." I still like the older, archaic phrasing, since that's the way I learned it; but never mind—it's a glorious hymn, however it's rendered, especially when you know the tender story behind it.

In 1641, a bright German youth, Georg Neumark, twenty, packed his few belongings and left his home in the Thuringian forests. By hard work and frugality, he had saved enough for his first year at the University of Königsberg. Seeking to travel with others because of roving thieves, Georg joined a group of merchants in Leipzig. But after passing through Magdeburg, they were waylaid and robbed on the Gardelegan Heath. Georg lost everything except his prayer book and a few hidden coins.

His university hopes dashed, the young man retraced his way through villages and towns, looking for work. Months passed, and the onset of winter found Georg poorly fed, scantily clothed, cold, and homeless. Just when he was near despair, a pastor named Nicolaus Becker of Kiel befriended him.

Becker wanted to help Georg secure employment, but how? There was nothing. Just then, a position opened unexpectedly—a tutoring job in the home of a local judge named Henning. Georg was hired on the spot, and that very day he composed "If Thou But Suffer God to Guide Thee."

While tutoring, Georg conserved his money, and the next year he proceeded to Königsberg and enrolled in the university on June 21, 1643. Shortly afterward, he again lost everything, this time in a fire. But by now, he had no doubt in God's ability to both guide and provide.

In 1657, "If Thou But Suffer God to Guide Thee" was published in Neumark's own book of songs, set to a melody he himself had written. The seven stanzas were entitled, "A hymn of consolation. That God will care for and preserve His own in His own time—based on the saying, 'Cast Thy burden upon the Lord, and He shall sustain thee' (Psalm 55:22)."

In later years, Neumark recorded the circumstances of the hymn, saying that his "good fortune, coming suddenly as if it had fallen from heaven, greatly rejoiced me, and on that very day I composed to the honor of my beloved Lord the well-known hymn, 'Wer nur den lieben Gott lässt walten.'"

The Lord's My Shepherd

Scottish Psalter, 1650

Jessie S. Irvine

1. The Lord's my shep - herd, I'll not want; He makes me down to lie In pas - tures green; He lead - eth me The qui - et wa - ters by.

2. My soul He doth re - store a - gain, And me to walk doth make With - in the paths of right - eous - ness, E'en for His own name's sake.

3. Yea, though I walk in death's dark vale, Yet will I fear no ill, For Thou art with me, and Thy rod And staff me com - fort still.

4. My ta - ble Thou hast fur - nish - ed In pres - ence of my foes; My head Thou dost with oil a - noint, And my cup o - ver - flows.

The Lord's My Shepherd

1650

The LORD is my shepherd; I shall not want. Psalm 23:1

O ur oldest hymnal is the Book of Psalms, and Christians throughout history have wanted to obey the biblical injunction to praise the Lord using *"psalms,* hymns, and spiritual songs" (Ephesians 5:19; Colossians 3:16).

John Calvin, quoting Augustine, wrote, "We shall not find better songs nor more fitting for the purpose than the Psalms of David, which the Holy Spirit spoke . . . . And moreover, when we sing them, we are certain that God puts in our mouths these, as if He Himself were singing in us to exalt His glory."

But the Psalms were originally written in Hebrew, and, when translated, they don't typically have the rhyme or rhythm for easy singing.

In the early 1640s, Francis Rouse, an English Puritan, rendered all 150 Psalms from the Hebrew into metrical English. The General Assembly of the Church of Scotland, meeting in Edinburgh, took Rouse's translation and submitted it to revision committees. These committees spent six years comparing the metered Psalms with the original Hebrew, seeking to develop a singable translation that was accurate to the original Hebrew. They worked as painstakingly as if creating a new translation of the Bible.

Finally, in 1650, the *Scottish Psalter* was released and approved for congregations of the Church of Scotland. Its full title was: *The Psalms of David in Meeter: Newly translated, and diligently compared with the original Text, and former Translations: More plain, smooth, and agreeable to the Text, than any heretofore.*

Though the Scottish Psalter of 1650 is one of the great treasures of hymnody, the only portion widely sung beyond Scotland is its beautiful rendition of Psalm 23, set to the tune CRIMOND, which begins:

> *The Lord's my Shepherd, I'll not want.*
> *He makes me down to lie*
> *In pastures green; He leadeth me*
> *The quiet waters by.*

The melody, CRIMOND, was composed about 1870 by a woman named Jessie Seymour Irvine. She was the daughter of the parish minister in the little Scottish town of Crimond, which is also famous for its unusual clock in the church tower. The clockmaker accidentally put six marks into one of the five minute sections on the clock face. As a result, each hour in Crimond is 61 minutes, making a day there 24 minutes longer than anywhere else on earth.

Well, it just gives a little extra time for singing "The Lord's My Shepherd."

29

We Sing, Emmanuel, Thy Praise

Paul Gerhardt

Nikolaus Hermann

1. We sing, Emmanuel, Thy praise,
   Thou Prince of Life and Fount of grace, Thou Flow'r of heav'n and Star of morn, Thou Lord of lords, Thou virgin born. Hallelujah!

2. For Thee, since first the world was made,
   So many hearts have watched and prayed; The patriarchs' and prophets' throng For Thee have hoped and waited long. Hallelujah!

3. Now art Thou here, Thou ever blest!
   In lowly manger dost Thou rest. Thou, making all things great, art small; So poor art Thou, yet clothest all. Hallelujah!

4. But I, Thy servant, Lord, today
   Confess my love and freely say, I love Thee truly, but I would That I might love Thee as I should. Hallelujah!

We Sing, Emmanuel, Thy Praise

1654

I will be glad and rejoice in You; I will sing praise to Your name, O Most High.
Psalm 9:2

Paul Gerhardt might be called the "Charles Wesley of Germany," for he was a prolific hymnist who gave Lutheranism some of its warmest hymns. Paul grew up in Grafenhaynichen, Germany, where his father was mayor. This village near Wittenberg was devastated by the Thirty Years' War, and Paul's childhood was marked by scenes of bloodshed and death. But he had a good mind and heart, and he enrolled at the University of Wittenberg at age twenty-one.

After graduation, Paul found a job in Berlin tutoring children. During this time, encouraged by Johann Crüger, choirmaster at Berlin's St. Nicholas Church, he began writing hymns. When Crüger published a hymnbook in 1648, Paul was delighted to find his hymns in it. Others were added to later editions. In all, Gerhardt wrote 123 hymns. His hymnody reflects the shift from the rugged theological hymns of Luther to the more subjective, devotional songs of German Pietistic revival. Best known are "Give to the Winds Your Fears," "Jesus, Thy Boundless Love to Me," and "O Sacred Head, Now Wounded" (which he translated).

Paul was ordained into the ministry at age forty-four and began preaching in and around Berlin. In 1651, he became chief pastor at Mittenwalde, just outside Berlin, and later he returned to Berlin to labor at St. Nicholas Church alongside his mentor, Johann Crüger.

At that point, however, Paul became embroiled in a conflict with the Elector Friedrich Wilhelm, who wanted Lutheran clergymen to sign an edict limiting their freedom of speech on theological matters. Refusing, Paul was deposed from his pulpit in February of 1666. He was even forbidden to lead private worship in his home. During this time, four of his five children died, and in 1668, his wife also passed away.

Late that year, 1668, Paul assumed the pastorate of the Lutheran church in Lübben an der Spree, where he ministered faithfully until his death on May 27, 1676. He was buried in the crypt beneath the altar of the church where he preached. Today the church is known locally as the "Paul Gerhardt Church," and a monument at the entrance reminds visitors of the church's famous pastor-poet.

This Christmas carol, "We Sing, Emmanuel, Thy Praise," has a hauntingly beautiful melody that seems to express the sorrows through which Gerhardt passed. But the words are full of praise, every verse ending in an exuberant "Hallelujah!"

Just like Paul Gerhardt's life.

Jesu, Joy of Man's Desiring

Martin Janus

Johann Schop
Arr. by J.S. Bach

Jesu, Joy of Man's Desiring
1661

. . . I heard a loud voice of a great multitude in heaven, saying, "Alleluia! Salvation and glory and honor and power belong to the Lord our God!" Revelation 19:1

Someone said that it doesn't matter who gets the credit so long as the work gets done. Here's Exhibit A: "Jesu, Joy of Man's Desiring," a lovely, lilting classical melody often played at weddings. A recent poll touted it as the overwhelming favorite of all the compositions of the great musician, Johann Sebastian Bach.

But it was actually composed by another Johann—the German musician, Johann Schop. Born about 1590, Schop was a musical prodigy, a gifted youth and accomplished instrumentalist who became one of seventeenth-century Europe's best known composers, conductors, and performers.

In 1614, Schop was appointed probationary musician in the Hofkapelle, the national or royal orchestra of Saxony. His performances on the lute, cornet, and trombone were lauded, but he was exceptionally gifted on the violin. As a result, he was invited to become a permanent member of the Hofkapelle in 1615.

Johann, however, had better offers, and he left Saxony for Copenhagen where he joined the musical staff of King Christian IV. He performed there until 1619 when the plague drove him from Denmark. He returned to Germany, and by 1621, he had become the leading musician in Hamburg, a city that paid him handsomely and was determined to keep him. Johann took charge of the choirs and orchestras, and planned church music for civic occasions. He became Hamburg's musical ambassador to the rest of Germany and to all of Europe, doing much to shape German religious and classical music in the seventeenth century. Many of his melodies found their way into Lutheran hymnals. "Jesu, Joy of Man's Desiring" is a good example, accompanied by words composed in 1661 by Martin Janus, an evangelical pastor in Silesia.

It was the famous Leipzig church musician, Johann Sebastian Bach, who "borrowed" this work and rearranged it into the beautiful piece it is today. Bach began working on this arrangement during the Christmas season of 1716, but it wasn't performed publicly until July 2, 1723, when it appeared as the final choral selection in one of his cantatas. Bach ended up with the credit, but always remember: Behind one Johann stands another. Behind every famous person is a host of faithful, gifted souls, and, in the end, all the glory goes to God.

Or as Bach would say: SDG—Soli Deo Gloria: *To God Alone Be the Glory.*

Praise God, from Whom All Blessings Flow

Thomas Ken

att. to Louis Bourgeois

Praise God from whom all bless - ings flow.

Praise Him, all crea - tures here be - low.

Praise Him a - bove, ye heav'n - ly host.

Praise Fa - ther, Son and Ho - ly Ghost. A - men.

Praise God, from Whom All Blessings Flow
1674

Blessed be the God and Father of our Lord Jesus Christ, who has blessed us with every spiritual blessing in the heavenly places in Christ. Ephesians 1:3

Before Charles Wesley or Isaac Watts, there was Thomas Ken who has been called "England's first hymnist." He was born in 1637 in Little Berkhampstead on the fringes of greater London. When his parents died, he was raised by his half-sister and her husband who enrolled him in Winchester College, an historic boys' school. Thomas was later ordained to the ministry and returned to Winchester as a chaplain.

To encourage the devotional habits of the boys, Thomas wrote three hymns in 1674. This was revolutionary because English hymns had not yet appeared. Only the Psalms were sung in public worship. Ken suggested the boys use the hymns privately in their rooms.

One hymn was to be sung upon waking, another at bedtime, and a third at midnight if sleep didn't come. His morning hymn had thirteen stanzas, beginning with:

> *Awake, my soul, and with the sun thy daily stage of duty run;*
> *Shake off dull sloth and joyful rise, to pay thy morning sacrifice.*

His evening hymn, equally meaningful, included this verse:

> *All praise to Thee, my God, this night, for all the blessings of the light!*
> *Keep me, O keep me, King of kings, beneath Thine own almighty wings.*

All three hymns ended with a common stanza, which has since become the most widely-sung verse in the world.

> *Praise God, from Whom all blessings flow; / Praise Him, all creatures here below; /*
> *Praise Him above, ye heavenly host; / Praise Father, Son, and Holy Ghost.*

In 1680, Thomas was appointed chaplain to England's King Charles II. It was a thankless job, as Charles kept a variety of mistresses. Once the king asked to lodge a mistress in the chaplain's residence. Thomas rebuked him, saying, "Not for the King's Kingdom!" Afterward the king referred to him as "that little man who refused lodging to poor Nellie."

During the reign of the next king, James II, Thomas, by now a bishop, was sent to the Tower of London for his Protestant convictions. After his release, Thomas retired to the home of a wealthy friend where he died on March 11, 1711. He was buried at sunrise, and the Doxology was sung at his funeral.

Sing Praise to God Who Reigns Above

Johann J. Schütz

Bohemian Brethren's *Kirchengesänge*

1. Sing praise to God who reigns a - bove, The God of all cre -
2. What God's al - might - y power hath made, His gra - cious mer - cy
3. The Lord is nev - er far a - way, But, thru all grief dis -
4. Thus all my toil - some way a - long, I sing a - loud His

a - tion; The God of pow'r the God of love, The
keep - eth; By morn - ing glow or even - ing shade, His
tress - ing, An ev - er - pre - sent help and stay, Our
prais - es; That men may hear the grate - ful song. My

God of our sal - va - tion. With heal - ing balm my soul is filled, And
watch - ful eye ne'er sleep - eth. With - in the king - dom of His might, Lo,
peace and joy and bless - ing. As with a mo - ther's ten - der hand, He
voice un - wear - ied rais - es, Be joy - ful in the Lord my heart; Both

ev - ery faith - less mur - mur stilled; To God, all praise and glo - ry!
all is just and all is right; To God, all praise and glo - ry.
leads His own, His cho - sen band, To God, all praise and glo - ry.
soul and bod - y bear your part, To God all praise and glo - ry.

Sing Praise to God Who Reigns Above

1675

If My people . . . will humble themselves, and pray and seek My face, and turn from their wicked ways, then I will . . . forgive their sin. . . . 2 Chronicles 7:14

Evangelist Vance Havner once quipped, "When I was a boy, preachers used to talk about 'holding a revival.' What we really need is somebody who will turn a revival loose."

Well, that's what Philip Spener did in Germany, spurred on by his friend and attorney, Johann Jakob Schütz.

Years before, Martin Luther had been all aflame as he established the Protestant Reformation, and the early Lutherans were firebrands of holy zeal. But a generation later, Lutheranism had lost its steam. By the 1600s, church life tended to be formal and shallow. The doctrine was correct but cold. That's when Philip Spener accepted the call to pastor the Lutheran Church in Frankfort am Main. Rather than preaching from the prescribed texts, he began preaching through the entire Bible, calling for repentance and serious discipleship. In 1669, as he preached from the Sermon on the Mount, revival broke out in the church. People were converted, lives changed, families transformed.

No one was more excited than Johann Schütz, a lifelong resident of Frankfort and prominent city attorney. He suggested Spener take some of these converts and disciple them in small, home prayer and Bible study groups. Spener did so, and it became the talk of the town. These people were called "Pietists" in derision, but the revival spread throughout Germany and is known to history as the "Pietistic Movement."

Out of his joy for what was happening, Johann Schütz wrote a hymn in 1675:

> *Sing praise to God Who reigns above, the God of all creation,*
> *The God of power, the God of love, the God of our salvation.*
> *With healing balm my soul is filled and every faithless murmur stilled:*
> *To God all praise and glory.*

Schütz died in Frankfort at age 49, on May 22, 1690. But his hymn lives on. It was first published in the United States in 1879, where it appeared in *Hymnbook for the Use of Evangelical Lutheran Schools and Congregations.* It is sung to a traditional Bohemian melody named "Kirchengesänge."

The story of Spener and Schütz reminds us we should never give up on revival. If you don't see a revival starting around you, let it begin in your own heart, then let it overflow to others.

Fairest Lord Jesus

Anonymous German Hymn

Schlesische Volkslieder arr. by Richard S. Willis

1. Fair-est Lord Je - sus; Rul-er of all na - ture,
2. Fair are the mead - ows; Fair-er still the wood-lands,
3. Fair is the sun - shine; Fair-er still the moon-light
4. Beau-ti-ful Sav - ior! Lord of the na - tions!

O Thou of God and man the Son.
Robed in the bloom-ing garb of spring.
And all the twin-kling star - ry host.
Son of God and Son of man!

Thee will I cher-ish; Thee will I hon-or,
Je - sus is fair - er; Je - sus is pur-er,
Je - sus shines bright - er; Je - sus shines pur-er
Glo - ry and hon - or, Praise, ad-o - ra-tion,

Thou my soul's glo - ry, joy, and crown.
Who makes the woe-ful heart to sing.
Than all the an-gels heav'n can boast.
Now and for-ev-er-more be Thine!

Fairest Lord Jesus

1677

For unto us a Child is born, unto us a Son is given . . . And His name will be called Wonderful, Counselor, Mighty God, Everlasting Father, Prince of Peace.
Isaiah 9:6

This hymn came from Roman Catholic Jesuits in Germany and originally had six verses. It first appeared in 1677 in a Jesuit hymnbook titled *Münster Gesangbuch*, but the text of the hymn was in existence at least fifteen years earlier, for it has been found in a manuscript dating back to 1662. Yet the origin of the words remains a mystery.

Who translated it into English? That, too, is largely a mystery. The first three stanzas are the work of an anonymous translator. The fourth stanza was by Joseph A. Seiss, and it first appeared in a Lutheran Sunday School book in 1873.

How appropriate that no human author draws attention from the great theme of this song. There's no source to distract from the subject, no story to detract from the Savior.

This hymn emphasizes the beauty and wonder of Christ, and it alludes to His dual nature, that He was both human and divine, God made flesh, the God-Man: *O Thou of God and man the Son . . . . Son of God and Son of Man . . . .*

It brings to mind one of the greatest observations ever made about Christ, uttered by the "Golden-mouthed" preacher of Antioch, John Chrysostom, in a fourth-century sermon: "I do not think of Christ as God alone, or man alone, but both together. For I know He was hungry, and I know that with five loaves He fed five thousand. I know He was thirsty, and I know that He turned the water into wine. I know He was carried in a ship, and I know that He walked on the sea. I know that He died, and I know that He raised the dead. I know that He was set before Pilate, and I know that He sits with the Father on His throne. I know that He was worshiped by angels, and I know that He was stoned by the Jews. And truly some of these I ascribe to the human, and others to the divine nature. For by reason of this He is said to have been both God and man."

Beautiful Savior! Lord of all the nations!
Son of God and Son of Man!
Glory and honor, praise, adoration,
Now and forever more be Thine.

Praise Ye the Lord, the Almighty

Joachim Neander

Straslund Gesangbuch

1. Praise to the Lord, the Al - might - y, The King of cre - a - tion!
2. Praise to the Lord, Who o'er all things So won-drous-ly reign - eth,
3. Praise to the Lord! O let all that is in me a - dore Him!
4. Praise to the Lord, Who doth pros - per Thy work and de - fend thee;

O my soul, praise Him, For He is thy health and sal - va - tion!
Shel - ters thee un - der His wings, Yes, so gent - ly sus - tain - eth!
All that hath life and breath, Come now with prais - es be - fore Him.
Sure - ly His good - ness and mer - cy Here dail - y at - tend thee.

All ye who hear, Now to His tem - ple draw near;
Hast Thou not seen How all thy long - ings have been
Let the a - men sound from His peo - ple a - gain:
Pon - der a - new what the Al - might - y can do,

Join me in glad ad - o - ra - tion!
Grant - ed in what He or - dain - eth?
Glad - ly for aye we a - dore Him.
If with His love He be - friend thee.

Praise Ye the Lord, the Almighty

1680

Where were you when I laid the foundations of the earth? Tell Me, if you have understanding. Job 38:4

This hymn was written by Joachim Neander, born in 1650, whose father, grandfather, great-grandfather, and great-great-grandfather—all Joachim Neanders—had been preachers of the gospel. But as a student, Joachim was wild and rebellious. At 20, he joined a group of students who descended on St. Martin's Church in Bremen to ridicule and scoff the worshippers. But the sermon that day by Rev. Theodore Under-Eyck arrested him and led to his conversion. A few years later, he was the assistant preacher at that very church.

Joachim often took long walks near his home in Hochdal, Germany. They were worship walks, and he frequently composed hymns as he strolled, singing them to the Lord. He was the first hymnwriter from the Calvinist branch of Protestantism. When he was 30—the year he died—he wrote this while battling tuberculosis:

> *Praise Ye The Lord, The Almighty, the King of Creation.*
> *O my soul praise Him, for He is Thy health and Salvation.*

One of Joachim's favorite walking spots was a beautiful gorge a few miles from Dusseldorf. The Dussel River flowed through the valley, and Joachim Neander so loved this spot that it eventually was named for him—Neander Valley. The Old German word for "valley" was "tal" or "thal" with a silent "h."

Two hundred years later Herr von Beckersdorf owned the valley, which was a source for limestone, used to manufacture cement. In 1856, miners discovered caves which contained human bones. Beckersdorf took the bones to a local science teacher who speculated they belonged to one who died in the Flood.

But when William King, an Irish professor of anatomy, saw the bones, he claimed they were proof of evolution's famous "missing link." Other Neanderthal fossils were found, and for many years they were used to "prove" Darwin's theory of evolution. Today we know the Neanderthal was fully human, an extinct people group of great strength.

But, as one expert put it, "when Joachim Neander walked in his beautiful valley so many years ago, he could not know that hundreds of years later his name would become world famous, not for his hymns celebrating creation, but for a concept that he would have totally rejected: human evolution."*

---

*Marvin L. Lubenow, *Bones of Contention* (Grand Rapids: Baker Book House, 1992), p. 77. I am indebted to Lubenow for much of the information in this story, gleaned from chapter 6 of this excellent book, subtitled "A Creation's Assessment of Human Fossils."

Behold the Savior of Mankind

Samuel Wesley, Sr.

William Daman's *Booke of Musicke*

1. Be - hold the Sav - ior of man - kind Nailed to the shame - ful tree! How vast the love that Him in - clined To bleed and die for thee!

2. Hark, how He groans, while na - ture shakes, And earth's strong pil - lars bend! The tem - ple's veil in sun - der breaks; The sol - id mar - bles rend.

3. 'Tis done! the pre - cious ran - som's paid! "Re - ceive my soul!" He cries; See where He bows His sa - cred head! He bows His head and dies!

4. But soon He'll break death's en - vious chain, and in full glo - ry shine; O Lamb of God, was ev - er pain, Was ev - er love, like thine?

Behold the Savior
of Mankind

1700

Christ has redeemed us from the curse of the law, having become a curse for us (for it is written, "Cursed is everyone who hangs on a tree"). Galatians 3:13

Samuel Wesley, Sr. was a penniless and unpopular Anglican pastor in tiny Epworth, England, and it riled him that his wife's kitchen Bible studies were more popular than his own sermons. Though they truly loved each other, Susanna once exclaimed, "It is a misfortune peculiar to our family that he and I seldom think alike."

Epworth's citizens, too, found Samuel dogmatic and often severe, and some expressed their disapproval in appalling ways. His crops were burned, his livestock maimed, and on February 9, 1709, his house was torched. Susanna was awakened by sparks falling onto the bed. Samuel cried, "Fire! Fire!" The thatched roof exploded, and the flames spread like a sheet of lightning. The parents, flying to rescue their children, were almost trapped. But everyone finally managed to escape through windows and the garden door. Or so they thought.

Peering back, they saw five-year-old John's terrified face pressed against an upstairs window. Instantly a human ladder formed; and just as the house caved in, John was snatched to safety. He never forgot the rescue: "I remember the circumstances as distinctly as though it were but yesterday. Seeing the room was very light, I put my head out and saw streaks of fire on top of the room. I . . . ran to the door, but could get no further, the floor beyond it being in a blaze. I climbed up a chest that stood near a window."

Among the things that perished that night was the manuscript of Samuel's compositions. He had often found relief in penning devotional poetry and hymns. He had hoped in this way to meet his family's financial needs—and to be remembered by posterity. That night, all was lost.

Well, almost all. Somehow one hymn was rescued. Appropriately, it was about another preacher with Whom Samuel identified, One Who was likewise disdained and attacked.

This is the only known surviving hymn from the father of the famous Wesley brothers, but it became the forerunner for the many wonderful hymns that later flowed from the pen of Samuel's famous hymn-writing son, Charles:

> *Behold the Savior of mankind*
> *Nailed to the shameful tree!*
> *How vast the love that Him inclined*
> *To bleed and die for thee!*

O That I Had a Thousand Voices

Johann Mentzer   Johann B. König

1. O that I had a thou-sand voic-es And with a thou-sand tongues could tell Of Him in Whom the earth re-joic-es, Who does all things wise-ly and well! My grate-ful heart would then be free To tell what God has done for me.

2. O all you pow'rs that God im-plant-ed, A-rise and si-lence keep no more; Put forth the strength that God has grant-ed, Your no-blest work is to a-dore. O soul and bod-y, join to raise With heart-felt joy our Mak-er's praise!

3. You for-est leaves so green and ten-der, That dance for joy in sum-mer air. You mead-ow grass-es bright and slen-der, You flow'rs so won-drous sweet so fair, You live to show God's praise a-lone. With me now make His glo-ry known.

4. All crea-tures that have breath and mo-tion, That throng the earth, the sea, the sky, Now join with me my heart's de-vo-tion, Help me to raise His prais-es high. My ut-most pow'rs can ne'er a-right De-clare the won-ders of God's might.

O That I Had a Thousand Voices

1704

Behold, bless the LORD, All you servants of the LORD, Who by night stand in the house of the LORD! Lift up your hands in the sanctuary, And bless the LORD.
Psalm 134:1, 2

salm 134, one of the shortest chapters in the Bible, instructs those who serve the Lord by night to bless Him, to lift up their hands in the sanctuary and bless the Lord. Sometimes our highest praise occurs during the darkest hours.

Johann Mentzer was pastor in the small village of Kemnitz, located in the middle of the forests of Eastern Germany, near the Polish and Czech borders. He began his ministry there in 1696, and became a trusted friend and mentor to the young count, Nicholas Ludwig von Zinzendorf, who was born in 1700 and frequently visited his grandmother in nearby Berthelsdorf (see the story for "Jesus, Thy Blood and Righteousness").

Most of Mentzer's parishioners, however, were poor serfs whose hard work primarily benefited their wealthy masters. Mentzer's heart went out to his people, toiling in poverty and trouble, and he often counseled them to praise the Lord whatever the circumstances.

One evening Johann was returning from a Bible study in a nearby village. The night was dark, but as he approached his church, he grew alarmed at a frightening red glow in the sky. Hurrying onward, he found his own home, the church parsonage, ablaze. It had been set afire during his absence.

As he later inspected the ashes and ruins, he was disturbed and downhearted. Just then a serf tapped him on the shoulder and asked, "So, Pastor, are you still in the mood for praise and thanksgiving?" Johann offered a silent prayer for grace, and at that moment his whole attitude changed. It seemed to him that his praise to God should be louder than the sound of the tongues of flame that had just consumed his own home. The next day, he composed this hymn: "O that I had a thousand voices / and with a thousand tongues could tell / of Him in whom the earth rejoices / who does all things wisely and well."

Years later, Charles Wesley, undoubtedly inspired by this hymn, wrote his more famous, "O for a Thousand Tongues to Sing."

If you're facing difficulty right now, try praise and thanksgiving.

Behold the Glories of the Lamb

Isaac Watts

William Tans'ur

1. Be - hold the glo - ries of the Lamb A - midst His Fa - ther's throne. Pre - pare new hon - ors for His Name, And songs be - fore un - known.

2. E - ter - nal Fa - ther, who shall look In - to Thy se - cret will? Who but the Son should take that Book And o - pen ev - er - y seal?

3. Now to the Lamb that once was slain Be end - less bless - ings paid; Sal - va - tion, glo - ry, joy re - main For ev - er on Thy head.

4. Thou hast re - deemed our souls with blood, Hast set the pris - oner free; Hast made us kings and priests to God, And we shall reign with Thee.

Behold the Glories of the Lamb

1707

Worthy is the Lamb who was slain to receive power and riches and wisdom, and strength and honor and glory and blessing! Revelation 5:12

Isaac Watts, Sr. was a clothier and a deacon in Above Bar Congregational Church in Southampton, England. He and his wife, Sarah were "Dissenters"—Non-Anglicans—a treasonous offense in those days. About the time Isaac, Jr. prematurely arrived, July 17, 1674, the elder Watts was arrested. Sarah reportedly nursed her newborn while seated on a stone outside the prison.

In time Watts was released, and the young couple soon discovered they had a precocious child. Young Isaac took to books almost from infancy. He learned Latin at age four, Greek at nine, and Hebrew at thirteen. He loved rhyme and verse. At age seven, he wrote this poem in childish script. Notice the acrostic—ISAAC:

> **I** am a vile polluted lump of earth
> **S**o I've continued ever since my birth
> **A**lthough Jehovah grace does give me
> **A**s sure this monster Satan will deceive me
> **C**ome, therefore, Lord, from Satan's claws relieve me.

After Isaac graduated from grammar school in Southampton, a wealthy benefactor offered to send him to Oxford. But that would have required his becoming Anglican. Politely declining, Isaac enrolled in a college-level school for Dissenters in Stoke Newington, London, where he excelled.

After graduation from college, Isaac, about 19, returned to Southampton. He complained to his father about the dismal singing at church. Only versified arrangements of the Psalms were used. Martin Luther taught his followers to sing hymns, but John Calvin allowed only the singing of Scriptures. After a heated discussion, his father challenged Isaac to write a hymn.

Centering his thoughts on Revelation 5, he did so. This was the first of Isaac's 600-plus hymns, and has been called the first English hymn designed for congregational use. (It was published in 1707.) Above Bar Congregational Church liked Isaac's hymn so much, they requested a new one each week. Isaac, about 20, gladly complied. Those two years in Southampton became the richest hymn-writing period in Isaac Watts' life. Though barely out of school, he composed hymns that are still sung nearly three centuries later, earning him the title, "Father of English Hymnody."

Alas! and Did My Savior Bleed

Isaac Watts

Hugh Wilson

1. A - las! and did my Sav - ior bleed And did my Sov - ereign die? Would He de - vote that sa - cred head, For such a worm as I.
2. Was it for crimes that I have done, He suf - fered on the tree? A - maz - ing pi - ty, grace un - known, And love be - yond de - gree!
3. Well might the sun in dark - ness hide And shut His glo - ries in; When Christ the might - y Ma - ker died For man, the crea - ture's sin.
4. Thus might I hide my blush - ing face While His dear cross ap - pears; Dis - solve my heart in thank - ful - ness And melt mine eyes to tears.
5. But drops of grief can ne'er re - pay, The debt of love I owe; Here, Lord, I give my - self a - way, 'Tis all that I can do.

Alas! and Did My Savior Bleed

1707

But God forbid that I should boast except in the cross of our Lord Jesus Christ.
Galatians 6:14

After his graduation from college, Isaac Watts returned to Southampton, England, and spent two years writing hymns for Above Bar Congregational Church. He then moved to London to tutor children in a wealthy family of Dissenters. While there he joined Mark Lane Independent Chapel. Soon he was asked to be a teacher in the church, and in 1698, he was hired as associate pastor. There, on his twenty-fourth birthday, he preached his first sermon. In 1702, he became senior pastor of the church, a position he retained the rest of his life. He was a brilliant Bible student, and his sermons brought the church to life.

In 1707, his *Hymns and Spiritual Songs* was published. Isaac had written most of these hymns in Southampton while in late teens and early twenties. Included was a hymn now considered the finest hymn ever written in the English language. It was based on Galatians 6:14: "But God forbid that I should boast except in the cross of our Lord Jesus Christ." Originally the first stanza said: *When I survey the wondrous cross / Where the young Prince of Glory died . . .* In an enlarged 1709 edition, Watts rewrote the lines to say:

> *When I survey the wondrous cross*
> *On which the Prince of glory died,*
> *My richest gain I count but loss,*
> *And pour contempt on all my pride.*

Also included in the 1707 hymnbook was "Heavenly Joy on Earth," better known today as, "Come, We That Love the Lord," or "We're Marching to Zion."

Another hymn was, "Godly Sorrow Arising from the Sufferings of Christ," better known as: "Alas! and Did My Savior Bleed." This hymn later played a major role in the conversion of a great American hymnist. In 1851, Fanny Crosby, 31, attended a revival service at John Street Methodist Church in New York. "After a prayer was offered," she recalled, "they began to sing the grand old consecration hymn, 'Alas! and Did My Savior Bleed' and when they reached the third line of the fifth stanza, 'Here, Lord, I give myself away,' my very soul was flooded with celestial light."

How right that Watts should, long after his death, play a part in winning to Christ the author of a new generation of hymns and gospel songs!

We're Marching to Zion

Isaac Watts

Robert Lowry

1. Come, we that love the Lord, And let our joys be known.
2. Let those re - fuse to sing Who nev - er knew our God;
3. Then let our songs a - bound, And ev - 'ry tear be dry.

Join in a song with sweet ac - cord, Join in a song with sweet ac - cord,
But chil - dren of the heav'n - ly King, But chil - dren of the heav'n - ly King,
We're march - ing thro' Im - man - uel's ground, We're march - ing thro' Im - man - uel's ground.

And thus sur - round the throne, And thus sur - round the throne.
May speak their joys a - broad, May speak their joys a - broad.
To fair - er worlds on high, To fair - er worlds on high.

We're march - ing to Zi - on, Beau - ti - ful, beau - ti - ful Zi - on. We're

march - ing up - ward to Zi - on, The beau - ti - ful cit - y of God.

We're Marching to Zion

1707

Out of Zion, the perfection of beauty, God will shine forth. Psalm 50:2

n the night of November 30, 1940, German planes bombed Southampton, England, and destroyed the Above Bar Congregational Church. The pastor and caretaker were able to rescue the church records, but all else was destroyed—except for a bust of Isaac Watts, the "Father of English Hymnody."

The destruction of those old buildings was a blow to Christian history, for within the walls of the Above Bar Church the hymns of young Isaac Watts were first sung.

Watts was born in Southampton on July 17, 1674, the oldest of nine children. He was a brilliant lad who started learning Latin at age four and Greek and Hebrew soon after. It's said that even before he could speak plainly, he would cry out, "A book! A book! Buy a book!" whenever anyone would give him money.

Isaac advanced so quickly in school that a local physician offered to finance his education at a major university. As members of Above Bar Congregational Church, however, the Watts were committed "Dissenters," Christians who didn't believe in joining the State Church. Dissenters opted instead for establishing independent congregations where they could worship without conforming to government regulations. As such, they were bitterly persecuted, and Isaac's father had even spent time in prison for his beliefs. Nor were dissenters allowed to attend the state universities. So at sixteen, Isaac enrolled instead in an independent academy in London and graduated with honors.

Returning home, Isaac spent two years more living with his parents and attending Above Bar Congregational Church. One day, discontented with the quality of the singing at the church, he wrote a hymn for the church to sing. This was a new and radical innovation, for at that time only the Psalms of David were sung in English churches.

Nonetheless, Above Bar Congregational Church gamely tried the young man's hymn and liked it so much they asked for another. For two and a half years, Isaac churned out hymns for that little congregation. Those two post-college years at home became the "Golden Years" of Watts's hymn writing.

How remarkable that some of the greatest hymns ever sung in the English language—such as "We're Marching to Zion"—should be produced by the "Father of Hymnody" who was only twenty years of age.

The old church building may be gone now, but the hymns first sung there will never die.

When I Survey the Wondrous Cross

Isaac Watts

Gregorian Chant
Arr. by Lowell Mason

1. When I sur - vey the won - drous cross
2. For - bid it, Lord, that I should boast,
3. See, from His head, His hands, His feet,
4. Were the whole realm of na - ture mine,

On which the Prince of glo - ry died,
Save in the death of Christ, my God;
Sor - row and love flow min - gled down;
That were a pres - ent far too small;

My rich - est gain I count but loss,
All the vain things that charm me most,
Did e'er such love and sor - row meet,
Love so a - maz - ing, so di - vine,

And pour con - tempt on all my pride.
I sac - ri - fice them all to His blood.
Or thorns com - pose so rich a crown?
De - mands my soul, my life, my all.

When I Survey the Wondrous Cross

1707

But God forbid that I should boast except in the cross of our Lord Jesus Christ, by whom the world has been crucified to me, and I to the world. Galatians 6:14

fter Isaac Watts finished his college studies and returned home to Southampton, he wrote many of his now-immortalized hymns for Above Bar Congregational Church. In 1696, Isaac, twenty-two, left home for London to become a tutor.

All the while, he was feeling a clear tug toward ministry. On his twenty-fourth birthday, July 17, 1698, Isaac preached his first sermon. The following year, he became assistant pastor of London's Mark Lane Church.

In March of 1700, Isaac received a long letter from his brother, Enoch, urging him to publish the hymns he had written at Southampton. The letter said:

Dear Brother, In your last [letter] you [mentioned] an inclination to oblige the world by showing it your hymns in print, and I heartily wish . . . that you were something more than inclinable thereunto. . . . I am very confident whoever has the happiness of reading your hymns (unless he be either sot or atheist) will have a very favorable opinion of their author. . . . There is . . . a great need of a pen, vigorous and lively as yours, to quicken and revive the dying devotion of the age. . . . Yours now is the old truth, stripped of its ragged ornaments, and appears, if we may say so, younger by ages in a new and fashionable dress.

Isaac, however, hesitated. He had other obligations on his time. On March 8, 1702, he became Mark Lane's pastor. The next year, 1703, the church chose Samuel Price of Wales to assist Isaac, due to the latter's fragile health. Under the preaching of these two, the old, dying church revived. The building grew too small for the crowds, and a new house of worship was built down the street.

Finally in 1707, Watts published his hymns, selling the copyright to a Mr. Lawrence, the publisher, for ten pounds. This volume was an instant success. It was enlarged and republished in 1709.

"When I Survey the Wondrous Cross" appeared in his 1707 book of hymns. Inspired by Galatians 6:14, it was originally titled, "Crucifixion to the World, by the Cross of Christ." Many consider it the finest hymn in English church history, and Charles Wesley reportedly said he would rather have written it than all his own.

Join All the Glorious Names

Isaac Watts

John Darwall

1. Join all the glo - rious names, Of wis - dom, love and pow'r, That ev - er mor - tals knew, That an - gels ev - er bore: All are too mean to speak His worth, Too mean to set my Sav - ior forth.

2. Great Proph - et of my God, My tongue would bless Thy name: By Thee the joy - ful news Of our sal - va - tion came, The joy - ful news of sins for - giv'n, Of hell sub - dued and peace with heav'n.

3. Je - sus, my great High Priest, Of - fered His blood, and died; My guilt - y con - science seeks No sac - ri - fice be - side; His pow'r - ful blood did once a - tone And now it pleads be - fore the throne.

4. Thou are my Coun - sel - or, My Pat - tern, and my Guide, And Thou my Shep - herd art; O keep me near Thy side; Nor let my feet e'er turn a - stray To wan - der in the crook - ed way.

5. My Sav - ior and my Lord, My Con - qu'ror and my King, Thy scep - ter and Thy sword, Thy reign - ing grace, I sing: Thine is the pow'r; be - hold I sit In will - ing bonds be - neath Thy feet.

Join All the Glorious Names

1709

His name will be called Wonderful, Counselor, Mighty God, Everlasting Father, Prince of Peace. Isaiah 9:6

Shortly after Isaac Watts assumed the pastorate of London's Mark Lane Church, his health broke. Though only in his twenties, he was already famous throughout England for his sermons, books, and hymns. The strain of it all, however, was too much for his constitution; he was very short, thin, and weak. When he offered to resign from his pastorate, Mark Lane Church would have none of it. They hired an able assistant and determined to care for their ailing young pastor.

A wealthy couple, Sir Thomas and Lady Abney, invited him to spend a week at Theobalds (pronounced Tib-balds), their manor house outside London. The week turned into thirty-six years. Theobalds was a perfect environment for the little poet.

An 1875 biography of Watts says of him, "One of the smallest of mortals, he had one of the largest of homes," with "rich rural scenes, the delightful garden, the spreading lawn, and the fragrant and embowered recess all wooing the body back to health and the heart to peace." Watts had his own suite of apartments packed with books, a sort of literary hermitage. During the wee hours, he would study, pray, write his books and sermons, and compose his poems.

His biographer wrote, "For many years he knew little of sleep, except such as could be obtained by medicine. Intense mental application, working upon a weak and nervous constitution, brought about the consequences of insomnia, or sleeplessness; yet his mind seems to have been too calm, too equally balanced, and too completely under the control of highest principles, ever to know such agitations as shake to their centre some poetic natures."

Perhaps it was during the evening hours of many sleepless nights that Isaac studied the wonderful subject of the names of Jesus as revealed in the Bible. There are nearly three hundred names and titles of Jesus in the Bible, and Watts packed some of the richest of them into the twelve original stanzas of "Join All the Glorious Names."

This is my favorite of all Watts's hymns. One of the verses often omitted from today's hymnals says:

> *Be Thou my Counselor,*
> *My Pattern, and my Guide,*
> *And through this desert land*
> *Still keep me near Thy side;*
> *Nor let my feet e'er run astray*
> *Nor rove nor seek the crooked way.*

I Sing the Mighty Power of God

Isaac Watts   from *Gesangbuch der Herzogl*, Württemberg

1. I sing the might-y power of God, That made the mountains rise;
2. I sing the good-ness of the Lord, That filled the earth with food;
3. There's not a plant or flow'r be-low But makes Thy glo-ries known,

That spread the flow-ing seas a-broad, And built the loft-y skies.
He formed the crea-tures with His word, And then pro-nounced them good.
and clouds a-rise and tem-pests blow, By or-der from Thy throne.

I sing the wis-dom that or-dained The sun to rule the day;
Lord, how Thy won-ders are dis-played, Wher-e'er I turn my eye;
While all that bor-rows life from Thee Is ev-er in Thy care;

The moon shines full at His com-mand, And all the stars o-bey.
If I sur-vey the ground I tread, Or gaze up-on the sky.
And ev-ery-where that man can be, Thou, God, art pres-ent there.

I Sing the Mighty Power of God

1715

He has made the earth by His power; He has established the world by His wisdom, and stretched out the heaven by His understanding. Jeremiah 51:15

As Isaac Watts quietly pastored Mark Lane Chapel in London, the growing popularity of his hymns was causing a tempest. "Christian congregations have shut out divinely inspired Psalms," one man complained, "and taken in Watts' flights of fancy." The issue of singing hymns versus Psalms split churches, including the one in Bedford, England, once pastored by John Bunyan.

The controversy jumped the Atlantic. In May, 1789, Rev. Adam Rankin told the General Assembly of the Presbyterian Church, meeting in Philadelphia: "I have ridden horseback all the way from my home in Kentucky to ask this body to refuse the great and pernicious error of adopting the use of Isaac Watts' hymns in public worship in preference to the Psalms of David."

We don't know Isaac's reactions. Dr. Samuel Johnson later reported that "by his natural temper he was quick of resentment; but, by his established and habitual practice, he was gentle, modest, and inoffensive." But in 1712, Isaac suffered a breakdown from which he never fully recovered. He asked his church to discontinue his salary; but they raised it and hired a co-pastor who assumed the bulk of the pastoral duties. Watts remained as pastor the rest of his life, preaching whenever he could.

A wealthy couple in the church, Sir Thomas and Lady Abney, invited him to spend a week on their estate. Isaac accepted—and lived with them until his death 36 years later. He enjoyed the children in the home, and in 1715, he published *Divine and Moral Songs for Children.* It sold 80,000 copies in a year and has been selling ever since. In his preface, he said, "Children of high and low degree, of the Church of England or Dissenters, baptized in infancy or not, may all join together in these songs. And as I have endeavored to sink the language to the level of a child's under-standing . . . to profit all, if possible, and offend none."

One hymn in this volume, intended for children, became popular with adults. Entitled, "Praise for Creation and Providence," it said:

> *I sing the mighty power of God, that made the mountains rise,*
> *That spread the flowing seas abroad, and built the lofty skies.*
> *I sing the wisdom that ordained the sun to rule the day;*
> *The moon shines full at God's command, and all the stars obey.*

Jesus Shall Reign

Isaac Watts

John Hatton

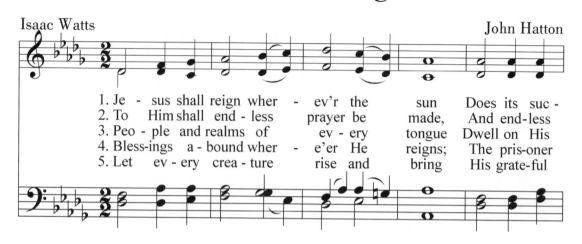

1. Je - sus shall reign wher - ev'r the sun   Does its suc-
2. To   Him shall end - less   prayer be   made,   And end-less
3. Peo - ple and realms of   ev - ery   tongue   Dwell on His
4. Bless-ings a - bound wher - e'er He   reigns;   The pris-oner
5. Let   ev - ery crea - ture   rise and   bring   His grate-ful

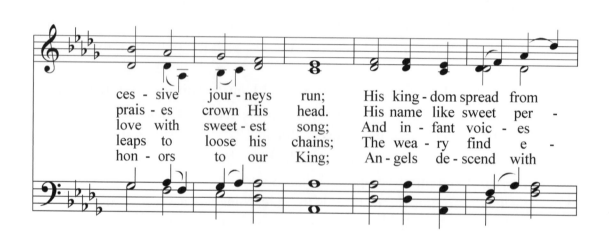

ces - sive   jour - neys   run;   His king - dom spread from
prais - es   crown His   head.   His name like sweet per -
love with   sweet - est   song;   And in - fant voic - es
leaps to   loose his   chains;   The wea - ry find   e -
hon - ors   to   our   King;   An - gels de - scend with

shore to   shore, 'Til   moons shall wax   and wane no   more.
fume shall   rise With   ev - ery morn - ing   sac - ri -   fice.
shall pro - claim Their   ear - ly bless - ings   on His   name.
ter - nal   rest, And   all   the sons   of   want are   blest.
songs a - gain, And   earth re - peat   the loud "A - men!"

Jesus Shall Reign

1719

His name shall endure forever; His name shall continue as long as the sun. And men shall be blessed in Him; All nations shall call Him blessed. Psalm 72:17

While living on the Abney estate, Isaac devoted himself to a massive project, adapting the Book of Psalms for Christian worship. In 1719, *The Psalms of David Imitated in the Language of the New Testament* was published. In it, Watts worked his way through most of the 150 Psalms, paraphrasing them, injecting them with New Testament truth, and framing them in singing form.

He explained his approach with these words: "Where the Psalmist describes religion by the fear of God, I have often joined faith and love to it. Where he speaks of the pardon of sin through the mercies of God, I have added the merits of a Savior. Where he talks of sacrificing goats or bullocks, I rather choose to mention the sacrifice of Christ, the Lamb of God. Where He promises abundance of wealth, honor, and long life, I have changed some of these typical blessings for grace, glory, and life eternal, which are brought to light by the gospel, and promised in the New Testament."

Several of these have become favorites that have withstood the ages. His rendition of Psalm 72, for example, has been called the first missions hymn: "Jesus Shall Reign Where'er The Sun."

This hymn played a role in the life of Eric Liddell, Scottish Olympic hero of the 1924 games in Paris, who became a missionary to China with the London Missionary Society. His departure from Edinburgh was never-to-be-forgotten. His friends escorted him in a festooned carriage from Scottish Congregational Church to Waverley Station where multitudes had gathered. Before boarding the train, Eric spoke to the crowds, saying he was going abroad to endeavor to do his part in trying to unify the countries of the world under Christ. "Let our motto be 'Christ for the World, for the World Needs Christ,'" he shouted. He then led in two verses of "Jesus Shall Reign Where'er the Sun."*

If, on that memorable day, Eric had sang *all* the verses of "Jesus Shall Reign," he would have come to this one:

> *The saints shall flourish in His days,*
> *Dressed in the robes of joy and praise;*
> *Peace, like a river, from His throne*
> *Shall flow to nations yet unknown.*

---

*Eric Liddell served courageously in China until his death in 1945 in a Japanese internment camp.

O God, Our Help in Ages Past

Isaac Watts

William Croft

1. O God, our Help in a - ges past, Our
2. Un - der the sha - dow of Thy throne Still
3. Be - fore the hills in or - der stood, Or
4. A thou - sand a - ges in Thy sight, Are
5. Time like an ev - er roll - ing stream, Bears
6. O God, our Help in a - ges past, Our

Hope for years to come, Our Shel - ter from the
may we dwell se - cure; Suf - fi - cient is Thine
earth re - ceived her frame, From ev - er - last - ing
like an eve - ning gone; Short as the watch that
all its sons a - way; They fly, for - got - ten,
Hope for years to come, Be Thou my Guide while

storm - y blast, And our e - ter - nal Home!
arm a - lone, And our de - fense is sure.
Thou art God, To end - less years the same.
ends the night, Be - fore the ris - ing sun.
as a dream Dies at the open - ing day.
life shall last, And our e - ter - nal Home.

O God, Our Help in Ages Past

1719

Lord, You have been our dwelling place in all generations. Before the mountains were brought forth, or ever You had formed the earth and the world, even from everlasting to everlasting, You are God. Psalm 90:1–2

Another hymn in Isaac Watts' 1719 *Psalms of David Imitated* is based on Psalm 90, and is perhaps Watts' most bracing hymn. It was played on the radio by the BBC as soon as World War II was declared, and was later sung at the funeral service of Winston Churchill. Some of the original verses have fallen into disuse, but as you read them, think of the ailing hymnist, sitting at the desk in his room on the Abney estate, pouring over Psalm 90 and penning these words:

Our God, our help in ages past, / Our hope for years to come, /
Our shelter from the stormy blast, / And our eternal home.

Under the shadow of Thy throne / Thy saints have dwelt secure; /
Sufficient is Thine arm alone, / And our defense is sure.

Before the hills in order stood, / Or earth received her frame, /
From everlasting Thou art God, / To endless years the same.

Thy Word commands our flesh to dust, / "Return, ye sons of men:" /
All nations rose from earth at first, / And turn to earth again.

A thousand ages in Thy sight / Are like an evening gone; /
Short as the watch that ends the night / Before the rising sun.

The busy tribes of flesh and blood, / With all their lives and cares, /
Are carried downwards by the flood, / And lost in following years.

Time, like an ever rolling stream, / Bears all its sons away; /
They fly, forgotten, as a dream / Dies at the opening day.

Like flowery fields the nations stand / Pleased with the morning light; /
The flowers beneath the mower's hand / Lie withering ere 'tis night.

Our God, our help in ages past, / Our hope for years to come, /
Be Thou our guard while troubles last, / And our eternal home.

P.S.   We also have a great Christmas carol from this 1719 collection. As Watts studied Psalm 98, especially verses 4–9, he worded them this way: *Joy to the world, the Lord is come! Let earth receive her King!*

God Is the Refuge of His Saints

Isaac Watts

Lowell Mason

1. God is the ref - uge of His saints, When
2. Let moun-tains from their seats be hurled Down
3. There is a stream, whose gen - tle flow Sup -
4. That sac - red stream, Thy ho - ly Word, That

storms of sharp dis - tress in - vade;
to the deep, and bur - ied there;
plies the cit - y of our God,
all our rag - ing fear con - trols;

Ere we can of - fer our com - plaints, Be -
Con - vul - sions shake the sol - id world: Our
Life, love, and joy, still guid - ing through, And
Sweet peace Thy prom - i - ses af - ford, And

hold Him pres - ent with His aid.
faith shall nev - er yield to fear.
wat'r - ing our di - vine a - bode.
give new strength to faint - ing souls.

God Is the Refuge of His Saints

1719

The LORD of hosts is with us; the God of Jacob is our refuge. Psalm 46:7

In appearance, Isaac Watts was . . . well, odd. Standing five feet in his stockings, he had an outsized head and prominent nose, and his skin was tallowy. One woman, Elizabeth Singer, having never met him, fell in love with him through his hymns and poems, but when she saw him face-to-face, she was unsettled. He fell in love with her, but she couldn't bring herself to marry him, later saying, "I only wish I could admire the casket (jewelry box) as much as I admire the jewel."

In 1739, Watts suffered a stroke that left him able to speak but unable to write. A secretary was provided to transcribe his dictated poems and books, but over the next several years he became increasingly weak and bedridden. He died on November 25, 1748, and is buried in Bunhill Fields in London.

In addition to his 600 hymns, he wrote 52 other works, including a book of logic widely used in universities, and books on grammar, astronomy, philosophy, and geography. But it's his hymns—most of them written in his early twenties—for which we're most grateful.

Here's a lesser known Watts hymn. It is his rendition of Psalm 46, the same Scripture that had inspired Luther's "A Mighty Fortress." Watts takes a gentler approach:

> *God is the refuge of His saints, / When storms of sharp distress invade; /*
> *Ere we can offer our complaints, / Behold Him present with His aid.*
>
> *Loud may the troubled ocean roar; / In sacred peace our souls abide; /*
> *While every nation, every shore, / Trembles, and dreads the swelling tide.*
>
> *There is a stream, whose gentle flow / Supplies the city of our God, /*
> *Life, love, and joy, still guiding through, / And wat'ring our divine abode.*
>
> *That sacred stream—Thy holy Word— / That all our raging fear controls; /*
> *Sweet peace Thy promises afford, / And give new strength to fainting souls.*
>
> *Zion enjoys her Monarch's love, / Secure against a threatening hour; /*
> *Nor can her firm foundations move, / Built on His truth, and armed with power.*

Joy to the World!

Isaac Watts

George Frederick Handel
Arr. by Lowell Mason

1. Joy to the world! the Lord is come; Let earth re - ceive her King. Let ev - ery heart pre - pare Him room, And heav'n and na - ture sing, And heav'n and na - ture sing, And heav'n, and heav'n and na - ture sing.

2. Joy to the world! the Sav - ior reigns; Let men their songs em - ploy, While fields and floods, Rocks, hills and plains Re - peat the sound - ing joy, Re - peat the sound - ing joy, Re - peat, re - peat the sound - ing joy.

3. No more let sin and sor - row grow, Nor thorns in - fest the ground. He comes to make His bless - ings flow Far as the curse is found, Far as the curse is found, Far as, far as the curse is found.

4. He rules the world with truth and grace And makes the na - tions prove The glo - ries of His righ - teous - ness And won - ders of His love, And won - ders of His love, And won - ders, and won - ders of His love.

1. And heav'n and na-ture sing, And heav'n and na-ture sing,

Joy to the World!

1719

Shout joyfully to the LORD, all the earth; Break forth in song, rejoice, and sing praises. Psalm 98:4

ntil Isaac Watts came along, most of the singing in British churches was from the Psalms of David. The church—especially the Church of Scotland—had labored over the Psalms with great effort and scholarship, translating them into poems with rhyme and rhythm suitable for singing. As a young man in Southampton, Isaac had become dissatisfied with the quality of singing, and he keenly felt the limitations of being able to only sing these Psalms. So he "invented" the English hymn.

He did not, however, neglect the Psalms. In 1719, he published a unique hymnal—one in which he had translated, interpreted, and paraphrased the Old Testament Psalms through the eyes of New Testament faith. He called it simply, *The Psalms of David Imitated in the Language of the New Testament.* Taking various Psalms, he studied them from the perspective of Jesus and the New Testament, and then formed them into verses for singing.

"I have rather expressed myself as I may suppose David would have done if he lived in the days of Christianity," Watts explained, "and by this means, perhaps, I have sometimes hit upon the true intent of the Spirit of God in those verses farther and clearer than David himself could ever discover."

Watt's archenemy, Thomas Bradbury, was greatly critical of Watts' songs, which he called *whims* instead of *hymns.* He accused Watts of thinking he was King David. Watts replied in a letter, "You tell me that I rival it with David, whether he or I be the sweet psalmist of Israel. I abhor the thought; while yet, at the same time, I am fully persuaded that the Jewish psalm book was never designed to be the only Psalter for the Christian church."

"Joy to the World!" is Isaac Watts' interpretation of Psalm 98, which says: "Shout joyfully to the Lord, all the earth" (verse 4). As he read Psalm 98, Isaac pondered the real reason for shouting joyfully to the Lord—the Messiah has come to redeem us. The result, despite the now-forgotten criticisms of men like Bradbury, has been a timeless carol that has brightened our Christmases for nearly three hundred years.

I'll Praise My Maker While I've Breath

Isaac Watts

Probably by Matthäus Greiter

1. I'll praise my Mak - er while I've breath; And when my voice
2. Hap - py the man whose hopes re - ly On Is - rael's God;
3. The Lord pours eye - sight on the blind; The Lord sup - ports
4. I'll praise Him while He lends me breath; And when my voice

is lost in death, Praise shall em - ploy my no - bler powers.
He made the sky And earth and seas with all their train.
the faint - ing mind; He sends the la - boring con - science peace,
is lost in death, Praise shall em - ploy my no - bler powers.

My days of praise shall ne'er be past, While life, and thought,
His truth for - ev - er stand se - cure, He saves th'op - pressed,
He helps the stran - ger in dis - tress, The wid - ow and
My days of praise shall ne'er be past, While life, and thought,

and be - ing last, Or im - mor - tal - i - ty en - dures.
He feeds the poor, And none shall find His prom - ise vain.
the fa - ther - less, And grants the pris - oner sweet re - lease.
and be - ing last, Or im - mor - tal - i - ty en - dures.

I'll Praise My Maker While I've Breath

1719

While I live I will praise the LORD; I will sing praises to my God while I have my being. Psalm 146:2

Several well-known hymns first appeared in Watts' *Psalms of David*, including "O God Our Help in Ages Past" (from Psalm 90), "Joy to the World!" (Psalm 98), "Jesus Shall Reign Where'er the Sun," (Psalm 72), and "I'll Praise My Maker While I've Breath," Watts' rendition of Psalm 146.

> *I'll praise my Maker while I've breath;*
> *And when my voice is lost in death,*
> *Praise shall employ my nobler powers.*
> *My days of praise shall ne'er be past . . .*

The theme of this hymn reflects Isaac's great interest in the afterlife. One of his most popular books was *The World to Come,* in which he vividly described the Bible's teaching about heaven, hell, and eternity. He wrote, "Death to a good man is but passing through . . . one little dusky room of his Father's house into another that is fair and large, lightsome and glorious, and divinely entertaining."

Then he added this personal note: "Oh, may the rays and splendors of my heavenly apartment shoot far downward and gild the dark entry with such a cheerful beam as to banish every fear when I shall be called to pass through."

It was as he wished. As he lay on his deathbed for three weeks in November of 1748, at age seventy-four, his friends gathered around. Mustering his strength, he exclaimed, "If God should raise me up again, I may finish some more of my papers, or God can make use of me to save a soul, and that will be worth living for. If God has no more service for me to do, through grace I am ready; it is a great mercy to me that I have no manner of fear or dread of death. . . ."

He was buried in London's Bunhill Fields, and this epitaph, prepared by himself, was placed at his tomb:

Isaac Watts, D.D., pastor of a church of Christ in London . . .
after fifty years of feeble labours in the gospel,
interrupted by four years of tiresome sickness, was at last dismissed to his rest . . .
2 Corinthians 5:8: Absent from the body, and present with the Lord.
Colossians 3:4: When Christ, who is my life, shall appear,
then shall I also appear with Him in Glory.

Am I a Soldier of the Cross?

Isaac Watts

Thomas A. Arne

1. Am I a sol - dier of the cross,
2. Must I be car - ried to the skies
3. Are there no foes for me to face?
4. Sure I must fight, if I would reign;
5. Thy saints in all this glo - rious war
6. When that il - lus - trious day shall rise,

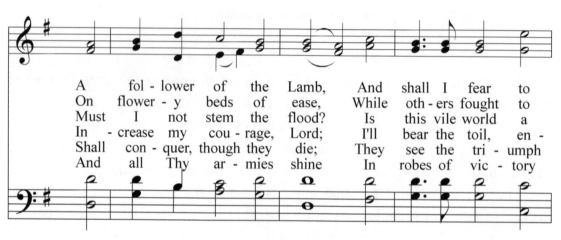

A fol - lower of the Lamb, And shall I fear to
On flower - y beds of ease, While oth - ers fought to
Must I not stem the flood? Is this vile world a
In - crease my cou - rage, Lord; I'll bear the toil, en -
Shall con - quer, though they die; They see the tri - umph
And all Thy ar - mies shine In robes of vic - tory

own His cause, Or blush to speak His name?
win the prize, And sailed through blood - y seas?
friend to grace, To help me on to God?
dure the pain, Sup - port - ed by Thy word.
from a - far, By faith they bring it nigh.
through the skies, The glo - ry shall be Thine.

Am I a Soldier of the Cross?

1724

Watch, stand fast in the faith, be brave, be strong. 1 Corinthians 16:13

This Isaac Watts hymn appeared after most of his others, not in a collection of hymns, but in a published volume of his sermons. It followed a sermon entitled "Holy Fortitude," based on 1 Corinthians 16:13: "Watch, stand fast in the faith, be brave, be strong."

Over a century later, this song played a role in American hymnology, bringing together the powerful gospel team of evangelist D. L. Moody and soloist Ira Sankey.

It happened this way. By the 1870s, D. L. Moody had become a world-famed evangelist, but he badly needed a musician to lead singing at his meetings. On a Saturday night in 1870, he preached at a convention in Indianapolis. At the last minute, a tax collector named Ira Sankey was asked to lead singing.

After the service, Moody assaulted Sankey with questions, "Where are you from? Are you married? What is your business?"

Sankey replied that he lived in Pennsylvania, was married, had two children, and worked for the government, whereupon Moody said abruptly, "You will have to give that up."

Sankey, dumbfounded, asked "What for?"

"To help me in my work. I have been looking for you for the last eight years."

The next day, Sankey received a card from Moody, suggesting they meet on a certain corner that evening at six. Sankey arrived first. When Moody showed up, he said nothing but entered a nearby store for a large box. He asked Sankey to stand on the box and sing.

Sankey dutifully hoisted himself up and sang Isaac Watts' *Am I a soldier of the cross, a follower of the Lamb, / and shall I fear to own His cause, or blush to speak His Name?*

Workers, going home from mills and factories, were arrested by Sankey's beautiful voice, and the crowd grew. Moody ascended the box and preached for twenty-five minutes before announcing that the meeting would continue in the Opera House. The Opera House was soon packed, and Moody preached the gospel with great power. Finally, he closed the meeting, saying, "Now we must close, as the brethren of the convention wish to come in to discuss the question, 'How to reach the masses!'"

That was the beginning of three remarkable decades. Moody and Sankey, soldiers of Christ, crisscrossed the world, singing and preaching and reaching the masses as few others, before or since.

Give to the Winds Thy Fears

Paul Gerhardt, trans. by John Wesley

Samuel Howard

1. Give to the winds Thy fears; Hope and be un-dis-mayed; God hears Thy sighs and counts Thy tears, God shall lift up Thy head.
2. Through waves and clouds and storms, He gent-ly clears Thy way; Wait Thou His time; So shall this night soon end in joy-ous day.
3. Leave to God's sov-'reign sway To choose and to com-mand; So shall Thou, won-d'ring, own that way, How wise, how strong His hand!
4. Let us in life, in death, Thy stead-fast truth de-clare, And pub-lish with our lat-est breath Thy love and guard-ian care.
5. Far, far a-bove thy thought His coun-sel shall ap-pear, When ful-ly He the work hath wrought That caused thy need-less fear.

Give to the Winds Thy Fears

1737

I sought the LORD, and He heard me, And delivered me from all my fears. Psalm 34:4

I t's hard to imagine two brothers making a larger impact on the Christian world than John and Charles Wesley. They were among the nineteen children born to Samuel and Susanna Wesley of little Epworth, England. John was four years older, and because he went off to school at an early age, the two didn't spend extended time together until they found themselves together at Oxford University. There they began praying in small groups, and both began planning for the ministry. Both were ordained in the Church of England. Both went to Georgia as missionaries and returned to England as failures. Both had a transforming experience with Christ the week of May 21, 1738. And both became powerful evangelists, accomplished hymnists, and the founders of the Methodist Movement.

But the two brothers often clashed when it came to personal issues or organizational matters within Methodism. Two examples stand out.

Once, during an illness, John fell in love with his nurse, Grace Murray. He more or less proposed to her, saying, "If I ever marry, I think you will be the person." She more or less accepted. But when Charles heard of it, he flew to Grace's house shouting, "Grace Murray! You have broken my heart," and fainted. When he recovered, he pelted her with objections, saying she would destroy his brother's ministry. She broke the engagement, leaving John to scribble painfully, "We were torn asunder by a whirlwind."

Another painful dispute involved the prospect of Methodism detaching itself from the Anglican Church. Charles spent his sunset years trying to prevent the split, prompting John, eighty-two, to write him, saying, "I do nothing rashly. It is not likely I should. . . . If you will go hand in hand with me, do. But do not hinder me if you will not help . . . With or without help, I creep on."

Despite their differences, however, these two brothers became a dynamic duo for revival, and they changed the world.

They also set the world to singing. Charles wrote most of their hymns, but John often edited Charles's hymns and wrote several of his own.

John also liked to translate German hymns for use by his English Methodists. "Give to the Winds Thy Fears" was originally written by the great German hymnist, Paul Gerhardt. John translated it in 1737, and it became a Methodist favorite, proclaiming the spirit of faith by which they lived.

And Can It Be That I Should Gain?

Charles Wesley

Thomas Campbell

1. And can it be that I should gain An in - t'rest
2. He left His Fa - ther's throne a - bove, So free, so
3. No con - dem - na - tion now I dread; Je - sus, and
4. Long my im - pris - oned spir - it lay Fast bound in

in the Sa - vior's blood? Died He for me, who caused His pain?
in - fi - nite His grace; Emp - tied Him - self of all but love,
all in Him, is mine! A - live in Him my liv - ing Head,
sin and na - ture's night; Thine eye dif - fused a quick - 'ning ray,

For me, who Him to death pur - sued? A - maz - ing love! How
And bled for A - dam's help - less race. 'Tis mer - cy all, im -
And clothed in righ - teous - ness di - vine, Bold I ap - proach th'e -
I woke, the dun - geon flamed with light; My chains fell off, my

can it be That Thou, my God, shouldst die for me?
mense and free! For, O my God it found out me!
ter - nal throne, And claim the crown, through Christ my own.
heart was free; I rose, went forth and fol - lowed Thee.

And Can It Be That I Should Gain?

1738

But He was wounded for our transgressions, He was bruised for our iniquities;
The chastisement for our peace was upon Him, and by His stripes we are healed.
Isaiah 53:5

 harles Wesley was born just before Christmas in 1707. He was premature and neither cried nor opened his eyes. His mother, Susanna, kept him tightly wrapped in wool until his actual due date, whereupon he opened his eyes and cried.

At age eight, he was taken to London to attend Westminster School. At thirteen, he became a King's Scholar at Westminster, and upon graduating, Charles enrolled at Oxford. He was nineteen and full of life. He later said, "My first year at college I lost in diversions."

During his second year at Oxford, he grew serious about spiritual things. Neither he nor his brother, John, had yet received Christ as Savior, but they began seeking to live the Christian life so methodically they were dubbed "Methodists" by fellow students.

Their studies completed, the brothers volunteered to go to Georgia, a new colony in America for those in Britain's debtors' prisons, founded by Colonel James Oglethorpe. But as a missionary, Charles was an utter failure. He was demanding and autocratic, and he insisted on baptizing infants, not by sprinkling, but by immersing them three times in succession. One angry woman fired a gun at him.

Charles left America ill and depressed. Some time later, John also returned in low spirits. Finding themselves in spiritual crisis, the brothers began attending meetings led by the Moravian Christian, Peter Boehler. Finally, on Sunday, May 21, 1738 Charles, 31, wrote, "I now found myself at peace with God, and rejoiced in hope of loving Christ. I saw that by faith I stood."

John came to Christ about the same time, saying, "I felt my heart strangely warmed."

On Tuesday, May 23, Charles wrote in his journal, "I began a hymn upon my conversion." We aren't certain which hymn he meant, but many historians think it was "And Can It Be," because of the vivid testimony of verse 4:

Long my imprisoned spirit lay,
Fast bound in sin and nature's night;
Thine eye diffused a quickening ray—
I woke, the dungeon flamed with light;
My chains fell off, my heart was free,
I rose, went forth, and followed Thee.

O for a Thousand Tongues to Sing

Charles Wesley

Carl G. Gläser; arr. by Lowell Mason

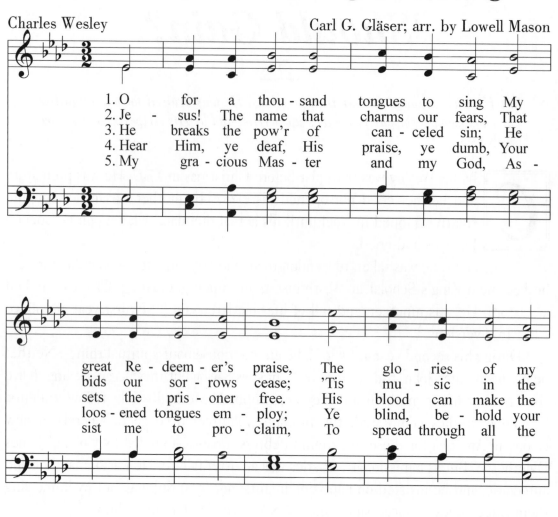

1. O for a thou - sand tongues to sing My
2. Je - sus! The name that charms our fears, That
3. He breaks the pow'r of can - celed sin; He
4. Hear Him, ye deaf, His praise, ye dumb, Your
5. My gra - cious Mas - ter and my God, As -

great Re - deem - er's praise, The glo - ries of my
bids our sor - rows cease; 'Tis mu - sic in the
sets the pris - oner free. His blood can make the
loos - ened tongues em - ploy; Ye blind, be - hold your
sist me to pro - claim, To spread through all the

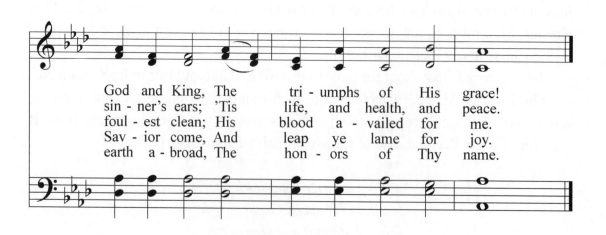

God and King, The tri - umphs of His grace!
sin - ner's ears; 'Tis life, and health, and peace.
foul - est clean; His blood a - vailed for me.
Sav - ior come, And leap ye lame for joy.
earth a - broad, The hon - ors of Thy name.

O for a Thousand Tongues to Sing

1739

. . . The whole multitude . . . began to rejoice and praise God with a loud voice for all the mighty works they had seen. Luke 19:37

The Wesley brothers sent word of their conversion to their sainted mother, Susanna, who didn't know what to make of it. "I think you have fallen into an odd way of thinking," she replied. "You say that till within a few months you had no spiritual life and no justifying faith . . . . I heartily rejoice that you have attained to a strong and lively hope in God's mercy through Christ. Not that I can think that you were totally without saving faith before, but it is one thing to have faith, and another thing to be sensible we have it."

Well, Charles was now very sensible of having it. His life changed, and he gained victory over both his temper and his unfortunate drinking habit. "I was amazed to find my old enemy, intemperance, so suddenly subdued, that I almost forgot I was ever in bondage to him."

He also began to spread the news of what had happened to him. "In the coach to London," he wrote, "I preached faith in Christ. A lady was extremely offended . . . (and) threatened to beat me. I declared I deserved nothing but hell; so did she; and must confess it, before she could have a title to heaven. This was most intolerable to her."

New vitality came into Charles' public preaching. He discontinued the practice of reading his sermons, and began preaching extemporaneously.

He found a fruitful arena for ministry at the infamous Newgate Prison, and allowed himself to be locked up with condemned men on nights before their executions, that he might comfort and witness to them during their final hours.

As the first anniversary of his conversion approached, Charles wrote an eighteen-stanza hymn describing his praise to the Lord. It was titled, "For the Anniversary Day of One's Conversion," and the first stanza began: "Glory to God, and praise, and love . . . ." Verse seven began, "O for a thousand tongues to sing," inspired by a statement Charles had once heard: "Had I a thousand tongues, I would praise Him with them all."

Beginning with a 1767 hymnbook, the seventh stanza was made the first, and when John Wesley complied his *Collection of Hymns* in 1780, he chose this for the first hymn in the book. Congregations today usually sing verses seven, eight, nine, and ten of Wesley's original, which we know today as "O for a Thousand Tongues to Sing."

Hark! The Herald Angels Sing

Charles Wesley

Felix Mendelssohn

1. Hark! the her - ald an - gels sing, "Glo - ry to the new - born King;
2. Christ, by high - est heav'n a - dored, Christ, the ev - er - last - ing Lord;
3. Hail the heav'n born Prince of Peace! Hail the Sun of Righ-teous-ness!

Peace on earth and mer - cy mild, God and sin - ners rec - on - ciled."
Late in time be - hold Him come, Off - spring of a vir-gin's womb.
Light and life to all He brings, Ris'n with heal - ing in His wings.

Joy - ful, all ye na - tions, rise, Join the tri - umph of the skies;
Veiled in flesh the God-head see, Hail, th'in - car - nate De - i - ty!
Mild He lays His glo - ry by, Born that man no more may die;

With an - gel - ic hosts pro-claim, "Christ is born in Beth - le - hem."
Pleased as man with men to dwell, Je - sus our Em - man - u - el.
Born to raise the sons of earth, Born to give them sec - ond birth.

Hark! The Herald Angels Sing
1739

Then the angel said to them, "Do not be afraid, for behold, I bring you good tidings of great joy which will be to all people." Luke 2:10

Upon his conversion, Charles Wesley immediately began writing hymns, each one packed with doctrine, all of them exhibiting strength and sensitivity, both beauty and theological brawn. He wrote constantly, and even on horseback his mind was flooded with new songs. He often stopped at houses along the road and ran in asking for "pen and ink."

He wrote over 6,000 hymns during his life, and he didn't like people tinkering with the words. In one of his hymnals, he wrote: "I beg leave to mention a thought which has been long upon my mind, and which I should long ago have inserted in the public papers, had I not been unwilling to stir up a nest of hornets. Many gentlemen have done my brother and me (though without naming us) the honor to reprint many of our hymns. Now they are perfectly welcome to do so, provided they print them just as they are. But I desire they would not attempt to mend them, for they are really not able. None of them is able to mend either the sense or the verse. Therefore, I must beg of them these two favors: either to let them stand just as they are, to take things for better or worse, or to add the true reading in the margin, or at the bottom of the page, that we may no longer be accountable either for the nonsense or for the doggerel of other men."

But one man did the church a great favor by polishing up one of Charles' best-loved hymns. When Charles was 32, he wrote a Christmas hymn that began:

> *Hark, how all the welkin rings,*
> *"Glory to the King of kings;*
> *Peace on earth, and mercy mild,*
> *God and sinners reconciled!"*
> *Joyful, all ye nations, rise,*
> *Join the triumph of the skies;*
> *Universal nature say,*
> *"Christ the Lord is born to-day!"*

The word "welkin" was an old English term for "the vault of heaven." It was Charles' friend, evangelist George Whitefield, who, when he published this carol in his collection of hymns in 1753, changed the words to the now-beloved, "Hark! The Herald Angels Sing."

Christ the Lord Is Risen Today

Charles Wesley

from *Lyra Davidica*

1. Christ the Lord is risen to-day, Al - - le - lu - ia!
2. Lives a - gain our glo - rious King, Al - - le - lu - ia!
3. Love's re - deem - ing work is done, Al - - le - lu - ia!
4. Soar we now where Christ has led, Al - - le - lu - ia!

Sons of men and an - gels say: Al - - le - lu - ia!
Where, O death, is now thy sting? Al - - le - lu - ia!
Fought the fight, the bat - tle won, Al - - le - lu - ia!
Fol - lowing our ex - alt - ed Head, Al - - le - lu - ia!

Raise your joys and tri - umphs high, Al - - le - lu - ia!
Dy - ing once He all doth save, Al - - le - lu - ia!
Death in vain for - bids Him rise, Al - - le - lu - ia!
Made like Him, like Him we rise, Al - - le - lu - ia!

Sing, ye heavens, and earth, re - ply: Al - - le - lu - ia!
Where thy vic - tor - y, O grave? Al - - le - lu - ia!
Christ hath o - pened par - a - dise, Al - - le - lu - ia!
Ours the cross, the grave, the skies, Al - - le - lu - ia!

Christ the Lord Is Risen Today

1739

And if Christ is not risen, then our preaching is empty and your faith is also empty.
1 Corinthians 15:14

John and Charles Wesley soon found themselves out of favor with many fellow Anglican ministers who spurned their fiery evangelistic preaching. Many pulpits were closed to them.

A friend from his Oxford days, George Whitefield, 22, who was having the same trouble, began preaching in the open air. In London, he asked Charles to stand with him as he preached to thousands in the open air at Blackheath, and Charles, too, got a vision for reaching the multitudes.

He made his first attempt in the outskirts of London. "Franklyn, a farmer, invited me to preach in his field," he wrote. "I did so to about 500. I returned to the house rejoicing." Soon he was preaching to thousands. "My load was gone, and all my doubts and scruples. God shone upon my path; and I knew this was his will concerning me."

A man named Joseph Williams heard Charles in Bristol: "I found him standing on a table-board, in an erect posture . . . surrounded by, I guess, more than a thousand people, some of them fashionable persons, but most of the lower rank of mankind. He prayed with uncommon fervency . . . He then preached about half an hour in such a manner as I have scarce ever heard any man preach . . . . I think I never heard any man labor so earnestly to convince his hearers they were all by nature in a sinful, lost, undone, damnable state; that notwithstanding, there was a possibility of their salvation, through faith in Christ . . . All this he backed up with many texts of Scripture, which he explained and illustrated, and then by a variety of the most forcible motives, arguments, and expostulation, did he invite, allure, quicken, and labor, if it were possible, to compel all, and every of his hearers, to believe in Christ for salvation."

Charles Wesley still preaches today in much the same way through his ageless hymns which are sung around the world each Sunday. Perhaps his most exuberant anthem is the one he simply called, "Hymn for Easter Day," published in 1739. It originally consisted of eleven stanzas. The "Alleluia's" were added later, but appropriately, for this is a hymn one never gets tired of singing:

Christ, the Lord, is risen today, Alleluia!
Sons of men and angels say, Alleluia!
Raise your joys and triumphs high, Alleluia!
Sing, ye heavens, and earth, reply, Alleluia!

Jesus, Thy Blood and Righteousness

Nickolaus von Zinzendorf

William Gardiner

1. Je - sus, Thy blood and righ - teous - ness
2. Bold shall I stand in Thy great day,
3. Lord, I be - lieve Thy pre - cious blood,
4. Lord, I be - lieve were sin - ners more

My beau - ty are, my glo - rious dress; 'Midst
For who aught to my charge shall lay? Ful -
Which, at the mer - cy seat of God, For -
Than sands up - on the o - cean shore, Thou

flam - ing worlds, in these ar - rayed, With
ly ab - solved through these I am, From
ev - er doth for sin - ners plead, For
hast for all a ran - som paid, For

joy shall I lift up my head.
sin and fear, from guilt and shame.
me, e'en for my soul, was shed.
all a full a - tone - ment made.

Jesus, Thy Blood and Righteousness

1739

But of Him you are in Christ Jesus, who became for us wisdom from God—and righteousness and sanctification and redemption. 1 Corinthians 1:30

Travel with me to Germany. After flying into Berlin, we rent a car and drive south to Dresden, then east toward the Polish and Czech borders. There on Highway 178 is the little town of Herrnhut. At first glance, it seems like any other German village; but there in the central square is a large, plainly furnished church, dazzling white on the inside. It's the Moravian Meeting House, rebuilt after having been destroyed by bombs during World War II.

On one side of town is a hillside called "God's Acre," the Moravian Cemetery containing the tomb of the city's founder, Count Nikolaus Ludwig von Zinzendorf. Just beyond "God's Acre," you'll find the ruins of the count's vast manor house.

These are some of the most significant sites in modern Church history.

Count Zinzendorf (1700–1760) was born into wealth, and his family insisted on his pursuing a career as diplomat and statesman. But from childhood, Zinzendorf had a tender heart toward the Lord and felt God's call to the ministry.

The opportunity came unexpectedly. In nearby Moravia, a group of Christians were being persecuted for their faith. They approached Zinzendorf, asking for refuge on his estate. He assisted them in building a community named Herrnhut, a word meaning "Under the Lord's Watch." Zinzendorf became their spiritual leader.

It was in Herrnhut on August 18, 1732, in an extraordinary, emotion-packed service, that two men were commissioned for overseas missionary work. It was a historic moment, for virtually no Protestant group had previously sent out missionaries; but between 1732 to 1742, more than 70 missionaries left Herrnhut, a community of six hundred. This has been called "The Golden Decade," the dawn of Protestant missions.

It was also Zinzendorf's London-based Moravians who later led John and Charles Wesley to genuine faith in Christ and helped launch their history-changing ministry.

The Moravians were a singing people. On the night the two missionaries were commissioned, the church sang one hundred hymns. Zinzendorf wrote many of these songs, the best-known of which is:

> *Jesus, Thy blood and righteousness*
> *My beauty are, my glorious dress;*
> *'Midst flaming worlds, in these arrayed,*
> *With joy shall I lift up my head.*

Where Shall My Wondering Soul Begin?

Charles Wesley

Attr. to Jeremiah Ingalls

Where Shall My Wondering Soul Begin?

1739

And now, LORD, what do I wait for? My hope is in You. Psalm 39:7

The great hymnist, Charles Wesley, was converted to Christ on Pentecost Sunday, May 21, 1738. He was staying in the London home of his friend, John Bray. He was ill at the time, and Bray was tending to him both physically and spiritually. Wesley's journal tracks the course of his remarkable conversion:

Thursday, May 11, 1738. *Mr. Bray read me many comfortable Scriptures . . . so that I was persuaded I should not leave his house before I believed with my heart unto righteousness.*

May 12. *This day . . . I spent in discoursing on faith, either with those that had it, or those that sought it.*

May 13. *I waked without Christ; yet still desirous of finding Him.*

May 14. *The beginning of the day I was very heavy, weary, and unable to pray . . . I longed to find Christ that I might show Him to all mankind. . . .*

May 17. *About midnight I was waked by the return of my pleurisy. I felt great pain and straitness at my heart; but found immediate relief by bleeding. I had some discourse with Mr. Bray; thought myself willing to die the next moment, if I might but believe. . . .*

May 19. *At five this morning the pain and difficulty in breathing returned. The surgeon was sent for; but I fell asleep before he could bleed me a second time. I was easier all day, after taking Dr. Cockburn's medicines. . . . I received the sacrament; but not Christ.*

May 20. *I waked much disappointed, and continued all day in great dejection. . . . Mr. Bray, too, seemed troubled at my not yet believing. . . .*

Sunday, May 21, 1738. *I rose and looked into the Scripture. The words that first presented were, "And now, Lord, what is my hope? Truly my hope is even in Thee. . . ." I now found myself at peace with God, and rejoiced in hope of loving Christ. . . . I saw that by faith I stood. . . . I went to bed. . . . confident of Christ's protection.*

Within just a day or two, Charles wrote "Where Shall My Wondering Soul Begin?" Some historians believe it is the first of his thousands of hymns, one that expressed the joy of his newfound faith.

Jesus, Lover of My Soul

Charles Wesley

Simeon B. Marsh

1. Je - sus, Lov - er of my soul, Let me to Thy bo - som fly,
2. Oth - er ref - uge have I none; Hangs my help-less soul on Thee.
3. Thou, O Christ, art all I want; More than all in Thee I find.
4. Plen - teous grace with Thee is found, Grace to cov - er all my sin.

While the near - er wa - ters roll, While the tem - pest still is high!
Leave, ah, leave me not a - lone; Still sup - port and com - fort me!
Raise the fall - en cheer the faint, Heal the sick and lead the blind.
Let the heal - ing streams a - bound; Make and keep me pure with - in.

Hide me O my Sav - ior hide, Till the storm of life is past.
All my trust on Thee is stayed; All my help from Thee I bring.
Just and ho - ly is Thy name; I am all un - righ-teous - ness.
Thou of life the Foun - tain art, Free - ly let me take of Thee.

Safe in - to the ha - ven guide. Oh, re-ceive my soul at last!
Cov - er my de - fense-less head, With the shad-ow of Thy wing.
False and full of sin I am; Thou art full of truth and grace.
Spring Thou up with - in my heart; Rise to all e - ter - ni - ty.

Jesus, Lover of My Soul
1740

For He Himself has said, "I will never leave you nor forsake you." So we may boldly say: "The Lord is my helper; I will not fear. What can man do to me?"
Hebrews 13:5b–6

Many stories have arisen around the writing of "Jesus, Lover of My Soul," but they all appear to be fictional. We don't know the exact occasion for his composition, but it was written shortly after Charles Wesley's conversion, and its words seem to anticipate the huge crowds, lawless mobs, midnight escapes, traveling dangers, and flea-infested beds he would encounter in coming years. Wesley's life, in brief, can be summed up as follows:

As the Methodist movement spread through England, Charles traveled horseback from place to place, an itinerant, homeless evangelist. His fiery preaching incited revival in some people and outrage in others.

In the midst of all this, his dear mother, Susanna, died on July 23, 1742. Her last words were, "Children, as soon as I am released, sing a psalm of praise to God." Later, preaching in Wales, Charles met Sally Gwynne, a beautiful girl half his age. A courtship followed, and Charles wanted to propose, but he was virtually penniless with no way of supporting a wife.

That's when he decided to publish his *Hymns and Sacred Poems,* as well as his journals and sermons, hoping the royalties would provide an income. Charles and Sally were married on April 8, 1749, Charles noting: "Not a cloud was to be seen from morning till night. I rose at four, spent three hours and a half in prayer or singing, with my brother . . . . At eight I led my Sally to church . . . . It was a most solemn season of love!"

They left immediately on a preaching tour, and Charles continued his itinerant ministry until 1756, when, at age 49, exhausted, he and Sally settled down. Charles busied himself preaching, visiting, counseling, fretting about his three unsaved children, trying to keep Methodism within the Church of England, and giving unsolicited advice to his brother, John. All the while, he worked tirelessly on his hymns and poems.

By early 1788, Charles was bedfast, not from sickness but from a lifetime of fatigue. By March, too weak to write, he dictated his last hymn to Sally:

In age and feebleness extreme, Who shall a sinful worm redeem?
Jesus, my only hope Thou art, strength of my failing flesh and heart;
Oh, could I catch a smile from Thee, and drop into eternity!

Hallelujah Chorus

from *The Messiah*

George Frideric Handel

George Frideric Handel

Hal - le - lu - jah! Hal - le - lu - jah! Hal - le - lu - jah! Hal - le - lu - jah! Hal-

le - lu - jah! Hal - le - lu - jah! Hal - le - lu - jah! Hal - le -

lu - jah! Hal - le - lu - jah! Hal - le - lu - jah! For the Lord

God om - nip - o - tent reign - eth. Hal - le - lu - jah!

Hallelujah Chorus
(from *The Messiah*)

1741

Let the heavens rejoice, and let the earth be glad; and let them say among the nations, the LORD reigns. 1 Chronicles 16:31

His father tried to discourage his musical interests, preferring that he enter the legal profession. But it was the organ, harpsichord, and violin that captured the heart of young George Frideric Handel. Once, accompanying his father to the court of Duke Johann Adolf, George wandered into the chapel, found the organ, and started improvising. The startled Duke exclaimed, "Who is this remarkable child?"

This "remarkable child" soon began composing operas, first in Italy then in London. By his 20s, he was the talk of England and the best paid composer on earth. He opened the Royal Academy of Music. Londoners fought for seats at his every performance, and his fame soared around the world.

But the glory passed. Audiences dwindled. His music became outdated, and he was thought of as an old fogey. Newer artists eclipsed the aging composer. One project after another failed, and Handel, now bankrupt, grew depressed. The stress brought on a case of palsy that crippled some of his fingers. "Handel's great days are over," wrote Frederick the Great, "his inspiration is exhausted."

Yet his troubles also matured him, softening his sharp tongue. His temper mellowed, and his music became more heartfelt. One morning Handel received by post a manuscript from Charles Jennens. It was a word-for-word collection of various biblical texts about Christ. The opening words from Isaiah 40 moved Handel: *Comfort ye, comfort ye my people. . . .*

On August 22, 1741, he shut the door of his London home and started composing music for the words. Twenty-three days later, the world had *Messiah.* "Whether I was in the body or out of the body when I wrote it, I know not," Handel later said, trying to describe the experience. *Messiah* opened in London to enormous crowds on March 23, 1743, with Handel leading from his harpsichord. King George II, who was present that night, surprised everyone by leaping to his feet during the *Hallelujah Chorus.* No one knows why. Some believe the king, being hard of hearing, thought it the national anthem.

No matter—from that day audiences everywhere have stood in reverence during the stirring words: *Hallelujah! For He shall reign forever and ever.*

Handel's fame was rekindled, and even after he lost his eyesight, he continued playing the organ for performances of his oratorios until his death in London, April 14, 1759.

O for a Heart to Praise My God

Charles Wesley

A Collection of Hymns and Sacred Poems
Probably arranged by John F. Lampe

1. O for a heart to praise my
2. A heart re - signed, sub - mis - sive,
3. A hum - ble, low - ly, con - trite
4. A heart in ev - ery thought re -

God, A heart from sin set free, A
meek, My great Re - deem - er's throne, Where
heart, Be - liev - ing, true and clean; Which
newed, And full of love di - vine; Per -

heart that al - ways feels Thy
on - ly Christ is heard to
nei - ther life nor death can
fect and right and pure and

blood, So free - ly shed for me!
speak, Where Je - sus reigns a - lone.
part, From Christ who dwells with - in!
good, A cop - y, Lord, of Thine.

O for a Heart to Praise My God

1742

. . . From childhood you have known the Holy Scriptures, which are able to make you wise for salvation through faith which is in Christ Jesus. 2 Timothy 3:15

Charles Wesley began preaching as soon as he'd been converted. He had already been ordained into the Anglican ministry, but his lack of genuine faith had robbed him of both motivation and message, and his ministry had been a failure. Upon his conversion, he found himself longing to proclaim the New Birth. He began preaching in religious meetings here and there, in a few churches, and in private homes.

At first, Charles followed the custom of the day in writing out his sermons and reading them word for word, but he felt inhibited by this practice. About five months after his conversion, he was invited to preach in a church with a small crowd. Deciding this was the time to experiment, he cast his notes aside. He recorded the results in his journal: "Seeing so few present at St. Antholin's, I thought of preaching extempore: afraid; yet ventured on the promise, 'Lo, I am with you always;' and spake on justification from Romans 3 for three quarters of an hour without hesitation. Glory be to God, who keepeth His promises forever."

Charles was a dynamic, emotional preacher, a bundle of zeal, an opinionated, strong-willed, stubborn evangelist. He was soon preaching to huge crowds; but he was at his best as a personal soul-winner. Here is an entry from his journal for September 27, 1738:

Wed., September 27th. *In our way to Oxford, I talked with my fellow-traveler, Mr. Combes. He expressed his desire of faith: I was moved to sing, "Salvation by Faith," then "Faith in Christ." I told him, if the Spirit had convinced him of unbelief, He could of righteousness also, even before we reached Oxford. I stopped and prayed that he might believe. Immediately he told me he was in such a blessed temper, as he never before experienced. We halted and went to prayers. He testified the great delight he felt, saying, it was heaven if it would but continue. While we were discoursing, the fire within him, he said, diffused itself through every part; he was brim full of joy . . . and eager to praise God. He called upon me to join. . . . We sang and shouted all the way to Oxford.*

Charles sang and shouted all the way through life, as reflected in "O for a Heart to Praise My God," one of his greatest hymns.

O Come, All Ye Faithful

ascribed to John Francis Wade
translated by Frederick Oakeley

John Francis Wade

1. O come all ye faith - ful, Joy - ful and tri - um - phant, O come ye, O come ye to Beth - le - hem. Come and be - hold Him, Born the King of an - gels.

2. Sing choirs of an - gels, Sing in ex - ul - ta - tion, O sing all ye bright Hosts of heav'n a - bove. Glo - ry to God, All glo - ry in the high - est.

3. Yea, Lord, we greet Thee, Born this hap - py morn - ing; Je - sus to Thee be all glo - ry giv'n. Word of the Fa - ther Now in flesh ap - pear - ing.

Refrain

O come let us a - dore Him, O come let us a - dore Him, O come let us a - dore Him, Christ the Lord.

O Come, All Ye Faithful

1743

And when they had come into the house, they saw the young Child with Mary His mother, and fell down and worshiped Him. And when they had opened their treasures, they presented gifts to Him: gold, frankincense, and myrrh. Matthew 2:11

John Francis Wade, author of this hymn, was hounded out of England in 1745. He was a Roman Catholic layman in Lancashire; but because of persecution arising from the Jacobite rebellion, streams of Catholics fled to France and Portugal, where communities of English-speaking Catholics appeared.

But how could he, a refugee, support himself? In those days, the printing of musical scores was cumbersome, and copying them by hand was an art. In the famous Roman Catholic College and Ministry Center in Douay, France, Wade taught music and became renowned as a copyist of musical scores. His work was exquisite.

In 1743, Wade, 32, had produced a copy of a Latin Christmas carol beginning with the phrase *Adeste Fidelis, Laeti triumphantes*. At one time historians believed he had simply discovered an ancient hymn by an unknown author, but most scholars now believe Wade himself composed the lyrics. Seven original hand-copied manuscripts of this Latin hymn have been found, all of them bearing Wade's signature.

John Wade passed away on August 16, 1786, at age 75. His obituary honored him for his "beautiful manuscripts" that adorned chapels and homes.

As time passed, English Catholics began returning to Britain, and they carried Wade's Christmas carol with them. More time passed, and one day an Anglican minister named Rev. Frederick Oakeley, who preached at Margaret Street Chapel in London, came across Wade's Latin Christmas carol. Being deeply moved, he translated it into English for Margaret Street Chapel. The first line of Oakeley's translation said: "Ye Faithful, Approach Ye."

Somehow, "Ye Faithful, Approach Ye," didn't catch on, and several years later Oakeley tried again. By this time, Oakeley, too, was a Roman Catholic priest, having converted to Catholicism in 1845. Perhaps his grasp of Latin had improved, because as he repeated over and over the Latin phrase *Adeste Fidelis, Laeti triumphantes* he finally came up with the simpler, more vigorous *O Come, All Ye Faithful, Joyful and Triumphant!*

So two brave Englishmen, Catholics, lovers of Christmas and lovers of hymns, living a hundred years apart, writing in two different nations, combined their talents to bid us come, joyful and triumphant, and adore Him born the King of angels.

O come, let us adore Him, Christ the Lord

When Morning Gilds the Skies

Katholisches Gesangbuch

Joseph Barnby

When Morning Gilds the Skies

1744

From the rising of the sun to its going down the LORD's name is to be praised.
Psalm 113:3

rom the rising of the sun to its going down the LORD's name is to be praised," exclaims Psalm 113:3. That's the theme behind this anonymous Catholic hymn, "Beim frühen Morgenlicht," which first appeared in the German hymnbook *Katholisches Gesangbuch* in 1744.

It was translated into English a hundred years later by Edward Caswall, a Roman Catholic priest. Edward had grown up in an Anglican parsonage in Yately, England, where his father was a Church of England minister. Following in his father's footsteps, Edward became an Anglican curate in Stratford-sub-Castle, Wiltshire. But in 1847, he converted to Catholicism. He delighted in translating ancient hymns from Latin into English and is the translator who gave us St. Bernard's "Jesus, the Very Thought of Thee."

In translating "When Morning Gilds the Skies," he rendered the verses freely and even added some of his own. Those who love this hymn as much as I do will be pleased to learn the original English version had twenty-eight (fourteen double) stanzas. Here are some new ones for you to sing:

When you begin the day, O never fail to say, | May Jesus Christ be praised! |
And at your work rejoice, to sing with heart and voice, | May Jesus Christ be praised!

Whene'er the sweet church bell peals over hill and dell, | May Jesus Christ be praised! |
O hark to what it sings, as joyously it rings, | May Jesus Christ be praised!

Be this at meals your grace, in every time and place; | May Jesus Christ be praised! |
Be this, when day is past, of all your thoughts the last | May Jesus Christ be praised!

When mirth for music longs, this is my song of songs: | May Jesus Christ be praised! |
When evening shadows fall, this rings my curfew call, | May Jesus Christ be praised!

When sleep her balm denies, my silent spirit sighs, | May Jesus Christ be praised! |
When evil thoughts molest, with this I shield my breast, | May Jesus Christ be praised!

Sing, sun and stars of space, sing, ye that see His face, | Sing, Jesus Christ be praised! |
God's whole creation o'er, for aye and evermore | Shall Jesus Christ be praised!

Ye Servants of God

Charles Wesley

Probably by William Croft

1. Ye ser-vants of God, your Mas-ter pro-claim,
2. God rul-eth on high, al-might-y to save;
3. "Sal-va-tion to God, who sits on the throne!"
4. Then let us a-dore and give Him His right;

And pub-lish a-broad His won-der-ful Name;
And still He is nigh, His pres-ence we have;
Let all cry a-loud and hon-or the Son:
All glo-ry and pow'r, all wis-dom and might,

The Name all-vic-to-rious of Je-sus ex-tol;
The great con-gre-ga-tion His tri-umph shall sing,
The prais-es of Je-sus the an-gels pro-claim,
All hon-or and bless-ing, with an-gels a-bove,

His king-dom is glo-rious, He rules o-ver all.
As-crib-ing sal-va-tion to Je-sus, our King.
Fall down on their fac-es and wor-ship the Lamb.
And thanks nev-er ceas-ing, and in-fi-nite love.

Ye Servants of God

1744

Praise the LORD! Praise the name of the LORD; Praise Him, O you servants of the LORD! Psalm 135:1

In the spring of 1739, Charles Wesley was recruited by his friend, evangelist George Whitefield, to begin preaching in the open air. This was highly unorthodox and would open Wesley up to harsh criticism. But after a period of inward struggling, Charles accepted it as God's will for him, and soon crowds of thousands were gathering in the cities and countryside of Great Britain listening to him and his brother, John, proclaim the gospel.

His journal records:

Tues., May 29th. *Franklyn, a farmer, invited me to preach in his field. I did so, to about five hundred, on, "Repent, for the kingdom of heaven is at hand." I returned to the house rejoicing.*

Wed., May 30th. *I invited near a thousand sinners (with whom the whole house was filled at night) to come weary and heavy-laden to Christ for rest.*

Thur., May 31st. *A Quaker sent me a pressing invitation to preach at Thackstead . . . Many Quakers, and near seven hundred others, attended, while I declared in the highways, "The Scripture hath concluded all under sin."*

Fri., June 1st. *My subject, to above one thousand attentive sinners, was, "He shall save his people from their sins." Many showed their emotion by their tears.*

Sun., June 17th. *My brother preached to above ten thousand people (as was supposed) in Moorfields, and to a still larger congregation on Kennington-Common. I preached twice in the prison.*

Sun., June 24th. *I found near ten thousand helpless sinners waiting for the word, in Moorfields. I invited them in my Master's words, as well as name: "Come unto me, all ye that travail, and are heavy laden and I will give you rest." The Lord was with me . . . At Newington, the Rector, Mr. Motte, desired me to preach. My text was, "All have sinned, and come short of the glory of God; being justified freely," & etc. I walked on to the Commons and cried to multitudes upon multitudes, "Repent ye, and believe the gospel." The Lord was my strength, and my mouth, and my wisdom.*

Charles Wesley's great hymn "Ye Servants of God" is an expression of his powerful evangelistic zeal. *Ye servants of God, your Master proclaim, / And publish abroad His wonderful Name.*

Rejoice, the Lord Is King

Charles Wesley

John Darwall

1. Re - joice, the Lord is King! Your Lord and King a - dore!
2. Je - sus, the Sav - ior reigns, The God of truth and love;
3. His king-dom can - not fail, He rules o'er earth and heaven;
4. Re - joice in glo-rious hope! Je - sus, the judge shall come,

Mor - tals, give thanks, and sing, And tri-umph ev - er - more:
When He had purged our stains, He took His seat a - bove:
The keys of death and hell Are to our Je - sus given:
And take His ser - vants up To their e - ter - nal home:

Lift up your heart; Lift up your voice!
Lift up your heart; Lift up your voice!
Lift up your heart; Lift up your voice!
Lift up your heart; Lift up your voice!

Re - joice, a - gain I say, re - joice!
Re - joice, a - gain I say, re - joice!
Re - joice, a - gain I say, re - joice!
Re - joice, a - gain I say, re - joice!

Rejoice, the Lord Is King

1744

Rejoice greatly, O daughter of Zion! Shout, O daughter of Jerusalem! Behold, your King is coming to you . . . Zechariah 9:9

By the 1740s, Charles Wesley was regularly preaching to thousands in the open air, but opposition was developing. He first encountered physical danger when a doctor in Wales, angry over Charles' sermon, stormed up to him and demanded an apology for having been called a "Pharisee."

Charles, who wasn't known for his tact, replied, "I still insist you are a Pharisee. . . . My commission is to show you your sins, and I shall make no apology for so doing. . . . You are a damned sinner."

The doctor struck Charles with his cane, causing a mêlée involving several men and women. This was the beginning of a period of dangerous ministry. Here's an entry in Charles' diary from July 22, 1743:

I had just named my text at St. Ives . . . when an army of rebels broke in upon us. . . . They began in a most outrageous manner, threatening to murder the people, if they did not go out that moment. They broke the sconces, dashed the windows in pieces, tore away the shutters . . . and all but the stone-walls. I stood silently looking on; but mine eyes were unto the Lord. They swore bitterly I should not preach there again; which I disproved, by immediately telling them Christ died for them all. Several times they lifted up their hands and clubs to strike me; but a stronger arm restrained them. They beat and dragged the women about, particularly one of a great age, and trampled on them without mercy. The longer they stayed, and the more they raged, the more power I found from above. . . .

It was during these days of danger that Charles wrote his triumphant hymn, "Rejoice, the Lord Is King," the third verse of which says:

His kingdom cannot fail, He rules o'er earth and heaven;
The keys of death and hell are to our Jesus given:
Lift up your heart; lift up your voice!
Rejoice, again I say, rejoice!

Interestingly, this entry appeared in Charles's journal a few years later, on Sunday, July 13, 1746: *At St. Ives no one offered to make the least disturbance. Indeed, the whole place is outwardly changed in this respect. I walk the streets with astonishment, scarce believing it St. Ives. It is the same throughout all the county. All opposition falls before us. . . .*

Come, Thou Long-Expected Jesus

Charles Wesley

Rowland H. Prichard

1. Come, Thou long ex- pect- ed Je- sus,
From our fears and sins re- lease us,
2. Born Thy peo- ple to de- liv- er,
Born to reign in us for- ev- er,

Born to set Thy peo- ple free;
Let us find our rest in Thee.
Born a Child and yet a King;
Now Thy gra- cious king- dom bring.

Is- rael's strength and con- so- la- tion, Hope of all the
By Thine own e- ter- nal Spir- it, Rule in all our

earth Thou art; Dear de- sire of ev- ery
hearts a- lone; By Thine all - suf- fi- cient

na- tion, Joy of ev- ery long- ing heart.
mer- it, Raise us to Thy glo- rious throne.

Come, Thou Long-Expected Jesus
1744

You therefore must endure hardship as a good soldier of Jesus Christ. 2 Timothy 2:3

t's hard to imagine the difficulties faced by John and Charles Wesley and their fellow evangelists as they traveled by horseback from town to town, facing mobs, enduring harsh conditions and severe weather. Here is a sampling from Charles' journal as he pressed into Wales in March of 1748.

Wed., March 23rd. *I was . . . not to set out till past seven. The continual rain and sharp wind were full in my teeth. I rode all day in great misery, and had a restless, painful night at Tan-y-bwlch.*

Thur., March 24th. *I resolved to push for Garth, finding my strength would never hold out for three more days riding. At five (a.m.), I set out in hard rain, which continued all day. We went through perils of water. I was quite gone when we came at night to a little village. There was no fire in the poor hut. A brother supplied us with some, nailed up our window, and helped us to bed. I had no more rest than the night before.*

Fri., March 23th. *I took horse again at five, the rain attending us still. . . . The weather grew more severe. The violent wind drove the hard rain full in our faces. I rode till I could ride no more; walked the last hour; and by five dropped down at Garth.*

Charles' primary purpose in going to Garth was to preach, but he had another motive as well. It was also to see Miss Sally Gwynee, whom he wanted to marry. Marriage required a regular income, however, and Sally's parents were concerned about Charles' ability to sustain a family with no regular source of finances. Charles agreed to publish two volumes of his *Hymns and Sacred Poems.*

The income from royalties more than satisfied Sally's parents, and the two were married on Saturday, April 8, 1749.

"Come, Thou Long-Expected Jesus" wasn't introduced in this two-volume set of *Hymns and Sacred Songs* containing a total of 455 hymns. It had been published earlier, in a 1745 edition of Christmas hymns entitled, *Hymns for the Nativity of Our Lord.* This little hymnal contained eighteen Christmas carols Charles had written, of which "Come, Thou Long-Expected Jesus" is the best known.

Guide Me, O Thou Great Jehovah

William Williams

John Hughes

1. Guide me, O Thou great Je-ho-vah, Pil-grim through this
2. O-pen now the crys-tal foun-tain, Whence the heal-ing
3. When I tread the verge of Jor-dan, Bid my an-xious

bar-ren land; I am weak, but Thou art might-y,
stream doth flow; Let the fire and cloud-y pil-lar
fears sub-side; Death of death and Hell's de-struc-tion

Hold me with Thy pow'r-ful hand. Bread of heav-en, Bread of heav-en,
Lead me all my jour-ney through. Strong De-liv-'rer, strong De-liv'-rer,
Land me safe on Ca-naan's side. Songs of prais-es, songs of prais-es,

Feed me till I want no more; Feed me till I want no more.
Be Thou still my strength and shield; Be Thou still my strength and shield.
I will ev-er give to Thee; I will ev-er give to Thee.

Guide Me, O Thou Great Jehovah

1745

When you pass through the waters, I will be with you; and through the rivers, they shall not overflow you. When you walk through the fire, you shall not be burned, nor shall the flame scorch you. Isaiah 43:2

The Great Awakening of the 1700s was a heaven-sent revival to many parts of the world. In America, the preaching of George Whitefield and Jonathan Edwards renewed Christian zeal and swept multitudes into the kingdom. In England, the open-air evangelism of Whitefield and the Wesley brothers did the same. In Wales, it was the electrifying preaching of Howell Harris and his convert, William Williams.

Williams, son of a wealthy farmer, graduated from the university as a physician, intending to become a medical doctor. But hearing a sermon that Harris preached while standing on a gravestone in Talgarth churchyard, he was converted. Soon thereafter, he changed professions to become a physician of the soul—a preacher.

During his 43 years of itinerant ministry, Williams traveled over 95,000 miles, drawing crowds of 10,000 or more. Once he spoke to an estimated 80,000, noting in his journal, "God strengthened me to speak so loud that most could hear."

Williams is best remembered, however, for his hymns. He has been called the "Sweet Singer of Wales," and the "Watts of Wales." In all, he composed over 800 hymns, his best known being this autobiographical prayer with its many Old Testament allusions, which first appeared in Williams' collection of Welsh hymns, *Alleluia* (1745), entitled "Strength to Pass Through the Wilderness."

Williams lived as a pilgrim, pressing through the snow of winter, the rains of springtime, and the heat of summer. He was both beaten by mobs (once nearly dying) and cheered by crowds, but in all his travels he sought only to do the will of God until his death at age 74.

Many years later, when President James Garfield was dying of an assassin's bullet, he seemed to temporarily rally and was allowed to sit by the window. His wife began singing this hymn, and the President, listening intently, began to cry. To his doctor, Willard Bliss, he said, "Glorious, Bliss, isn't it?"

This hymn was also sung at the funeral of England's Princess Diana.

Several stanzas of this hymn are today seldom sung. One of the best reads:

Musing on my habitation, musing on my heav'nly home;
Fills my soul with holy longings: Come, my Jesus, quickly come.
Vanity is all I see; Lord, I long to be with Thee.

101

Love Divine, All Loves Excelling

Charles Wesley

John Zundel

1. Love divine, all loves ex-cel-ling, Joy of heav'n, to earth come down!
2. Breathe, O breathe, Thy lov-ing Spir-it In-to ev-'ry trou-bled breast!
3. Come, Al-might-y to de-liv-er; Let us all Thy life re-ceive.
4. Fin-ish, then, Thy new cre-a-tion; Pure and spot-less let us be.

Fix in us Thy hum-ble dwell-ing; All Thy faith-ful mer-cies crown.
Let us all in Thee in-her-it; Let us find Thy prom-ised rest.
Sud-den-ly re-turn, and nev-er, Nev-er-more Thy tem-ples leave.
Let us see Thy great sal-va-tion, Per-fect-ly re-stored in Thee:

Je-sus, Thou art all com-pas-sion; Pure, un-bound-ed love Thou art.
Take a-way our bent to sin-ning; Al-pha and O-me-ga be.
Thee we would be al-ways bless-ing, Serve Thee as Thy hosts a-bove,
Changed from glo-ry in-to glo-ry, 'Til in heav'n we take our place,

Vis-it us with Thy sal-va-tion; En-ter ev-'ry trem-bling heart.
End of faith, as its Be-gin-ning, Set our hearts at lib-er-ty.
Pray, and praise Thee with-out ceas-ing, Glo-ry in Thy per-fect love.
Till we cast our crowns be-fore Thee, Lost in won-der, love, and praise.

Love Divine, All Loves Excelling

1747

His divine power has given to us all things that pertain to life and godliness, through the knowledge of Him who called us by glory and virtue. 2 Peter 1:3

After their marriage, Charles and Sally Wesley set up housekeeping in Bristol, England, heading up the Methodist activities there. Later they moved to London so Charles could work more closely with his brother, John. All the while, however, he was writing hymns. There are few stories behind specific hymns because Charles was just always writing them. He didn't need events to inspire him or quiet stretches of meditative time in which to develop his thoughts. He was just always writing hymns, and afterward he had few if any dramatic stories to tell about the occasions for writing them.

Biographer Arnold Dallimore says about his poetry: "He had inherited this gift from his father and although it had undoubtedly been resident in him since childhood, his conversion unlocked it and set it free. During [his] early ministry he says little in his journal about his composing hymns and, indeed, this is true throughout his life. But he had within him virtually a treasury of poetry. He constantly experienced the emotions of the true poet, his mind instinctively invested words with harmony, and hymn after hymn flowed from his pen."

Henry Moore, one of his friends, later described Charles like this: "When he was nearly eighty he rode a little horse, gray with age. . . . Even in the height of summer he was dressed in winter clothes. As he jogged leisurely along, he jotted down any thought that struck him. He kept a card in his pocket for this purpose, on which he wrote his hymn in shorthand. Not infrequently he had come to our house in City Road, and, having left the pony in the garden in front, he would enter, crying out, 'Pen and ink! Pen and ink!' These being supplied he wrote the hymn he had been composing."

How many hymns did Wesley compose? No one has been able to count them. In all, Charles wrote over nine thousand literary texts of one kind or another, but not all of them should be classified as hymns. Experts put the number somewhere between three thousand and six thousand. Among all of them, "Love Divine, All Loves Excelling" is the favorite of many.

Charles's last hymn was dictated to his beloved Sally as he was on his deathbed, in March, 1788. It was short, simple, and picturesque. Predictably, it, too, became a popular one-verse song among the Methodists:

In age and feebleness extreme, / Who shall a helpless worm redeem?
Jesus, my only hope Thou art, / Strength of my failing flesh and heart,
Oh, could I catch a smile from Thee / And drop into eternity!

Be Still, My Soul

Katherina A. von Schlegel

Jean Sibelius

1. Be still, my soul; the Lord is on thy side. Bear pa - tient - ly the
2. Be still, my soul; Thy God doth un - der - take To guide the fu - ture
3. Be still, my soul! The hour is hast'ning on When we shall be for -

cross of grief or pain; Leave to thy God to or - der and pro - vide.
as He has the past. Thy hope, Thy con - fi - dence let noth - ing shake;
ev - er with the Lord, When dis - ap - point - ment, grief, and fear are gone,

In ev - 'ry change He faith - ful will re - main. Be still, my soul; Thy
All now mys - te - rious shall be bright at last. Be still, my soul; the
Sor - row for - got, love's pur - est joys re - stored. Be still, my soul; when

best, Thy heaven - ly Friend Thro' thorn - y ways leads to a joy - ful end.
waves and winds still know His voice Who ruled them while He dwelt be - low.
change and tears are past, All safe and bless - ed we shall meet at last.

Be Still, My Soul

1752

Truly my soul silently waits for God; From Him comes my salvation. Psalm 62:1

L ittle is known about Katharina von Schlegel, the German author of this poem. Her words, joined with the haunting strains of "Finlandia" by Sibelius, have made this a classic hymn. It was widely sung during World War II when it comforted an entire nation. Virgil J. Bachman of Our Saviour Lutheran Church in Port Huron, Michigan, is a good example. Writing in his church newsletter, he said:

"I had probably sung 'Be Still, My Soul' many times before, but it was not until I sang it in a small stucco church in a tiny village in France during World War II that [it] became part of my life.

"The war in Europe was going badly. The news from the front was disheartening. We had suffered reverses. We were edgy, confused, and discouraged. It was at this crucial time that some Chaplain arranged a service in this quaint church somewhere in France. It seemed the roof of that little village church actually opened up as we weary, dirty, GIs blended our voices under the leadership of that Chaplain and the church's old pump organ.

"Halfway through the service it happened. Softly the organ began and we sang, 'Be still my soul, the Lord is on thy side.' How badly it was needed. It was as though the Lord was speaking to me in a very personal way. 'Bear patiently the cross of grief or pain'—the cross of war with its hardships, misery, separation and pain.

"As we began the second stanza, 'Be still my soul, Thy God doth undertake to guide the future as he hath the past,' God seemed to whisper, 'Don't give up, I'm still in command, yes, even here. I'll guide the future as I have the past.'

"The thoughts of dead and missing friends came as through a choked-up throat I sang, 'Be still my soul, though dearest friends depart. . . .' Soothing, personal assurance [came] at that moment and in that spot. With renewed spirit I was able to sing the final stanza, 'Be still my soul, when change and tears are past, all safe and blessed we shall meet at last.'

"Peace! Either here or in eternity.

"As we left that little church, the peace I felt among the horrors of war was nothing but a gift of the Holy Spirit. God did spare me and allow me to return to my loved ones and His service and still preserves me."

O Happy Day, That Fixed My Choice

Philip Doddridge

Edward F. Rimbault

1. O hap-py day that fixed my choice On Thee, my Sav-ior and my God!
2. O hap-py bond that seals my vows To Him who mer-its all my love!
3. 'Tis done, the great trans-ac-tion's done; I am my Lord's and He is mine.

Well may this glow-ing heart re - joice, And tell its rap-tures all a - broad.
Let cheer-ful an-thems fill His house, While to that sa-cred shrine I move.
He drew me and I fol-lowed on, Charmed to con-fess the voice di - vine.

Hap-py day, hap-py day, When Je-sus washed my sins a-way!

He taught me how to watch and pray, And live re-joic-ing ev-ery day.

Hap-py day, hap-py day, When Je-sus washed my sins a-way!

O Happy Day, That Fixed My Choice

1755

Likewise, I say to you, there is joy in the presence of the angels of God over one sinner who repents. Luke 15:10

Eighteen of Monica Doddridge's nineteen children died in infancy. When number twenty arrived on June 26, 1702, he, too, appeared stillborn. But while being laid aside, he cried out. Monica determined then and there to raise Philip for the Lord. As a young child, he sat on her knees at the fireplace, which was lined with Delft tiles illustrating the history of the Bible. Using those tiles, Monica taught her son the lessons of Scripture.

When he was later orphaned, Philip wrote in his diary, "God is an immortal Father, my soul rejoices in Him; He hath hitherto helped me and provided for me; may it be my study to approve myself a more affectionate, grateful, and dutiful child."

But he was destitute, and though he longed to be a minister, there seemed no way to afford the necessary education. Friends advised him to prepare for another profession, but before making a final decision, Philip set apart a day for earnest prayer. While he was praying, the postman arrived with a letter from a wealthy benefactor offering to finance his training. It was such a timely answer that Philip resolved henceforth to live a life of prayer, and he trained himself to pray without ceasing, even while getting washed and dressed in the morning.

At age 27, Philip was asked to become the head of a seminary for Dissenting (non-Anglican) ministerial students in Northampton, England. His health was frail, and he didn't think he was well enough for the new responsibilities. But while passing a house, he overheard a child reading Deuteronomy 33:25: "As your days, so shall your strength be." He took it as from God and accepted the call.

The reputation of Northampton Academy radiated through England, and students flocked there, in part, because of Philip's chapel sermons and his powerful prayer life. For twenty-two years, Philip trained students, and his books became "must reading" for the Christians of his day—and ours.

By age 48, however, he was exhausted. Consumption struck his lungs, and he traveled to Lisbon for a therapeutic holiday. There he passed away on October 26, 1751.

Today Philip is best remembered for his book, *The Rise and Progress of Religion in the Soul,* and for his collection of nearly 400 hymns, published posthumously in 1755, and which included "O Happy Day."

Come, Thou Fount of Every Blessing

Robert Robinson   Traditional American Melody

1. Come, Thou fount of ev-ery bless-ing, Tune my heart to sing Thy grace.
2. Here I raise my Eb-e-ne-zer; Hith-er by Thy help I come.
3. Oh, to grace how great a debt-or Dai-ly I'm con-strained to be!

Streams of mer-cy, nev-er ceas-ing, Call for songs of loud-est praise.
And I hope, by Thy good plea-sure, Safe-ly to ar-rive at home.
Let thy grace, Lord, like a fet-ter, Bind my wan-d'ring heart to Thee:

Teach me some me-lo-dious son-net, Sung by flam-ing tongues a-bove.
Je-sus sought me when a stran-ger Wand'ring from the fold of God;
Prone to wan-der, Lord, I feel it, Prone to leave the God I love.

Praise the mount! I'm fixed up-on it, Mount of God's un-chang-ing love.
He, to res-cue me from dan-ger, In-ter-posed His pre-cious blood.
Here's my heart, Lord, take and seal it, Seal it for Thy courts a-bove.

Come, Thou Fount of Every Blessing

1758

The Lord is not slack concerning His promise, as some count slackness, but is longsuffering toward us, not willing that any should perish but that all should come to repentance. 2 Peter 3:9

Robert Robinson had a rough beginning. His father died when he was young, and his mother, unable to control him, sent him to London to learn barbering. What he learned instead was drinking and gang-life. When he was 17, he and his friends reportedly visited a fortune-teller. Relaxed by alcohol, they laughed as she tried to tell their futures. But something about the encounter bothered Robert, and that evening he suggested to his buddies they attend the evangelistic meeting being held by George Whitefield.

Whitefield was one of history's greatest preachers, with a voice that was part foghorn and part violin. That night he preached from Matthew 3:7: "But when he saw many of the Pharisees and Sadducees coming to his baptism, he said to them, 'Brood of vipers! Who warned you to flee from the wrath to come?'" Bursting into tears, Whitefield exclaimed, "Oh, my hearers! The wrath to come! The wrath to come!"

Robert immediately sobered up and sensed Whitefield was preaching directly to him. The preacher's words haunted him for nearly three years, until December 10, 1755, when he gave his heart to Christ.

Robert soon entered the ministry, and three years later at age 23, while serving Calvinist Methodist Chapel in Norfolk, England, he wrote a hymn for his sermon on Pentecost Sunday. It was a prayer that the Holy Spirit flood into our hearts with His streams of mercy, enabling us to sing God's praises and remain faithful to Him. "Come, Thou Fount of Every Blessing," has been a favorite of the church since that day.

Robinson continued working for the Lord until 1790, when he was invited to Birmingham, England, to preach for Dr. Joseph Priestly, a noted Unitarian. There, on the morning of June 8, he was found dead at age 54, having passed away quietly during the night.

Take a few moments to offer this hymn as a personal prayer, especially remembering those last insightful lines:

> *Let thy goodness, like a fetter, bind my wandering heart to thee.*
> *Prone to wander, Lord, I feel it, prone to leave the God I love;*
> *Here's my heart, O take and seal it, seal it for thy courts above.*

I Will Arise and Go to Jesus

Joseph Hart

American Melody

1. Come, ye sin - ners, poor and need - y, Weak and wound-ed, sick and sore;
2. Come, ye thirst - y, come and wel - come, God's free boun - ty glo - ri - fy;
3. Come, ye wea - ry, heav - y - la - den, Lost and ru - ined by the Fall;
4. Let not con-science make you lin - ger, Nor of fit - ness fond - ly dream;

Je - sus read - y stands to save you, Full of pit - y, love and pow'r.
True be - lief and true re - pen - tance, Ev - ery grace that brings you nigh.
If you tar - ry 'til you're bet - ter, You will nev - er come at all.
All the fit - ness He re - quir - eth Is to feel your need of Him.

I will a - rise and go to Je - sus, He will em - brace me in His arms.

In the arms of my dear Sav - ior, O there are ten thou - sand charms.

I Will Arise and Go to Jesus

1759

Because you have kept My command to persevere, I also will keep you from the hour of trial which shall come upon the whole world, to test those who dwell on the earth. Revelation 3:10

When visiting London, make sure to go to Bunhill Fields, a little cemetery located across City Road from Wesley's House and Chapel. This old graveyard became the final resting place of a host of "Dissenters," spiritual giants who refused to follow the State Church and thus were not allowed burial on "consecrated ground." They were taken to Bunhill Fields. Among the graves, you'll find John Bunyan, author of *Pilgrim's Progress*, Daniel Defoe, author of *Robinson Crusoe*, and the great Puritan, John Owen.

You'll also find some of Britain's greatest hymnwriters. Isaac Watts, Father of English Hymnody, is buried here, as is Susanna Wesley, mother of Charles. William Shrubsole, who wrote the hymn tune, "Miles' Lane," is here. So are hymnists Joseph Swain, David Denham, Samuel Stennett ("On Jordan's Stormy Banks"), and John Rippon ("How Firm a Foundation").

Here also lies Joseph Hart, author of "Come, Ye Sinners, Poor and Needy." Born in London in 1712, he was raised a Christian and given a splendid education. He turned away from the Lord in his twenties and became an enemy of the Cross. Later describing himself as a "monstrous sinner," he wrote, "I ran such dangerous lengths both of carnal and of spiritual wickedness that I outwent professed infidels."

Joseph even wrote an anti-Christian pamphlet entitled, "The Unreasonableness of Religion," in response to a sermon John Wesley had preached from Romans 8:32.

Finally, at age forty-five, after a bout of depression, Joseph fell under deep spiritual conviction. Attending a Moravian service in Fetter Lane, London, on Pentecost Sunday 1757, he was struck by a sermon from Revelation 3:10. Hurrying home, he flung himself on his knees in broken repentance. "My horrors were immediately dispelled," he said, "and such light and comfort flowed into my heart, as no words can paint."

Soon Joseph was writing Christian poems, and when he published them in 1759, they became so popular that he felt compelled to enter the ministry. Acquiring an old wooden meetinghouse on London's Jewin Street, Joseph pastored an independent congregation until his death on May 24, 1768. By then, he was so beloved that 20,000 people attended his funeral at Bunhill Fields.

His greatest hymn is an expression of his testimony:

I will arise and go to Jesus, / He will embrace me in His arms.
In the arms of my dear Savior, / O, there are ten thousand charms.

Father, Whate'er of Earthly Bliss

Anne Steele

Hans G. Nägeli

1. Fa - ther, what - e'er of earth - ly bliss Thy sov - 'reign will de - nies, Ac - cept - ed at Thy throne, let this My hum - ble prayer, a - rise:

2. Give me a calm and thank - ful heart, From ev - - ery mur - mur free; The bless - ing of Thy grace im - part, And make me live to Thee.

3. Let the sweet hope that Thou art mine My life and death at - tend, Thy pres - ence through my jour - ney shine, And crown my jour - ney's end.

Father, Whate'er
of Earthly Bliss

1760

But may the God of all grace, who called us to His eternal glory by Christ Jesus, after you have suffered a while, perfect, establish, strengthen, and settle you. 1 Peter 5:10

The Lord never wastes suffering in the lives of His children; He always blesses their sacrifices. That's the lesson of this once-widely-sung, now-seldom-heard hymn.

Anne Steele was born in Broughton, England, in 1716, the oldest daughter of a timber merchant. She faced her first tragedy at age three when her mother died. Her father, however, raised her for the Lord. Growing affluent in his business, he was able to pastor Broughton's Baptist church without salary, serving forty years. Anne joined the church at age 14, and became her dad's co-worker.

When she was 19, a severe hip injury left her an invalid. She nonetheless fell in love with one Robert Elscurot, who proposed to her. But he drowned the day before their wedding.

Out of her suffering, Anne began writing devotional material, and her ministry alongside her dad to the people of Broughton blossomed. In her mid-forties, Anne submitted her *Poems on Subjects Chiefly Devotional* for publication. Her father wrote in his diary, "This day Annie sent part of her composition to London to be printed. I entreat a gracious God, who enabled and stirred her up to such a work, to direct in it and bless it for the good of many . . . . I pray God to make it useful and keep her humble."

So many of these poems were converted to hymns that Anne is remembered as one of the foremost women hymnists of the eighteenth century. Her best-known hymn, "Desiring Resignation and Thankfulness," was written as a personal prayer:

Father, whate'er of earthly bliss / Thy sovereign will denies, /
Accepted at Thy throne, let this / My humble prayer, arise:

Give me a calm and thankful heart, / From every murmur free; /
The blessing of Thy grace impart, / And make me live to Thee.

Let the sweet hope that Thou art mine / My life and death attend, /
Thy presence through my journey shine, / And crown my journey's end.

The prayer of the final stanza was answered on November 11, 1778, the day of her death. As her weeping friends gathered around, she closed her eyes and whispered her last words: "I know that my Redeemer liveth."

There Is a Fountain

William Cowper

Traditional American Melody arranged by Lowell Mason

1. There is a foun-tain filled with blood Drawn from Im - man - uel's veins;
2. The dy - ing thief re - joiced to see That foun-tain in his day;
3. Dear dy - ing Lamb, Thy pre - cious blood Shall nev - er lose its pow'r
4. E'er since by faith I saw the stream Thy flow-ing wounds sup - ply,

And sin - ners, plunged be - neath that flood, Lose all their guilt - y stains:
And there may I, though vile as he, Wash all my sins a - way:
Till all the ran - somed Church of God Are saved, to sin no more:
Re - deem - ing love has been my theme, And shall be till I die:

Lose all their guilt - y stains, Lose all their guilt - y stains;
Wash all my sins a - way, Wash all my sins a - way;
Are saved, to sin no more, Are saved, to sin no more;
And shall be till I die, And shall be till I die;

And sin - ners, plunged be - neath that flood, Lose all their guilt - y stains.
And there may I, though vile as he, Wash all my sins a - way.
Till all the ran - somed Church of God Are saved, to sin no more.
Re - deem - ing love has been my theme, And shall be till I die.

There Is a Fountain

1772

Whom God set forth as a propitiation by His blood, through faith, to demonstrate His righteousness, because in His forbearance God had passed over the sins that were previously committed. Romans 3:25

illiam Cowper is one of God's gracious gifts to those suffering from depression. Like the Psalmist who cried, "Why are you cast down, O my soul?" (Psalm 42:5), Cowper shows us that our emotional struggles often give us heightened sensitivity to the heart of God and to the needs of others.

Cowper (pronounced Cooper), born in 1731, was the fourth child of a British clergyman and his wife. William's three siblings died, then his mother died while giving birth to the fifth child. William was six when he lost his mother, and it was a blow from which he never recovered. Years later, when someone sent him a picture of her, he wrote:

> *My mother! when I learn'd that thou wast dead,*
> *Say, wast thou conscious of the tears I shed?*
> *Hover'd thy spirit o'er thy sorrowing son,*
> *Wretch even then, life's journey just begun? . . .*
> *I heard the bell toll'd on thy burial day,*
> *I saw the hearse that bore thee slow away,*
> *And, turning from my nurs'ry window, drew*
> *A long, long sigh, and wept a last adieu!*

William, emotionally frail, was sent to a boarding school where for two years he was terrorized by a bully which further shattered his nerves. From ages 10 to 18, he had a better experience at Westminster School, developing a love for literature and poetry. His father wanted him to be an attorney, but, preparing for his bar exam, he experienced runaway anxiety. Concluding himself damned, he threw away his Bible and attempted suicide.

Friends recommended an asylum run by Dr Nathaniel Cotton, a lover of poetry and a committed Christian. Under Dr. Cotton's care, William slowly recovered. In the asylum in 1764, he found the Lord while reading Romans 3:25: ". . . whom God set forth as a propitiation by His blood, through faith . . . ." His life was still to hold many dark days of intense depression, but at least he now had a spiritual foundation. As he later put it:

> *There is a fountain filled with blood | Drawn from Immanuel's veins, |*
> *And sinners plunged beneath that flood, | Lose all their guilty stains.*

O for a Closer Walk with God

William Cowper

Johann G. Nägeli

1. O for a clos-er walk with God, A calm and heaven-ly frame, A light to shine up-on the road That leads me to the Lamb!

2. Where is the bless-ed-ness I knew, When first I saw the Lord? Where is the soul-re-fresh-ing view Of Je-sus and His Word?

3. What peace-ful hours I once en-joyed! How sweet their mem-ory still! But they have left an ach-ing void The world can nev-er fill.

4. Re-turn, O ho-ly Dove, re-turn, Sweet mes-sen-ger of rest! I hate the sins that made Thee mourn, And drove Thee from my breast.

5. The dear-est i-dol I have known, What-e'er that i-dol be, Help me to tear it from Thy throne, And wor-ship on-ly Thee.

6. So shall my walk be close with God, Calm and se-rene my frame; So pur-er light shall mark the road That leads me to the Lamb.

O for a Closer Walk with God

1772

As you therefore have received Christ Jesus the Lord, so walk in Him. Colossians 2:6

Soon after William Cowper was discharged from Cotton's mental asylum, he met Morley and Mary Unwin coming out of church. Morley, an evangelical clergyman, invited William to spend two weeks with them—and William ended up staying in the Unwin home for 22 years. He took up gardening as a hobby, which helped ward off his depressions.

When Morley was killed from falling off a horse, Mrs. Unwin, wanting to sit under the ministry of another evangelical preacher, decided to move to the village of Olney, population 2,000, where John Newton was vicar. Newton, ex-scoundrel and slave trader, had become a celebrated preacher in England. William moved with her, and he and Newton were soon fast friends. They frequently met in the lawn between their houses, and William begin assisting John in visiting the sick and dying, and in distributing benevolent funds.

In December, 1769, Mary Unwin fell ill and appeared to be dying. William's anxiety and depression returned with a vengeance. Mary, being quite a bit older than William, was a mother-figure to him. He prayed earnestly for her, and it was during this time that, examining his own spiritual condition, he wrote "O For a Closer Walk with God."

He said, "(Mary) is the chief of blessings I have met with in my journey since the Lord was pleased to call me . . . . Her illness has been a sharp trial to me. Oh, that it may have a sanctified effect . . . . I began to compose (these verses) yesterday morning before daybreak, but I fell asleep at the end of the first two lines. When I awaked, the third and fourth verses were whispered to my heart in a way I have often experienced."

The hymn begins, "O, for a closer walk with God, a calm and heavenly frame," then goes on to ask:

*Where is the blessedness I knew, / When first I saw the Lord? /
Where is the soul refreshing view / Of Jesus and His Word?*

*Return, O holy Dove, return, / Sweet messenger of rest! /
I hate the sins that made Thee mourn / And drove Thee from my breast.*

*The dearest idol I have known, / Whate'er that idol be /
Help me to tear it from Thy throne, / And worship only Thee.*

Fortunately, the danger passed, William's prayers were answered, and Mary recovered.

God Moves in a Mysterious Way

William Cowper

Scottish Psalter, 1615

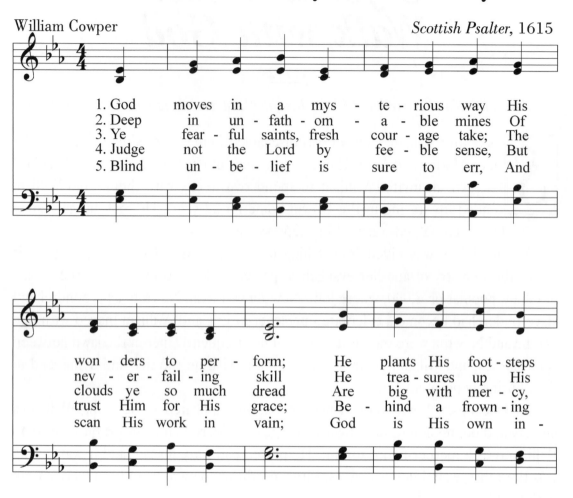

1. God moves in a mys - te - rious way His
2. Deep in un - fath - om - a - ble mines Of
3. Ye fear - ful saints, fresh cour - age take; The
4. Judge not the Lord by fee - ble sense, But
5. Blind un - be - lief is sure to err, And

won - ders to per - form; He plants His foot - steps
nev - er - fail - ing skill He trea - sures up His
clouds ye so much dread Are big with mer - cy,
trust Him for His grace; Be - hind a frown - ing
scan His work in vain; God is His own in -

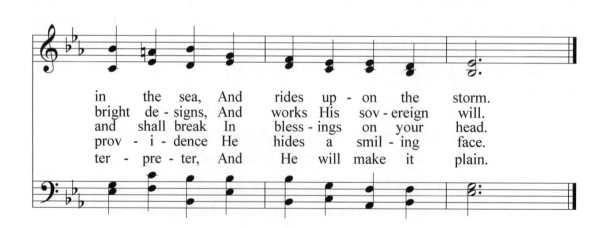

in the sea, And rides up - on the storm.
bright de - signs, And works His sov - ereign will.
and shall break In bless - ings on your head.
prov - i - dence He hides a smil - ing face.
ter - pre - ter, And He will make it plain.

God Moves in a Mysterious Way

1774

Jesus answered and said to him, "What I am doing you do not understand now, but you will know after this." John 13:7

illiam Cowper suffered another blow when his friend, John Newton, left Olney to become London's most celebrated pastor. Turning again to writing, William this time devoted his energy to secular poetry rather than spiritual hymns, earning him a prominent place in English literature. The publication of "The Task" made him famous throughout Britain. "Pity for Poor Africans," which appeared in 1788, contributed to John Newton and William Wilberforce's efforts to abolish slavery in the British Empire. William's translation of Homer, published in 1791, was widely lauded.

His depression was never far away, and it intensified as he aged. Shortly before his death he wrote *The Castaway*, in which he described himself as a sailor swept overboard into the Atlantic to perish. In this melancholia, William died on April 25, 1800.

There is a report, however, that on his deathbed his face suddenly lit up as he exclaimed, "I am not shut out of heaven after all!" And one of Cowper's lesser-known poems would make a fitting epitaph:

Sometimes a light surprises the Christian while he sings;
It is the Lord, Who rises with healing in His wings . . .

In holy contemplation we sweetly then pursue
The theme of God's salvation, and find it ever new.

Set free from present sorrow, we cheerfully can say,
Let the unknown tomorrow bring with it what it may.

It can bring with it nothing but He will bear us through;
Who gives the lilies clothing will clothe His people, too;

Beneath the spreading heavens, no creature but is fed;
And He Who feeds the ravens will give His children bread.

Though vine nor fig tree neither their wonted fruit should bear,
Though all the field should wither, nor flocks nor herds be there;

Yet God the same abiding, His praise shall tune my voice,
For while in Him confiding, I cannot but rejoice.

Or as William put it elsewhere: "God moves in a mysterious way His wonders to perform."

119

Rock of Ages

Augustus M. Toplady

Thomas Hastings

1. Rock of A - ges, cleft for me, Let me
2. Could my tears for - ev - er flow? Could my
3. While I draw this fleet - ing breath, When my

hide my - self in Thee. Let the wa - ter and the
zeal no lan - guor know? These for sin could not a -
eyes shall close in death, When I rise to worlds un -

blood, From Thy wound - ed side which flowed, Be of
tone; Thou must save, and Thou a - lone. In my
known, And be - hold Thee on Thy throne, Rock of

sin the dou - ble cure, Save from wrath and make me pure.
hand no price I bring; Sim - ply to thy cross I cling.
A - ges cleft for me, Let me hide my - self in Thee.

Rock of Ages
1776

My Father, who has given them to Me, is greater than all; and no one is able to snatch them out of My Father's hand. John 10:29

n November 4, 1740, a baby in Farnham, England, was given the formidable name of Augustus Montague Toplady. His father died in a war, his mother spoiled him, his friends thought him "sick and neurotic," and his relatives disliked him.

But Augustus was interested in the Lord. "I am now arrived at the age of eleven years," he wrote on his birthday. "I praise God I can remember no dreadful crime; to the Lord be the glory." By age 12 he was preaching sermons to whoever would listen. At 14 he began writing hymns. At 16 he was soundly converted to Christ while attending a service in a barn. And at 22 he was ordained an Anglican priest.

As a staunch Calvinist, he despised John Wesley's Arminian theology and bitterly attacked the great Methodist leader. "I believe him to be the most rancorous hater of the gospel-system that ever appeared on this island," Augustus wrote.

"Wesley is guilty of satanic shamelessness," he said on another occasion, "of acting the ignoble part of a lurking, shy assassin."

In 1776 Augustus wrote an article about God's forgiveness, intending it as a slap at Wesley. He ended his article with an original poem:

> *Rock of Ages, cleft for me,*
> *Let me hide myself in Thee;*
> *Let the water and the blood,*
> *From Thy wounded side which flowed,*
> *Be of sin the double cure,*
> *Save from wrath and make me pure.*

Augustus Toplady died at age 38, but his poem outlived him and has been called "the best known, best loved, and most widely useful" hymn in the English language. Oddly, it is remarkably similar to something Wesley had written 30 years before in the preface of a book of hymns for the Lord's Supper: "O Rock of Salvation, Rock struck and cleft for me, let those two Streams of Blood and Water which gushed from thy side, bring down Pardon and Holiness into my soul."

Perhaps the two men were not as incompatible as they thought.*

---

*Taken from the author's book, *On This Day* (Nashville: Thomas Nelson Publishers, 1997), installment for November 4th.

All Hail the Power of Jesus' Name

All Hail the Power of Jesus' Name
1779

Who has gone into heaven and is at the right hand of God, angels and authorities and powers having been made subject to Him. 1 Peter 3:22

n the November, 1799, issue of *The Gospel Magazine*, edited by Augustus Toplady, there appeared an anonymous hymn entitled "On the Resurrection, the Lord is King":

> *All hail the power of Jesus' Name! Let angels prostrate fall;*
> *Bring forth the royal diadem, and crown Him Lord of all.*

The author, it was later revealed, was Rev. Edward Perronet.

Edward's Protestant grandparents had fled Catholic France, going first to Switzerland, then to England. Edward's father had become a vicar in the Anglican Church, and Edward followed in his footsteps.

For several years, he became closely allied with the Wesleys, traveling with them and sometimes caught up in their adventures. In John Wesley's journal, we find this entry: "Edward Perronet was thrown down and rolled in mud and mire. Stones were hurled and windows broken."

In time, however, Edward broke with the Wesleys over various Methodist policies, and John Wesley excluded his hymns from Methodist hymnals. Edward went off to pastor a small independent church in Canterbury, where he died on January 22, 1792. His last words were: *Glory to God in the height of His divinity! Glory to God in the depth of His humanity! Glory to God in His all-sufficiency! Into His hands I commend my spirit.*

Edward Perronet's hymn, "All Hail the Power," has earned him an indelible place in the history of church music. It also has a place in missionary history, being greatly used in evangelistic endeavors. Rev. E. P. Scott, for example, missionary to India, wrote of trying to reach a savage tribe in the Indian subcontinent. Ignoring the pleadings of his friends, he set off into the dangerous territory. Several days later, he met a large party of warriors who surrounded him, their spears pointed at his heart.

Expecting to die at any moment, Scott took out his violin, breathed a prayer, closed his eyes, and began singing, "All Hail the Power of Jesus' Name!" When he reached the words, "Let every kindred, every tribe," he opened his eyes. There stood the warriors, some in tears, every spear lowered. Scott spent the next two years evangelizing the tribe.

Amazing Grace

John Newton

Traditional American Melody

1. A - maz - ing grace! How sweet the sound! That saved a wretch like me! I once was lost, but now am found; Was blind, but now I see.
2. 'Twas grace that taught my heart to fear, And grace my fears re - lieved. How pre - cious did that grace ap - pear, The hour I first be - lieved.
3. Thro' man - y dan - gers, toils and snares I have al - read - y come. 'Tis grace that brought me safe thus far, And grace will lead me home.
4. When we've been there ten thou - sand years, Bright shin - ing as the sun, We've no less days to sing God's praise, Than when we first be - gun.

Amazing Grace

1779

In Him we have redemption through His blood, the forgiveness of sins, according to the riches of His grace. Ephesians 1:7

I t's hard to shake off a mother's influence. John Newton's earliest memories were of his godly mother who, despite fragile health, devoted herself to nurturing his soul. At her knee he memorized Bible passages and hymns. Though she died when he was about seven, he later recalled her tearful prayers for him.

After her death, John alternated between boarding school and the high seas, wanting to live a good life but nonetheless falling deeper and deeper into sin. Pressed into service with the British Navy, he deserted, was captured, and after two days of suspense, was flogged. His subsequent thoughts vacillated between murder and suicide. "I was capable of anything," he recalled.

More voyages, dangers, toils, and snares followed. It was a life unrivaled in fiction. Then, on the night of March 9, 1748, John, 23, was jolted awake by a brutal storm that descended too suddenly for the crew to foresee. The next day, in great peril, he cried to the Lord. He later wrote, "That tenth of March is a day much remembered by me; and I have never suffered it to pass unnoticed since the year 1748—the Lord came from on high and delivered me out of deep waters."

The next several years saw slow, halting spiritual growth in John, but in the end he became one of the most powerful evangelical preachers in British history, a powerful foe of slavery, and the author of hundreds of hymns.

Here are some things you may not know about Newton's most famous hymn. His title for it wasn't originally "Amazing Grace" but "Faith's Review and Expectation." It is based in Newton's study of 1 Chronicles 17:16–17: "King David . . . said: 'Who am I, O Lord God? And what is my house, that You have brought me this far? And yet . . . You have also spoken of Your servant's house for a great while to come, and have regarded me according to the rank of a man of high degree. . . .'"

And here's a nearly forgotten verse that Newton added near the end of "Amazing Grace." Try singing it for yourself:

> *The earth shall soon dissolve like snow, the sun forbear to shine;*
> *But God, Who called me here below, shall be forever mine.*

Though Troubles Assail Us

John Newton

Traditional Welsh Melody

1. Though trou - bles as - sail us and dan - gers af - fright,
2. The birds, with - out gar - ner or store - house, are fed;
3. When Sa - tan as - sails us to stop up our path,
4. No strength of our own and no good - ness we claim;

Though friends should all fail us and foes all u - nite,
From them let us learn to trust God for our bread.
And cour - age all fails us, we tri - umph by faith.
Yet, since we have known of the Sav - ior's great name,

Yet one thing se - cures us, what - ev - er be - tide,
His saints what is fit - ting shall ne'er be de - nied,
He can - not take from us, though oft He has tried,
In this our strong tow - er for safe - ty we hide:

The prom - ise as - sures us, "The Lord will pro - vide."
So long as 'tis writ - ten, "The Lord will pro - vide."
This heart - cheer - ing prom - ise, "The Lord will pro - vide."
The Lord is our pow - er, "The Lord will pro - vide."

Though Troubles Assail Us

1779

And Abraham called the name of the place, The-LORD-Will-Provide; as it is said to this day, "In the Mount of the LORD it shall be provided." Genesis 22:14

W hen he quit the seafaring life, John Newton worked in the docks of Liverpool as a surveyor of tides from 1755 to 1760. During these years he settled down spiritually and began to mature. He came into contact with the great evangelist, George Whitefield, and was energized by thoughts of preaching the evangelical faith. Encouraged by his godly wife, Mary, he began studying Hebrew and Greek and preparing for the ministry.

At age 39, he was ordained, and shortly thereafter appointed to the Anglican church in Olney, England. He labored there fifteen years, during which he and the great British poet, William Cowper, developed a lasting friendship. The two men met virtually every day in the garden between their homes, and together they produced a volume of hymns.

In 1779, Newton was appointed rector of St. Mary's Woolnoth, a quaint church in the heart of London's financial district. Here he preached for 28 years until his death at age 82.

Late in life, when his mind began failing, he told his friend William Jay, "My memory is nearly gone; but I remember two things, that I am a great sinner and that Christ is a Great Savior."

"Amazing Grace" is Newton's best-known hymn, but its popularity has obscured some of his other compositions. He wrote with incredible insight, yet his words are simple enough for children. Here is Newton's hymn based on Genesis 22:14:

Though troubles assail us and dangers affright,
Though friends should all fail us and foes all unite,
Yet one thing secures us, whatever betide,
The promise assures us, "The Lord will provide."

The birds, without garner or storehouse, are fed;
From them let us learn to trust God for our bread.
His saints what is fitting shall ne'er be denied.
So long as 'tis written, "The Lord will provide."

When Satan assails us to stop up our path,
And courage all fails us, we triumph by faith.
He cannot take from us, though oft he has tried,
This heart cheering promise, "The Lord will provide."

The Saints Should Never Be Dismayed

William Cowper   Alexander R. Reinagle

1. The saints should nev - er be dis - mayed, Nor
2. This A - br'am found: he raised the knife; God
3. Once Da - vid seemed Saul's cer - tain prey; But
4. When Jo - nah sunk be - neath the wave, He
5. Blest proofs of pow'r and grace di - vine, That
6. Wait for His sea - son - a - ble aid, And

sink in hope - less fear; For when they least ex -
saw, and said, "For - bear! Yon ram shall yield his
hark! the foe's at hand; Saul turns his arms an -
thought to rise no more; But God pre - pared a
meet us in His Word! May ev - ery deep felt
though it tar - ry, wait: The pro - mise may be

pect His aid, The Sav - ior will ap - pear.
mean - er life; Be - hold the vic - tim there."
oth - er way, To save th'in - vad - ed land.
fish to save, And bear him to the shore.
care of mine Be trust - ed with the Lord.
long de - layed, But can - not come too late.

The Saints Should Never Be Dismayed

1779

Oh, love the LORD, all you His saints! For the LORD preserves the faithful . . .
Psalm 31:23

The little town of Olney, England, quaintly situated by the River Ouse, is best known for two things. The first is its "Pancake Race," held every year since the mid-fifteenth century. According to legend, the women of Olney, needing to use up their accumulated cooking fats at the beginning of Lent, made pancakes every year on Shrove Tuesday. In 1445, one woman became so engrossed in her pancakes that she forgot the time until the church bells pealed. Dashing from the house in her apron, she raced to the church, skillet in hand. Thus began the custom of Pancake Racing that continues to this day.

Olney's other claim to fame is its association with the famous hymnists John Newton and William Cowper (pronounced Cooper).

All his life, William suffered severe bouts of depression. The son of a minister, he had intended to become a lawyer until disabled by his depression. He found relief in poetry; and when he came to Christ, the poems flowing from his pen were set to music and sung throughout England. Together he and Newton compiled the famous *Olney Hymnal,* still in print today. That's where you'll find hymns like "Amazing Grace," "There Is a Fountain Filled with Blood," and "God Moves in a Mysterious Way."

Here's a lesser-known Olney hymn, one that shows us from biblical examples how we, like Cowper, can fight off the blues:

> *The saints should never be dismayed, nor sink in hopeless fear;*
> *For when they least expect His aid, the Savior will appear.*

> *This Abr'am found: he raised the knife; God saw, and said, "Forbear!*
> *Yon ram shall yield his meaner life; behold the victim there."*

> *Once David seemed Saul's certain prey; but hark! the foe's at hand;*
> *Saul turns his arms another way, to save th'invaded land.*

> *When Jonah sunk beneath the wave, he thought to rise no more;*
> *But God prepared a fish to save, and bear him to the shore.*

> *Blest proofs of power and grace divine, that meet us in His Word!*
> *May every deep felt care of mine be trusted with the Lord.*

> *Wait for His seasonable aid, and though it tarry, wait:*
> *The promise may be long delayed, but cannot come too late.*

Glorious Things of Thee Are Spoken

John Newton   Franz Joseph Haydn

1. Glorious things of Thee are spoken, Zion, city of our God;
2. See, the streams of living waters, Springing from eternal Love,
3. Round each habitation hovering, See the cloud and fire appear

He whose word cannot be broken Formed thee for His own abode.
Well supply thy sons and daughters, And all fear of want remove.
For a glory and a covering, Showing that the Lord is near!

On the Rock of Ages founded, What can shake thy sure repose?
Who can faint while such a river Ever flows their thirst assuage?
Thus deriving from our banner Light by night and shade by day;

With salvation's walls surrounded, Thou mayst smile at all thy foes.
Grace which, like the Lord, the Giver, Never fails from age to age!
Safe they feed upon the manna Which He gives them when they pray.

Glorious Things of Thee Are Spoken

1779

Glorious things are spoken of you, O city of God! Psalm 87:3

If you visit England in the future, plan to stop in quaint little Olney, home of John Newton and William Cowper. An excellent museum is dedicated to them, housed in Orchard Side, Cowper's home on Olney's triangular market-place. Cowper had moved to Olney to be under the ministry of John Newton, who preached in the village church. The two became friends and would often meet in the garden between their houses for long talks. Out of their friendship came one of history's most famous books—the *Olney Hymns*, first published in 1779.

Prior to his conversion, Newton had been a slave trader on the high seas, and a very wicked man. After his conversion, he became a powerful preacher, a leader in the fight against slavery, and a renowned hymnist. His most famous hymn, "Amazing Grace," is an expression of his testimony.

This song, "Glorious Things of Thee Are Spoken," Number 60 in the Olney hymnal, is a powerful hymn about the church, which is metaphorically described here as "Zion." It originally had five verses, built around seven biblical passages, which Newton footnoted in the original hymnal.

If you hear this hymn being played in Germany, you'd better stand to your feet for you'll be hearing the German national anthem. Franz Joseph Haydn's majestic composition, AUSTRIA, was played for the first time on February 12, 1797, to honor the Austrian Emperor Franz Josef on his birthday. It was an immediate hit, and was almost instantly adopted as the Austrian national anthem. Thus it remained until Adolf Hitler rose to power. In 1938 when Austria was annexed into the German Third Reich during the Anschluss, Hitler not only seized Austria, but he seized AUSTRIA, adapting Haydn's musical score as the Nazi national anthem.

After the War, the Austrian people, feeling they could no longer use Haydn's tune as their national song because of its association with the Nazis, chose another melody. The Germans, however, kept Haydn's tune, AUSTRIA, as their own anthem.

As far back as 1802, however, Christians in America and Britain were using Haydn's AUSTRIA as a hymn accompaniment, and this majestic composition is best known today as the melody for John Newton's famous hymn about the church of Jesus Christ, "Glorious Things of Thee Are Spoken."

How Firm a Foundation

Rippon's *Selection of Hymns*

Early American Melody

1. How firm a foun - da - tion, ye saints of the Lord,
2. Fear not; I am with thee. O be not dis - mayed,
3. When through fi - ery tri - als Thy path - way shall lie,
4. The soul that on Je - sus Hath leaned for re - pose,

Is laid for your faith In His ex - cel - lent Word!
For I am thy God, I will still give thee aid.
My grace, all suf - fi - cient, Shall be thy sup - ply.
I will not, I will not De - sert to its foes;

What more can He say Than to you He hath said,
I'll strength - en thee, help thee, And cause thee to stand,
The flames shall not hurt thee; I on - ly de - sign
That soul, though all hell Should en - deav - or to shake,

To you who for ref - uge To Je - sus have fled?
Up - held by My righ - teous, Om - nip - o - tent hand.
Thy dross to con - sume and thy gold to re - fine.
I'll nev - er, no nev - er, No nev - er for - sake.

How Firm a Foundation

1787

Fear not, for I am with you; be not dismayed, for I am your God. I will strengthen you, Yes, I will help you, I will uphold you with My righteous right hand. Isaiah 41:10

Talk about long pastorates! John Rippon pastored Carter's Lane Baptist Church in London for 63 years, beginning in 1775. He had been born in 1751, so he was in his mid-twenties when he first mounted the Carter's Lane pulpit following his education at the Baptist College in Bristol, England.

During the years of Carter's Lane, John developed a vision for a church hymnal, which he edited, assisted by his Minister of Music, Robert Keene. The resulting volume, *A Selection of Hymns from the Best Authors, Intended to Be an Appendix to Dr. Watts' Psalms and Hymns*, was published in 1787. It was a runaway hit, especially among the Baptists, going through eleven British editions during Rippon's lifetime. An American edition appeared in 1820.

"How Firm a Foundation" first appeared here. No one knows its author, for the line reserved for the author's name simply bore the letter "K." Many scholars attribute the composition to Keene.

The unique power of this hymn is due to the fact that each of the seven original stanzas were based on various biblical promises. The first verse established the hymnist's theme—God's Word is a sufficient foundation for our faith. The author then selected precious promises from the Bible, and converted these into hymn stanzas, among them:

- Isaiah 41:10—*Fear not, for I am with you; be not dismayed, for I am your God. I will strengthen you, yes, I will help you, I will uphold you with My righteous right hand.*
- Isaiah 43:2—*When you pass through the waters, I will be with you; and through the rivers, they shall not overflow you. When you walk through the fire, you shall not be burned, nor shall the flame scorch you.*
- 2 Corinthians 12:9—*My grace is sufficient for you, for My strength is made perfect in weakness. Therefore most gladly I will rather boast in my infirmities, that the power of Christ may rest upon me.*
- Hebrews 13:5—*For He Himself has said, "I will never leave you nor forsake you."*

No wonder this hymn was first published under the title, "Exceedingly Great and Precious Promises."

On Jordan's Stormy Banks

Samuel Stennett

American Folk Melody

1. On Jor-dan's storm - y banks I stand, And cast a wish - ful eye
2. O'er all those wide ex - tend - ed plains Shines one e - ter - nal day;
3. No chill-ing winds nor poi - s'nous breath Can reach that health - ful shore;
4. When I shall reach that hap - py place, And be for - ev - er blest,

To Ca-naan's fair and hap - py land, Where my pos - ses - sions lie.
There God the Son for - ev - er reigns And scat-ters night a - way.
Sick - ness and sor-row, pain and death Are felt and feared no more.
For I shall see my Fa-ther's face, And in His bos - om rest.

I am bound for the Prom - ised Land, I am bound for the Prom - ised Land;

O who will come and go with me? I am bound for the Prom-ised Land.

On Jordan's Stormy Banks

1787

Greater love has no one than this, than to lay down one's life for his friends. John 15:13

S amuel Stennett, the Seventh Day Baptist who wrote "On Jordan's Stormy Banks," originally titled it "Heaven Anticipated," a sentiment that later comforted a dying twenty-one-year-old spy.

Sam Davis was a student in Nashville when the Civil War broke out. He joined the Confederate army and proved such a fearless soldier that he was selected for an elite group of spies named, "Coleman's Scouts." Sam excelled as an undercover agent. Once he even shared a table at Nashville's St. Cloud Hotel with General William Rosecrans, listening to a discussion of Yankee battle plans.

In November, 1863, Sam was seized in Giles County, Tennessee, and thrown into jail. The maps and papers under his saddle exposed him as a spy. His captors promised to spare his life if he would only reveal the identity of the mysterious "Coleman."

Sam refused, and it fell to Private C. B. Van Pelt to inform him of his sentence. "I read him a copy of his death sentence," Van Pelt later said. "A reprieve was extended which I [also] read to him, if he would inform us where 'Coleman' was. He stood before me, an uncrowned hero, his eyes flashing, and said: 'I will die a thousand deaths rather than betray my [friends].' We were both moved to tears and remained silent for a time."

Unknown to the Yankee soldiers, "Coleman" was really Dr. H. B. Shaw, who at that moment was being held in an adjacent cell and who was later released.

On the eve of his execution, Sam wrote to his dear mother, saying: *Oh, how painful it is to write you! I have got to die tomorrow morning—to be hanged by the Federals. Mother, do not grieve for me. I must bid you good-by forevermore.*

Chaplain James Young spent the day before the hanging praying with Sam. That night in a small worship service, Sam asked if they would sing, "On Jordan's Stormy Banks." Young later said he would never forget the young soldier's animated voice as he sang: "I am bound for the Promised Land; I am bound for the Promised Land."

Today there is a monument honoring Sam Davis on the grounds of the Tennessee State Capitol. Underneath are the words: "Greater love hath no man than this, that a man lay down his life for his friends."

Praise the Lord! Ye Heavens Adore Him

Published by Thomas Coram

John H. Wilcox

1. Praise the Lord! Ye heav'ns a - dore Him; praise Him, angels, in the height; Sun and moon, re - joice be - fore Him; praise Him, all ye stars of light. Praise the Lord! for He hath spo - ken; worlds His might - y voice o - beyed: Laws which nev - er shall be bro - ken for their guid-ance He hath made.

2. Praise the Lord! For He is glo - rious; nev - er shall His prom - ise fail; God hath made His saints vic - to - rious; sin and death shall not pre - vail. Praise the God of our sal - va - tion! hosts on high, His pow'r pro - claim; Heav'n and earth and all cre - a - tion, laud and mag - ni - fy His name.

Praise the Lord! Ye Heavens Adore Him

1796

Sing praise to the LORD, you saints of His, And give thanks at the remembrance of His holy name. Psalm 30:4

One of Christianity's legacies is its concern for the fatherless. The Bible tells us forty-four times that God regards the plight of the orphans, and that we should do the same. But in seventeenth-century England, little was being done. It was commonplace to see babies left on the doorsteps or abandoned in latrines. London had its fashionable spots, but much of the city was gripped by poverty and disease with thousands living atop one another in mucky slums.

Captain Thomas Coram (1668—1751), a devout Anglican and friend of the Wesleys, determined to do something. Coram (who wasn't really a captain; the title was honorary), was a trader on the high seas who had been sent by a group of merchants to set up the first shipyard in Massachusetts. Returning to London after ten years in the colonies, he was shocked to learn that London had become a city of abandoned babies. "Left to die on dung heaps," he complained to anyone who would listen.

Not being a wealthy man, Coram approached the rich men of London, soliciting donations for a hospital and orphanage for "foundlings" (infants found on the streets). No one would help. "I could no more prevail with them than if I had asked them to pull down their breeches and present their backsides to the King and Queen," he wrote in disgust.

But when he appealed to the wives of London's wealthy men, he found a responsive audience. Finally, the charter was granted, the funds procured, and the foundling hospital opened in 1741. On its first night, hundreds of desperate women gathered at its doors, each with a child in her arms.

Soon London's artists threw their support behind the project, filling the institution with their paintings and music. The great composer George Handel gave benefit performances of his *Messiah* to help raise funds. The London Foundling Hospital became known for its beautiful singing and children's choirs.

In 1796, Coram published a hymnbook entitled *Psalms, Hymns, and Anthems of the Foundling Hospital, London*. Pasted into the cover of this book was an anonymous hymn entitled "Praise the Lord! Ye Heavens Adore Him." To this day, no one knows who wrote it, but it will forever be associated with God's love for children and His concern for the fatherless.

There Is a Balm in Gilead

Traditional Spiritual

Traditional Spiritual

There is a balm in Gil-e-ad to make the wound-ed whole;

There is a balm in Gil-e-ad to heal the sin-sick soul.

1. Some - times I feel dis - cour - aged, And think my work's in vain,
2. If you can't preach like Pet - er, If you can't pray like Paul,

But then the Ho - ly Spir - it Re - vives my soul a - gain.
Just tell the love of Je - sus, And say He died for all.

There Is a Balm in Gilead

About 1800

Who Himself bore our sins in His own body on the tree, that we, having died to sins, might live for righteousness—by whose stripes you were healed. 1 Peter 2:24

The first Africans on American shores arrived in chains. Their hellish voyage aboard slave ships was only the beginning of their sorrows. The breakup of their families, the oppression of bondage, the whips and shackles, their loss of dignity . . . it all combined to kill both body and spirit.

But the souls of the slaves found release through singing, and a unique form of music evolved called the "Negro Spiritual." Spirituals differed greatly from the hymns we've thus far studied. The classics of English hymnody were largely written by pastors like Isaac Watts and John Newton out of their studies of Scripture. African-American slaves, on the other hand, composed their songs in the fields and barns, the words dealing with daily pain and future hope.

Often the slaves were allowed to sing while working. If, for example, they were hauling a fallen tree, they would combine muscles and voices, using the musical rhythms for a "heave-ho" effect. Other times, risking the lash or branding iron, they'd slip into torch-lit groves to worship the Lord. With swaying bodies, they would stand, eyes half-closed, singing, "Go Down, Moses," "Roll, Jordan, Roll, "He's Got the Whole World in His Hands," and the classic "There Is a Balm in Gilead" based on Jeremiah 8:22.

"Hymns more genuine than these have never been sung since the psalmists of Israel relieved their burdened hearts," wrote Edith A. Talbot.

Fisk University, in Nashville, Tennessee, was established after the Civil War, and the famous Fisk Jubilee Singers popularized these Negro spirituals around the world. Composers began arranging spirituals in a way that appealed to the larger population and this gave rise to another type of Christian music, tagged by composer Thomas A. Dorsey as "gospel songs."

Few Negro spirituals can be precisely dated, nor are many specific authors known, but they have mightily influenced American Christian music. The roots of the children's Sunday school chorus, "Do Lord," for example, is in this old spiritual:

O do, Lord, remember me!
For Death is a simple thing,
And he go from door to door
And he knock down some, and he cripple up some,
And he leave some here to pray.
O do Lord, remember me!

I Love Thy Kingdom, Lord

Timothy Dwight

Aaron Williams

1. I love Thy king - dom Lord, The
2. I love Thy Church, O God! Her
3. For her my tears shall fall, For
4. Be - yond my high - est joy I
5. Sure as Thy truth shall last, To

house of Thine a - bode, The Church our blest Re -
walls be - fore Thee stand Dear as the ap - ple
her my prayers as - cend, To her my cares and
prize her heaven - ly ways, Her sweet com - mu - nion,
Zi - on shall be given The bright - est glo - ries

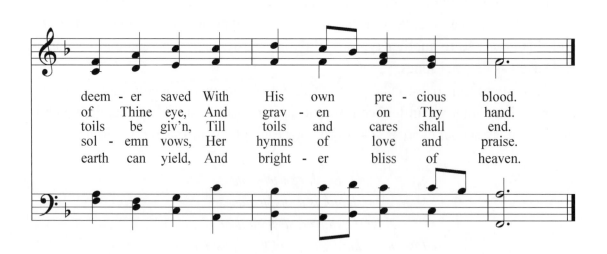

deem - er saved With His own pre - cious blood.
of Thine eye, And grav - en on Thy hand.
toils be giv'n, Till toils and cares shall end.
sol - emn vows, Her hymns of love and praise.
earth can yield, And bright - er bliss of heaven.

I Love Thy Kingdom, Lord

1800

If I forget you, O Jerusalem, let my right hand forget its skill! If I do not remember you, let my tongue cling to the roof of my mouth— if I do not exalt Jerusalem above my chief joy. Psalm 137:5–6

Those of us praying for a spiritual revival in America should remember the last two decades of the 1700s. It was a low-water mark for morality, especially on college campuses. The Rationalist movement, sweeping over classroom and dormitory, had turned most professors and students into infidels.

"During the last decade of the eighteenth century," wrote J. Edwin Orr, "the typical Harvard student was atheist. Students at Williams College conducted a mock celebration of Holy Communion. When the Dean at Princeton opened the chapel Bible to read, a pack of playing cards fell out, some radical having cut a rectangle out of each page to fit the pack! Christians were so unpopular they met in secret and kept their minutes in code."

Yale University in Hartford, Connecticut, was no exception. The college church was almost extinct, and Christian students—if there were any—were underground. But God was preparing a man named Timothy Dwight (grandson of Jonathan Edwards) to turn the tide.

As a child, Timothy had been precocious. He learned the alphabet in one lesson and read the Bible at an early age. Once when he didn't show up for dinner, his worried parents found him in the orchard teaching the catechism to a group of Native Americans. He was only four.

Timothy entered Yale at age thirteen, and was so devoted to his studies that he neglected exercise and sleep. He even limited himself to twelve mouthfuls of vegetables at meals, so as not to overeat and dull his mind. He went on to become a pastor and community leader. In 1795, he was elected president of Yale.

Soon he was debating upperclassmen on the subject: "Are the Scriptures of the Old and New Testament the Word of God?" In small numbers, students began considering Christianity, and within a couple of years there were about a dozen believers on campus.

After seven years of preaching, teaching, and praying, Dwight saw a revival break out at Yale in which one-third of the student body was converted. This spiritual resurgence touched other colleges, too: Harvard, Brown, Dartmouth, and many others. This "Second Great Awakening," provided the spiritual leadership America needed for the next generation.

The spirit of revival permeates Dwight's "I Love Thy Kingdom, Lord," which is based on a portion of Psalm 137. It's the oldest American hymn in continual use.

Praise the Savior, Ye Who Know Him!

Thomas Kelly   Traditional German Melody

1. Praise the Sav - ior, ye who know Him! Who can
2. Je - sus is the name that charms us, He can
3. Trust in Him, ye saints, for - ev - er; He is
4. Keep us, Lord, O keep us cleav - ing to Thy

tell how much we owe Him? Glad - ly
con - flict fits and arms us; Noth - ing
faith - ful, chang - ing nev - er. Neith - er
self And still bel - iev - ing; 'Til the

let us ren - der to Him All we
moves and noth - ing harms us While we
force nor guile can sev - er Those He
hour of our re - ceiv - ing, Prom - ised

are and have.
trust in Him.
loves from Him.
joys with Thee.

Praise the Savior, Ye Who Know Him!

1806

Now therefore, our God, we thank You and praise Your glorious name. 1 Chronicles 29:13

Thomas Kelly of Kellyville, Ireland, was born July 13, 1769. His father, the Honorable Thomas Kelly, was an Irish judge. Planning to walk in his father's footsteps, Thomas enrolled at Trinity College, Dublin, and majored in law. But while in school, he was converted to Christ, and the Lord so convicted him about the ministry that, following graduation, he was ordained in the Irish Episcopal Church.

Thomas was aflame for Christ, and his robust messages about justification by faith troubled the Archbishop of Dublin who frowned on evangelical preaching. Eventually, Thomas was forbidden to preach in that diocese. He preached anyway, leaving the Irish church to become a Dissenter, a non-Anglican.

His keen biblical scholarship and splendid sermons flowed from a warm and winsome personality. Being a man of means, he devoted himself to helping those in need. He is forever remembered because of his acts of mercy during the Dublin famine of 1847.

Thomas also became the "Isaac Watts" of Ireland. He wrote 765 hymns, many of them published in 1802 in *A Collection of Psalms and Hymns.* Two years later, more were issued under the title, *Hymns on Various Passages of Scripture.* In 1815, another volume came out entitled, *Hymns of Thomas Kelly Not Before Published.*

Best known is his great Ascension hymn, "Look Ye Saints, the Sight is Glorious!" The easiest to sing and happiest to hear is his "Praise the Savior, Ye Who Know Him."

> *Praise the Savior, ye who know Him! Who can tell how much we owe Him?*
> *Gladly let us render to Him all we are and have.*
>
> *Jesus is the Name that charms us; He for conflict fits and arms us;*
> *Nothing moves and nothing harms us while we trust in Him.*
>
> *Trust in Him, ye saints, forever—He is faithful, changing never;*
> *Neither force nor guile can sever those He loves from Him.*
>
> *Keep us, Lord, O keep us cleaving to Thyself, and still believing;*
> *Till the hour of our receiving, promised joys with Thee.*
>
> *Then we shall be where we would be; then we shall be what we should be;*
> *Things that are not now, nor could be, soon shall be our own.*

Look, Ye Saints, the Sight Is Glorious

Thomas Kelly

William Owen

1. Look ye saints! The sight is glo-rious; See the Man of Sor-rows now;
2. Crown the Sav-iour, an-gels, crown Him; Rich the tro-phies Je-sus brings;
3. Sin-ners in de-ri-sion scorned Him, Mock-ing thus the Sav-ior's claim;
4. Hark, those bursts of ac-cla-ma-tion! Hark, those loud tri-um-phant chords!

From the fight re-turned vic-to-rious, Ev-ery knee to Him shall bow:
In the seat of power en-throne Him, While the vault of heav-en rings:
Saints and an-gels crowd a-round Him, Spread a-broad the vic-tor's fame.
Je-sus takes the high-est sta-tion; O what joy the sight af-fords:

Crown Him, crown Him, Crown Him, crown Him, Crown Him, crown Him.
Crown Him, crown Him, Crown Him, crown Him, Crown Him, crown Him.
Crown Him, crown Him, Crown Him, crown Him, Crown Him, crown Him.
Crown Him, crown Him, Crown Him, crown Him, Crown Him, crown Him.

Crowns be-come the vic-tor's brow, Crowns be-come the vic-tor's brow.
Crown the Sav-iour King of kings, Crown the Sav-iour King of kings.
Spread a-broad the vic-tor's fame, Spread a-broad the vic-tor's fame.
King of kings, and Lord of lords! King of kings, and Lord of lords!

Look, Ye Saints, the Sight Is Glorious

1809

. . . And there were loud voices in heaven, saying, "The kingdoms of this world have become the kingdoms of our Lord and of His Christ, and He shall reign forever and ever!" Revelation 11:15

Thomas Kelly (1769—1855) was a prolific Irish hymnist who gave us "Praise the Savior, Ye Who Know Him" and many other great hymns—over 750 in all. He's the "Isaac Watts" of Ireland.

As a young man, Thomas honored his father's wishes and enrolled at Dublin University to study law. But while pursing his studies, he came across a book that piqued his interest in Hebrew. This led to his studying the Scriptures with greater diligence and reading books of a spiritual nature. Deeply moved, Thomas abandoned his pursuit of the law, committed his life to Christ, and began studying theology.

In 1792, Thomas was ordained into the Anglican ministry and became friends with the well-known open-air evangelist, Rowland Hill. (It was Rowland Hill who, when asked about the upbeat tempo of some of the Christian music of his day, quipped, "Why should the devil have all the good tunes?")

Such evangelical fervor wasn't welcome in the Anglican Church of that day, and as a result Thomas was suspended from ministry and forbidden to preach. Thus he became a Dissenter—a non-Anglican preacher whose passionate sermons, winning personality, and zealous work with the poor made him a local hero. In one famous incident, a poor Irishman encouraged his wife during an unusually difficult period, saying, "Hold up, Bridget! There's always Mr. Kelly to pull us off of the bog after we've sunk for the last time."

In this way, Kelly pastored in Dublin throughout his life. On his deathbed at age eighty-six, he was heard to pray, "Not my will, but Thine be done." A friend read the 23rd Psalm to him, and Thomas whispered his last words: "The Lord is my all."

Though Kelly's hymn, "Look, Ye Saints, the Sight Is Glorious" was inspired by Revelation 11:15, it's usually associated with the Ascension of Christ. Forty days after His resurrection, Christ took His disciples to the Mount of Olives, where "He was taken up and a cloud received Him out of their sight." According to Acts 1:9–11, the stunned disciples continued staring into the sky until two angels dressed in white broke the spell, asking, "Men of Galilee, why do you stand gazing up into heaven? This same Jesus, who was taken up from you into heaven, will so come in like manner."

The Star-Spangled Banner

Francis Scott Key

Attributed to John Stafford Smith

The Star-Spangled Banner
1814

For our citizenship is in heaven, from which we also eagerly wait for the Savior, the Lord Jesus Christ. Philippians 3:20

I t was a deadly September attack on America. Casualties on our own shores. The nation's capitol targeted. The White House in danger. Terror. Heroes.

One hero was Francis, a Georgetown attorney heavily involved in national politics. An evangelical Christian, Francis taught Bible classes and witnessed boldly, once telling a friend in Congress, "Christ alone can save you from the sentence of condemnation."

He also wrote hymns like this one:

Lord, with glowing heart I'd praise Thee, | For the bliss Thy love bestows, |
For the pardoning grace that saves me, | And the peace that from it flows; |
Help, O God, my weak endeavor; | This dull soul to rapture raise;
Thou must light the flame, or never
Can my love be warmed to praise.

But nothing prepared Francis for the hostage-recovery mission he undertook at the request of the President of the United States. He was seeking the release of a prominent physician, Dr. Beanes, who had been taken captive. During that assignment he was detained by enemy troops and forced to watch a brutal assault on the eastern seaboard.

Toward the morning of September 14, 1814, when it became clear that American forces had withstood the 25-hour bombardment, Francis Scott Key penned another hymn, scribbling it on the back of an envelope. The first stanza we all know, but have you ever sung the last stanza of "The Star-Spangled Banner"?

Blest with victory and peace, may the heaven-rescued land
Praise the Power that hath made and preserved us a nation!
Then conquer we must when our cause it is just.
And this be our motto: "In God is our trust."
And the star-spangled banner in triumph shall wave
O'er the land of the free and the home of the brave.

After sunrise, the British released Francis, and back in Baltimore he wrote out this hymn in fuller form and showed it to his brother-in-law who promptly gave it to a printer who ran off handbills for distribution on the streets. One copy landed in the hands of an unknown musician who adapted it to the tune "To Anacreon in Heaven." So was born the patriotic hymn that was to become our national anthem.

Angels, from the Realms of Glory

James Montgomery

Henry T. Smart

1. An - gels from the realms of glo - ry, Wing your flight o'er
2. Shep - herds in the fields a - bi - ding, Watch - ing o'er your
3. Sag - es, leave your con - tem - pla - tions, Bright - er vi - sions
4. Saints, be - fore the al - tar bend - ing, Watch - ing long in
5. All cre - a - tion, join in prais - ing, God, the Fath - er,

all the earth; Ye who sang cre - a - tion's sto - ry,
flocks by night; God with man is now re - sid - ing,
beam a - far; Seek the great De - sire of na - tions,
hope and fear; Sud - den - ly the Lord, de - scend - ing,
Spir - it, Son; Ev - er - more your voic - es rais - ing,

Now pro - claim Mes - si - ah's birth.
Yon - der shines the in - fant Light.
Ye have seen His na - tal star.
In His tem - ple shall ap - pear.
To th'et - er - nal Three in One.

Come and wor-ship, come and wor-ship; Wor-ship Christ, the new-born King!

Angels, from the Realms of Glory
1816

Praise Him, all His angels; Praise Him, all His hosts! Psalm 148:2

L ike all Moravians, John Montgomery had a burden for world evangelism. He was the only Moravian pastor in Scotland, but he and his wife felt God's call to be missionaries to the island of Barbados. Tearfully placing their six-year-old son, James, in a Moravian settlement in Bracehill near Ballymena, County Antrim, Ireland, they sailed away. James never saw them again, for they perished in Barbados.

Left with nothing, James was enrolled in a school in England. When he didn't do well, he was apprenticed by school authorities to a baker. Baking wasn't for James. He ran away and spent his teenage years drifting from pillar to post, writing poetry and trying his hand at one thing then another. He eventually settled down in Sheffield, England.

In his early twenties, James began working for the local newspaper, the *Sheffield Register*, and there he found his niche. He loved writing. It was a politically active newspaper, and when its owner had to suddenly flee the country to avoid persecution and imprisonment, James purchased the paper and renamed it the *Sheffield Iris*. His editorials, too, proved unpopular with local officials. On two separate occasions he was thrown into jail. But he emerged from prison a celebrity, and he used his newly acquired fame to promote his favorite issues.

Chief among them was the gospel. Despite the loss of his parents, James Montgomery remained devoted to Christ and to the Scriptures, and he championed the cause of foreign missions and of the British Bible Society.

As the years passed, he became the most respected leader in Sheffield, and his writings were eagerly read by its citizens. Early on Christmas Eve, 1816, James, 45, opened his Bible to Luke 2, and was deeply impressed by verse 13. Pondering the story of the heralding angels, he took his pen and started writing. By the end of the day, his new Christmas poem was being read in the pages of his newspaper. It was later set to music and was first sung on Christmas Day, 1821, in a Moravian Church in England: "Angels, from the Realms of Glory."

His parents would have been proud.

Silent Night

Joseph Mohr

Franz Gruber

1. Silent night, holy night, All is calm, all is bright. Round yon virgin mother and child; Holy infant, so tender and mild, Sleep in heavenly peace; Sleep in heavenly peace.

2. Silent night, holy night, Shepherds quake at the sight. Glories stream from heaven afar, Heavenly hosts sing "Alleluia. Christ the Savior is born; Christ the Savior is born."

3. Silent night, holy night, Wondrous star, lend thy light. With the angels, let us sing, Alleluia to our King. Christ the Savior is born; Christ the Savior is born.

4. Silent night, holy night, Son of God, love's pure light. Radiant beams from Thy holy face, With the dawn of redeeming grace. Jesus, Lord, at Thy birth; Jesus, Lord, at Thy birth.

Silent Night
1818

Therefore the Lord Himself will give you a sign: Behold, the virgin shall conceive and bear a Son, and shall call His name Immanuel. Isaiah 7:14

I t was Christmas Eve in the Austrian Alps. At the newly constructed Church of St. Nicholas in Oberndorf, a Tyrol village near Salzburg, Father Joseph Mohr prepared for the midnight service. He was distraught because the church organ was broken, ruining prospects for that evening's carefully planned music. But Father Joseph was about to learn that our problems are God's opportunities, that the Lord causes all things to work together for good to those who love Him. It came into Father Joseph's mind to write a new song, one that could be sung organless. Hastily, he wrote the words, "Silent night, holy night, all is calm, all is bright . . . ." Taking the text to his organist, Franz Gruber, he explained the situation and asked Franz to compose a simple tune.

That night, December 24, 1818, "Silent Night" was sung for the first time as a duet accompanied by a guitar at the aptly named Church of St. Nicholas in Oberndorf.

Shortly afterward, as Karl Mauracher came to repair the organ, he heard about the near-disaster on Christmas Eve. Acquiring a copy of the text and tune, he spread it throughout the Alpine region of Austria, referring to it as "Tiroler Volkslied."

The song came to the attention of the Strasser Family, makers of fine chamois-skin gloves. To drum up business at various fairs and festivals, the four Strasser children would sing in front of their parent's booth. Like the Von Trapp children a century later, they became popular folk singers throughout the Alps.

When the children—Caroline, Joseph, Andreas, and Amalie—began singing "Trioler Volkslied" at their performances, audiences were charmed. It seemed perfect for the snow-clad region, and perfect for the Christian heart. "Silent Night" even came to the attention of the king and queen, and the Strasser children were asked to give a royal performance, assuring the carol's fame.

"Silent Night" was first published for congregational singing in 1838 in the German hymnbook, *Katholisches Gesang—und Gebetbuch für den öffentlichen und häuslichen Gottesdienst zunächst zum Gebrauche der katholischen Gereinden im Königreiche Sachsen.* It was used in America by German-speaking congregations, then appeared in its current English form in a book of Sunday school songs in 1863.

Were it not for a broken organ, there would never have been a "Silent Night."

The First Noel

Traditional English Carol

Traditional English Melody

1. The first No - el, the an - gel did say, Was to cer - tain poor
2. They look - ed up and saw a star Shin - ing in the
3. And by the light of that same star, Three Wise Men
4. Then en - tered in those Wise Men three, Full rev - erent-

shep - herds, in fields as they lay; In fields where they lay
east, be - yond them far, And to the earth it
came from coun - try far; To seek for a King was
ly up - on their knee, And of - fered there, in

keep - ing their sheep, On a cold win - ter's night that was so deep.
gave great light, And so it con - tin - ued both day and night.
their in - tent, And to fol - low the star, wher - ev - er it went.
His pres - ence, Their gold, and myrrh, and frank - in - cense.

No - el, No - el, No - el, No - el, Born is the King of Is - ra - el.

The First Noel

1823

And there were shepherds living out in the fields nearby, keeping watch over their flocks at night. Luke 2:8 (NIV)

N o other carol casts such a spell. The sweet, plaintive strains of "The First Noel," quietly sung on a snow-clad Christmas Eve, bring tears to the eyes and gentle peace to the heart. *Noel, noel, noel, noel. Born is the King of Israel.*

If only we knew who wrote it! It first appeared anonymously in *Some Ancient Christmas Carols*, published by Davis Gilbert in 1823, and the traditional music evidently came from an unknown source in the west of England.

The poetry itself is plain. If we were to recite this rather lengthy piece, we'd get only a garbled sense of the Christmas story. There's no indication in Scripture, for example, that the shepherds saw the Magi's star. And the final verse of the original carol seems anticlimactic. But when combined with its wistful music, the words glow and our hearts are strangely warmed.

The word "Noel" seems to be a French word with Latin roots: *Natalis*, meaning birthday. Modern hymns omit several of the verses. Here is the complete version:

The first Noel the angels did say was to certain poor shepherds in fields as they lay;
In fields where they lay keeping their sheep on a cold winter's night that was so deep.
Noel, Noel, Noel, Noel; Born is the King of Israel.

They looked up and saw a star shining in the East, beyond them far,
And to the earth it gave great light, and so it continued, both day and night.

And by the light of that same star three wise men came from country far,
To seek for a King was their intent, and to follow the star wherever it went.

This star drew nigh to the northwest; o'er Bethlehem it took its rest.
And there it did both stop and stay, right over the place where Jesus lay.

Then they did know assuredly within that house, the King did lie
One entered in then for to see and found the babe in poverty.

Then entered in those wise men three, full reverently, upon bended knee,
And offered there, in His presence, their gold and myrrh and frankincense.

If we in our time do well we shall be free from death and hell
For God hath prepared for us all a resting place in general.
Noel, Noel, Noel, Noel; Born is the King of Israel.

Jesus, I My Cross Have Taken

Henry F. Lyte

attributed to Wolfgang A. Mozart

1. Je - sus, I my cross have tak - en, All to leave and fol - low Thee;
2. Let the world de - spise and leave me; They have left my Sav - ior, too.
3. Hast-en on from grace to glo - ry, Armed by faith and winged by prayer;

Des - ti - tute, de - spised, for - sa - ken, Thou from hence my all shalt be.
Hu - man hearts and looks de-ceive me; Thou art not, like man, un - true.
Heav'n's e - ter - nal days be - fore me, God's own hand shall guide me there.

Per - ish ev - ery fond am - bi - tion, All I've sought, and hoped and known;
And while Thou shalt smile up - on me, God of wis - dom, love and might,
Soon shall close my earth - ly mis - sion, Swift shall pass my pil - grim days;

Yet how rich is my con - di - tion. God and heav'n are still my own!
Foes may hate and friends may shun me. Show Thy face and all is bright.
Hope shall change to glad fru - i - tion; Faith to sight, and prayer to praise.

Jesus, I My Cross Have Taken

1824

Then Jesus said to His disciples, "If anyone desires to come after Me, let him deny himself, and take up his cross, and follow Me." Matthew 16:24

Just as the most beautiful skies combine billowing clouds with shimmering sunlight, Henry Francis Lyte's colorful, bittersweet life contributed to the pensive depth of his beautiful hymns. Henry was born in Scotland in 1793. His father, Captain Thomas Lyte, moved the family to Ireland, then abandoned them, and young Henry was raised by his mother who taught him the Bible and instructed him about prayer. After he entered Portora Royal School in Northern Ireland, his mother died, leaving Henry a nine-year-old orphan with no means of support.

Portora Royal School was superintended by wise and kindly Rev. Robert Burrows, who saw something special in Henry. He invited him into his home, accepted him as part of his family, and paid for his education. Henry excelled. At age 16, he was awarded financial assistance to Trinity College in Dublin, and he traveled there intending to enter the medical school. But something was pulling him toward the ministry, and he wound up instead in the Divinity School.

By this time, Henry had grown into a handsome teenager, six feet tall with dark curly hair and a winning personality. He proved a hard worker, a brilliant student, and a gifted poet who repeatedly won awards for his compositions.

After college, Henry, 21, was ordained and began preaching at St. Munn's Church in Taghmon, Ireland, an inland city south of Dublin. There he made friends with another pastor, Rev. Abraham Swanne. When Swanne became critically ill, Henry cared for him and for his family, spending long hours talking to the dying man. The two clergymen realized they were both blind guides, lost, without adequate personal relationships with Christ. As they searched the Scriptures together, both Henry and his dying friend came to a deeper faith. He later wrote, "I began to study my Bible and preach in another manner than I had done previously." It was this incident that inspired his wonderful hymn, written in 1824 (revised in 1833):

Jesus, I my cross have taken, / All to leave and follow Thee. /
Destitute, despised, forsaken, / Thou from hence my all shall be. /

Man may trouble and distress me, / 'Twill but drive me to Thy breast, /
Life with trials hard may press me, / Heaven will bring me sweeter rest.

In the Cross of Christ I Glory

John Bowring

Ithamar Conkey

1. In the cross of Christ I glory,
2. When the woes of life o'er - take me,
3. When the sun of bliss is beam - ing
4. Bane and bless - ing, pain and plea - sure,

Tow'r - ing o'er the wrecks of time;
Hopes de - ceive and fears an - noy;
Light and love up - on my way;
By the cross are sanc - ti - fied;

All the light of sa - cred sto - ry
Nev - er shall the cross for - sake me,
From the cross the ra - diance stream - ing
Peace is there that knows no mea - sure,

Gath - ers round its head sub - lime.
Lo! it glows with peace and joy.
Adds more lus - ter to the day.
Joys that thro' all time a - bide.

In the Cross of Christ I Glory

1825

So Moses made a bronze serpent, and put it on a pole; and so it was, if a serpent had bitten anyone, when he looked at the bronze serpent, he lived. Numbers 21:9

When the World Trade Center collapsed following the terrorist attacks of September 11, 2001, workers excavating the site found a cross-shaped beam that, standing upright amid the ruin and debris, became a makeshift center of worship. The picture of that cross was published around the world and served as a symbol of hope.

A similar story is associated with this hymn. On the island of Macao in the region of Hong Kong, a magnificent cathedral was destroyed. Only the front wall remained. Atop it was a great metal cross, blackened with age, silhouetted against the sky. It is said that hymnist John Bowring was so inspired by the story of this cathedral that he wrote the hymn, "In the cross of Christ I glory, tow'ring o'er the wrecks of time."

The validity of that story is questionable, but we do have a verified story about RATHBUN, the tune to which this hymn is set. It was composed by Ithamar Conkey, organist at Central Baptist Church in Norwich, Connecticut.

In 1849, Central's pastor had planned a series of sermons on the seven last words of Christ on the Cross. According to the *Norwich Bulletin:* "One Sunday during the series it was a very rainy day. Mr. Conkey was sorely disappointed that the members of the choir did not appear, as only one soprano came. Mr. Conkey was so discouraged and disheartened that after the prelude he closed the organ and locked it and went to his home on Washington Street. The pastor and choir gallery were at opposite ends of the church, and he could leave without attracting the attention of the congregation. That afternoon, as he sat down at the piano for practice, his mind was distracted with the thoughts of the sermons Dr. Hiscox had prepared and the words of the hymn, 'In the Cross of Christ I Glory.' He then and there composed the music that is now so universally familiar in churches of every denomination, known as RATHBUN. He admitted afterward the inspiration was a vivid contradiction of his feelings at the morning service."

But why did he name his tune RATHBUN?

The one choir member who showed up on that rainy Sunday in 1849 . . . that one faithful soprano . . . was named Mrs. Beriah S. Rathbun.

Holy, Holy, Holy! Lord God Almighty

Reginald Heber

John B. Dykes

1. Ho-ly, ho-ly, ho - ly, Lord God Al - might - y!
2. Ho-ly, ho-ly, ho - ly! All the saints a - dore Thee,
3. Ho-ly, ho-ly, ho - ly! Though the dark - ness hide Thee,
4. Ho-ly, ho-ly, ho - ly! Lord God Al - might - y!

Ear - ly in the morn - ing our song shall rise to Thee.
Cast - ing down their gold - en crowns A - round the glass - y sea;
Though the eye of sin - ful man Thy glo - ry may not see.
All Thy works shall praise Thy name In earth, and sky, and sea.

Ho - ly, ho - ly, ho - ly! Mer - ci - ful and might - y!
Cher - u - bim and ser - a - phim Fall - ing down be - fore Thee,
On - ly Thou art ho - ly; There is none be - side, Thee
Ho - ly, ho - ly, ho - ly! Mer - ci - ful and might - y!

God in three Per - sons, Bless - ed Trin - i - ty!
Which wert, and art, And ev - er - more shall be.
Per - fect in power, In love, and pur - i - ty.
God in three Per - sons, Bless - ed Trin - i - ty.

Holy, Holy, Holy!
Lord God Almighty

1826

And they do not rest day or night, saying: "Holy, holy, holy, Lord God Almighty, Who was and is and is to come!" Revelation 4:8

Reginald Heber was born April 21, 1783, to a minister and his wife in an English village. After a happy childhood and a good education in the village school, he enrolled at Oxford where he excelled in poetry and became fast friends with Sir Walter Scott. Following graduation, he succeeded his father as vicar in his family's parish, and for sixteen years he faithfully served his flock.

His bent toward poetry naturally gave him a keen and growing interest in hymnody. He sought to lift the literary quality of hymns, and he also dreamed of publishing a collection of high-caliber hymns corresponding to the church year for use by liturgical churches. But the Bishop of London wouldn't go along with it, and Heber's plans were disappointed.

He continued writing hymns for his own church, however, and it was during the sixteen years in the obscure parish of Hodnet that Heber wrote all 57 of his hymns, including the great missionary hymn, "From Greenland's Icy Mountains," which exhorted missionaries to take the gospel to faraway places like "Greenland's icy mountains," and "India's coral strand."

> *From Greenland's icy mountains, / From India's coral strand, /*
> *Where Afric's sunny fountains / Roll down their golden sand; /*
> *From many an ancient river, / From many a palmy plain, /*
> *They call us to deliver / Their land from error's chain.*

This hymn represented an earnest desire for Reginald, for he felt God was calling him as a missionary to "India's coral strand." His desire was fulfilled in 1822, when, at age 40, he was appointed to oversee the Church of England's ministries in India.

Arriving in Calcutta, he set out on a 16-month tour of his diocese, visiting mission stations across India. In February of 1826, he left for another tour. While in the village of Trichinopoly on April 3, 1826, he preached to a large crowd in the hot sun, and afterward plunged into a pool of cool water. He suffered a stroke and drowned.

It was after his death that his widow, finding his 57 hymns in a trunk, succeeded in publishing his *Hymns Written and Adapted to the Weekly Service of the Church Year.* In this volume was the great Trinitarian hymn based on Revelation 4:8–11, "Holy, Holy, Holy, Lord God Almighty."

My Faith Looks Up to Thee

Ray Palmer

Lowell Mason

1. My faith looks up to Thee, Thou Lamb of Cal - va - ry, Sa - vior di - vine! Now hear me while I pray; Take all my guilt a - way. Oh let me from this day Be whol - ly Thine!

2. May Thy rich grace im - part Strength to my faint - ing heart, My zeal in - spire. As Thou hast died for me, Oh may my love to Thee Pure, warm and change - less be, A liv - ing fire.

3. While life's dark maze I tread, And griefs a - round me spread Be Thou my Guide. Bid dark - ness turn to day; Wipe sor - row's tears a - way; Nor let me ev - er stray From Thee a - side!

4. When ends life's tran - sient dream, When death's cold sul - len stream Shall o'er me roll, Blest Sa - vior, then in love, Fear and dis - trust re - move. Oh bear me safe a - bove, A ran - somed soul.

My Faith Looks Up to Thee

1830

But rejoice to the extent that you partake of Christ's sufferings, that when His glory is revealed, you may also be glad with exceeding joy. 1 Peter 4:13

I n the early 1830s, Lowell Mason moved to Boston from Savannah, where for sixteen years he had worked in a bank while directing church choirs on the side. In relocating to Boston, he wanted to focus exclusively on his musical interests. Soon he was directing three choirs, publishing hymns, compiling a songbook, and trying to get music education in the Boston public schools.

One day in 1832, he bumped into Ray Palmer. Palmer, 24, was exhausted. For years, he had burned the candle on both ends, working as a clerk in a dry goods store, attending classes at Yale, teaching at a girl's school in New York City, and preparing for the ministry.

Now, Mason wanted Palmer to write for him, to compose some hymns for his projected hymnbook.

Palmer, too tired to produce anything new, hesitatingly opened his little leather journal and showed Mason a poem he had written two years before. It was a personal prayer for renewed zeal and courage, composed in his rented room one night in 1830 when he had felt sick, tired, and lonely.

He later explained that he had wept that winter's evening upon finishing this poem: "The words for these stanzas were born out of my own soul with very little effort," he said. "I recall that I wrote the verses with tender emotion. There was not the slightest thought of writing for another eye, least of all writing a hymn for Christian worship."

After reading the words, Mason ducked into a nearby store for a piece of paper and hurriedly copied them down. That evening in his studio, he poured over this poem, hammering out the perfect tune for it. Shortly after, the two men met again and Mason told the young man, "Mr. Palmer, you may live many years and do many good things, but I think you will be best known to posterity as the author of 'My Faith Looks Up to Thee.'"

Lowell Mason was right. Ray Palmer did go on to do many good things and to write many fine hymns. But he is remembered by posterity for his first hymn, one written before he had even entered the ministry.

O For a Faith that Will Not Shrink

William H. Bathurst

J. C. Lowry

1. O for a faith that will not shrink, Tho' pressed by ev-'ry foe, That will not trem-ble on the brink Of an-y earth-ly woe!
2. That will not mur-mur nor com-plain, Be-neath the chas-tening rod But in the hour of grief or pain, Will lean up-on its God.
3. A faith that shines more bright and clear When tem-pests rage with-out; That when in dan-ger knows no fear, In dark-ness feels no doubt.
4. Lord give us such a faith as this; And then what-e'er may come, We'll taste e'en here the hal-lowed bliss, Of an e-ter-nal home.

O For a Faith that Will Not Shrink

1831

And the apostles said to the Lord, "Increase our faith." So the Lord said, "If you have faith as a mustard seed, you can say to this mulberry tree, 'Be pulled up by the roots and be planted in the sea,' and it would obey you. Luke 17:5–6

This hymn strikes a chord in most Christians, for we often find ourselves *worrying* when we should be *worshipping* and *waiting*. The German Christian, George Müeller, was a man who learned to replace fear with faith. When asked about his ability to trust God in crises, he replied, "My faith is the same faith which is found in every believer. It has been increased little by little for the last 26 years. Many times when I could have gone insane from worry, I was at peace because my soul believed the truth of God's promises. God's Word, together with the whole character of God, as He has revealed Himself, settles all questions. His unchangeable love and His infinite wisdom calmed me . . . . It is written, 'He who did not spare His own Son, but delivered Him up for us all, how shall He not with Him also freely give us all things.'"

If your faith needs bolstering, make this hymn your own personal prayer. It was written by William Bathurst, who was born near Bristol, England, on August 28, 1796. He grew up in privileged surroundings. His father, Charles Bragge, a member of Parliament, changed his name to Bathurst when he inherited the family estate at Lydney Park, Gloucestershire.

After graduating from Oxford, William became an Anglican minister in a village near Leeds, England, for 32 years (1820–1852). But he grew uncomfortable with the Anglican Church, especially regarding the baptism and burial practices demanded by the Book of Common Prayer. He eventually resigned his pulpit and assumed the family estate at Lydney Park. He died at the estate on November 25, 1877, and was buried in the nearby churchyard.

"O For a Faith that Will Not Shrink" is the best-known of William's 200 hymns. Originally entitled, "The Power of Faith," it was written as William studied Luke 17:5–6, where the disciples asked Jesus, "Lord, increase our faith."

O for a faith that will not shrink | Though pressed by ev'ry foe, |
That will not tremble on the brink | Of any earthly woe.

A faith that shines more bright and clear | When tempests rage without; |
That when in danger knows no fear, | In darkness feels no doubt.

My Country, 'Tis of Thee

Samuel F. Smith

Thesaurus Musicus

My Country, 'Tis of Thee

1831

Blessed is the nation whose God is the LORD . . . Psalm 33:12

This patriotic hymn was written by Samuel Francis Smith, a native Bostonian, born on October 21, 1808. After attending Boston Latin School, he enrolled in Harvard, then attended Andover Seminary. While there, Samuel became fascinated by the work of Adoniram Judson, America's first missionary, and he developed a lifelong passion for world evangelism.

It was also during Samuel's first year at Andover that hymn publisher, Lowell Mason, sought his help. Mason had a stack of German songs and materials needing translation. Learning that Samuel was proficient in German, he recruited the young student to translate them.

On a cold February afternoon, about a half hour before sunset, Samuel sat in his sparsely furnished room, pouring over the materials. He was struck by the words of "Gott segne Sachsenland" ("God Bless our Saxon Land"), set to the tune we know as "America" (used in Great Britain for "God Save the Queen").

"I instantly felt the impulse to write a patriotic hymn of my own adapted to this tune," Samuel later said. "Picking up a scrap of paper which lay near me, I wrote at once, probably within half an hour, the hymn, 'America' as it is now known."

A friend, William Jenks, took a copy to the pastor of Boston's Park Street Congregational Church. There "America" was first sung by the Juvenile Choir at a Sunday School Rally, on July 4, 1831.

In the years that followed, Samuel Francis Smith grew into a powerful Baptist preacher, pastor, college professor, hymnist, linguist, writer, and missionary advocate. He traveled the world in support of evangelism, and he rejoiced when his son became a missionary to Rangoon. Samuel lived to ripe old age and remained active till the end. He died suddenly in his late-eighties at the Boston train station en route to a preaching appointment.

But he has always been most revered for the patriotic hymn he wrote as a 23-year-old student. As his friend and Harvard classmate, Oliver Wendell Holmes, put it at a class reunion:

> And there's a nice youngster of excellent pith,—
> Fate tried to conceal him by naming him Smith;
> But he shouted a song for the brave and the free,—
> Just read on his medal, "My country, of thee!"

Lead, Kindly Light

John Henry Newman

John B. Dykes

1. Lead, kind-ly Light, a-mid th'en-cir-cling gloom, lead Thou me on!
2. I was not ev-er thus, nor prayed that Thou shouldst lead me on;
3. So long Thy power hath blest me, sure it still will lead me on.

The night is dark, and I am far from home; lead Thou me on!
I loved to choose and see my path; but now lead Thou me on!
O'er moor and fen, o'er crag and tor-rent, till the night is gone,

Keep Thou my feet; I do not ask to see
I loved the gar-ish day, and, spite of fears,
And with the morn those an-gel fac-es smile,

The dis-tant scene; one step e-nough for me.
Pride ruled my will. Re-mem-ber not past years!
which I have loved long since, and lost a-while!

Lead, Kindly Light
1833

The steps of a good man are ordered by the LORD. Psalm 37:23

I n the 1800s, more than 250 Church of England pastors converted to Roman Catholicism, largely through the influence of John Henry Newman.

Newman, born in London on February 21, 1801, was raised to love and read the Bible. He was a sensitive youth, and concluded early in life that God intended him to stay single. After graduating from Trinity College, Oxford, at age 19, he was ordained and became Vicar of St. Mary's, the university church at Oxford. His preaching attracted large crowds.

By 1833, his hard work and sensitive nature left him exhausted, and he embarked on a therapeutic voyage to the coasts of North Africa, Italy, Greece, and Sicily. While in Rome he found himself attracted to Catholicism. Proceeding on to Sicily, he contracted a fever and nearly died. Emotionally spent, homesick, weak, and worried, he sailed for home, but the winds died, stranding the vessel motionless on the Mediterranean for weeks.

The dispirited young man nearly broke under the strain. On June 16, 1833, alone in his cabin, he wrestled with God until he gained victory in his heart. From this experience, he penned one of the most famous hymns in the English language:

Lead, kindly Light! Amid th' encircling gloom, | Lead Thou me on; |
The night is dark, and I am far from home, | Lead Thou me on; |
Keep thou my feet; | I do not ask to see the distant scene; | One step enough for me.

"Lead, Kindly Light" was published the next year in a British magazine under the title, "Faith—Heavenly Leanings." It later appeared under the titles, "Light in the Darkness," and "The Pillar of Cloud."

By 1841 Newman was clearly turning away from the Anglican Church. On October 9, 1845, he shocked England by converting to Roman Catholicism. Two years later, he was ordained a priest and, eventually, a cardinal.

Try praying this hymn the next time you need guidance. The Lord leads us step by step. He provides for us day by day. And He cares for us moment by moment.

God never gives guidance for two steps at a time. I must take one step, and then I get light for the next. This keeps the heart in abiding dependence upon God.—C. H. Mackintosh

O Worship the King

Robert Grant

Johann Michael Haydn

1. O wor-ship the King, All glo-rious a-bove, And
2. O tell of His might, And sing of His grace, Whose
3. Thy boun-ti-ful care, What tongue can re-cite? It
4. Frail child-ren of dust, And fee-ble as frail, In

grate-ful-ly sing His power and His love: Our
robe is the light, Whose can - o - py space. His
breathes in the air; It shines in the light. It
Thee do we trust, Nor find Thee to fail. Thy

Shield and De - fend-er, The An-cient of Days, Pa -
char - iots of wrath, The deep thun-der-clouds form, And
streams from the hills; It de - scends to the plain, And
mer - cies how ten-der! How firm to the end! Our

vil - ioned in splen-dor, And gird - ed with praise.
dark is His path On the wings of the storm.
sweet-ly dis-tills In the dew and the rain.
Mak-er, De-fend-er, Re-deem - er, and Friend!

O Worship the King

1833

I will sing to the LORD as long as I live; I will sing praise to my God while I have my being. Psalm 104:33

harles Grant, director of the East India Company, was respected through-out India as one of Britain's finest statesmen. He was also a deeply commit-ted Christian, an evangelical in the Anglican Church, who used his position in India to encourage missionary expansion there.

In 1778, just as England was reeling from the American Revolution, Charles returned to the British Isles to become a Member of Parliament from Inverness, Scotland.

His son, Robert, six years old at the time, grew up in a world of power, politics, and privilege. But he also grew up as a devout and dedicated follower of Christ. As a young man, Robert attended Magdalene College, Cambridge, then entered the legal profession. His intelligence and integrity were obvious. He became King's Sargent in the Court of the Duchy of Lancaster, and, in 1818, he entered Parliament. Among his legislative initiatives was a bill to remove civil restrictions against the Jews.

One day in the early 1830s, as Robert studied Psalm 104, he compared the greatness of the King of kings with the majesty of British royalty. Psalm 104:1 says of God: "O Lord my God, You are very great: You are clothed with honor and majesty." Verses 2–3 add that God covers Himself "with light as with a garment" and "makes the clouds His chariot." Verse 5 reminds us that God "laid the foundations of the earth." All of creation reflects God's greatness, verse 24 proclaiming, "O Lord, how manifold are Your works!" Verse 31 says, "May the glory of the Lord endure forever."

Robert filled his heart with these verses, and from his pen came one of the most magnificent hymns in Christendom:

> *O worship the King, all glorious above,*
> *And gratefully sing His power and His love;*
> *Our Shield and Defender, the Ancient of Days,*
> *Pavilioned in splendor and girded with praise.*

In 1832, Robert was appointed Judge Advocate General, this hymn was published in 1833, and he was knighted in 1834. Soon thereafter, at age 50, Sir Robert returned to India, land of his early childhood, to be Governor of Bombay. He died there on July 9, 1838. A nearby medical college was built in his honor and named for him. But his most lasting memorial is this majestic hymn of praise, calling us to worship the King of kings.

The Solid Rock

Edward Mote

William B. Bradbury

1. My hope is built on noth-ing less Than Je-sus' blood and
2. When dark-ness seems to hide His face, I rest on His un-
3. His oath, His cov-e-nant, His blood, Sup-port me in the
4. When He shall come with trum-pet sound, O may I then in

righ-teous-ness. I dare not trust the sweet-est frame, But whol-ly
chang-ing grace. In ev-ery high and storm-y gale, My an-chor
whelm-ing flood. When all a-round my soul gives way, He then is
Him be found! Dressed in His righ-teous-ness a-lone, Fault-less to

lean on Je-sus' name.
holds with -in the veil. On Christ the sol-id Rock I stand, All
all my Hope and Stay.
stand be -fore the throne!

oth-er ground is sink-ing sand. All oth-er ground is sink-ing sand.

The Solid Rock

1834

For no other foundation can anyone lay than that which is laid, which is Jesus Christ. 1 Corinthians 3:11

Edward Mote was born into poverty on January 21, 1797, in London. His parents, innkeepers, wouldn't allow a Bible in their house, but somehow Edward heard the gospel as a teenager and came to Christ. He eventually became a skilled carpenter and the owner of his own cabinet shop.

"One morning," he recalled, "it came into my mind as I went to labor to write a hymn on the 'Gracious Experience of a Christian.' As I went up to Holborn I had the chorus: *On Christ the solid Rock I stand / All other ground is sinking sand.* In the day I had four verses complete, and wrote them off.

"On the Sabbath following, I met brother King . . . who informed me that his wife was very ill, and asked me to call and see her. I had an early tea and called afterwards. He said that it was his usual custom to sing a hymn, read a portion, and engage in prayer before he went to meeting. He looked for his hymnbook but could find it nowhere. I said, 'I have some verses in my pocket; if he liked, we would sing them.' We did, and his wife enjoyed them so much that after service he asked me, as a favor, to leave a copy of them for his wife.

"I went home, and by the fireside composed the last two verses, wrote the whole off, and took them to sister King . . . As these verses so met the dying woman's case, my attention to them was the more arrested, and I had a thousand printed for distribution."

In 1852, Edward, 55, gave up his carpentry to pastor the Baptist Church in Horsham, Sussex, where he ministered 21 years. He resigned in 1873, in failing health, saying, "I think I am going to heaven; yes, I am nearing port. The truths I have been preaching, I am now living upon and they'll do very well to die upon. Ah! The precious blood." He passed away at age 77.

Here's an interesting verse from Mote's original that is omitted from most hymnals today:

> *I trust His righteous character,*
> *His council, promise, and His power;*
> *His honor and His Name's at stake*
> *To save me from the burning lake;*
> *On Christ, the solid Rock, I stand,*
> *All other ground is sinking sand.*

Praise, My Soul, the King of Heaven

Henry F. Lyte

John Goss

1. Praise, my soul, the King of heav - en, to His feet thy tri - bute bring; Ran - somed, healed, re - stored, for - giv - en, ev - er - more His prais - es sing: Al - le - lu - ia! Al - le - lu - ia! Praise the ev - er - last - ing King!

2. Praise Him for His grace and fa - vor to our fa - thers in dis - tress; Praise Him, still the same as ev - er, slow to chide and swift to bless: Al - le - lu - ia! Al - le - lu - ia! Glo - rious in His faith - ful - ness!

3. Fa - ther - like He tends and spares us; well our fee - ble frame He knows; In His hands He gent - ly bears us, res - cues us from all our foes: Al - le - lu - ia! Al - le - lu - ia! Wide - ly yet His mer - cy flows!

4. Frail as sum - mer's flow'r we flour - ish, blows the wind and it is gone; But, while mor - tals rise and per - ish, God en - dures un - chang - ing on: Praise Him, Praise Him, Hal - le - lu - jah! Praise the High E - ter - nal One.

5. An - gels help us to a - dore Him; ye be - hold Him face to face; Sun and moon, bow down be - fore Him, dwell - ers all in time and space: Al - le - lu - ia! Al - le - lu - ia! Praise with us the God of grace!

Praise, My Soul, the King of Heaven

1834

Praise the LORD, O my soul; all my inmost being, praise His holy name. Psalm 103:1

Would you like to spend the night in the home of one of England's greatest hymnists? Reserve a room at the elegant Berry Head Hotel in Brixham, on England's southern coast. Years ago, this was the home of Henry Lyte, author of "Abide with Me," "Jesus, I My Cross Have Taken," and "God of Mercy, God of Grace."

For twenty-three years, Henry Lyte pastored the local church in Brixham, on the "English Riviera." How Henry and his wife, Anne, acquired this elegant estate is something of a mystery, but it was most likely provided for them by the King of England in appreciation for Henry's ministry. The estate was at water's edge, and there in the tranquility of that house and grounds Henry wrote most of his sermons, poems, and hymns.

Despite frail health and weak lungs, Henry established a Sunday school of eight hundred children in Brixham. In addition to preaching and tending his flock, he ministered to sailors on the docks and wrote his hymns and poems. In 1834, he published a small book that included this now-famous hymn, based on Psalm 103. (It was later chosen by Princess Elizabeth, now Queen Elizabeth II, for her wedding hymn in Westminster Abbey on November 20, 1947—the one hundredth anniversary of Lyte's death.)

> *Praise, my soul, the King of heaven;*
> *To His feet thy tribute bring.*
> *Ransomed, healed, restored, forgiven,*
> *Evermore His praises sing.*

While in his early fifties Henry realized his lung disorder had deteriorated into tuberculosis. On September 4, 1847, at age fifty-four, he entered his pulpit with difficulty and preached what was to be his last sermon. Henry closed the service by presiding over the Lord's Supper. That afternoon, he walked pensively over the grounds of Berry Head, working on his most enduring hymn, "Abide with Me."

Shortly afterward, Henry departed for warmer climes. Arriving on the French Riviera, he checked into the Hotel de Angleterre in Nice, and there on November 20, 1847, his lungs finally gave out. He was buried in Nice and a white cross now marks his grave.

After Anne's death, Berry Head passed to the Lyte daughter, Mrs. John Hogg, and it remained in the family until 1949, when it was converted into a hotel.

Just As I Am

Charlotte Elliott

William B. Bradbury

1. Just as I am, with – out one plea, But
2. Just as I am, and wait – ing not To
3. Just as I am, though tossed a – bout With
4. Just as I am, poor, wretch – ed, blind; Sight,
5. Just as I am, Thou wilt re – ceive, Wilt

that Thy blood was shed for me, And that Thou bidst me
rid my soul of one dark blot; To Thee whose blood can
many a con – flict, many a doubt, Fight – ings and fears with-
rich – es, heal – ing of the mind. Yea, all I need, in
wel – come, par – don, cleanse, re – lieve. Be – cause Thy prom – ise

come to Thee, O Lamb of God, I come, I come!
cleanse each spot, O Lamb of God, I come, I come!
in, with – out, O Lamb of God, I come, I come!
Thee to find, O Lamb of God, I come, I come!
I be – lieve, O Lamb of God, I come, I come!

Just As I Am

1836

All that the Father gives Me will come to Me, and the one who comes to Me I will by no means cast out. John 6:37

She was an embittered woman, Charlotte Elliott of Brighton, England. Her health was broken, and her disability had hardened her. "If God loved me," she muttered, "He would not have treated me this way."

Hoping to help her, a Swiss minister, Dr. Cesar Malan, visited the Elliotts on May 9, 1822. Over dinner, Charlotte lost her temper and railed against God and family in a violent outburst. Her embarrassed family left the room, and Dr. Malan was left alone with her.

"You are tired of yourself, aren't you?" he asked. "You are holding to your hate and anger because you have nothing else in the world to cling to. Consequently, you have become sour, bitter, and resentful."

"What is your cure?" asked Charlotte.

"The faith you are trying to despise."

As they talked, Charlotte softened. "If I wanted to become a Christian and to share the peace and joy you possess," she finally asked, "what would I do?"

"You would give yourself to God just as you are now, with your fightings and fears, hates and loves, pride and shame."

"I would come to God just as I am? Is that right?"

Charlotte did come just as she was, and her heart was changed that day. As time passed she found and claimed John 6:37 as a special verse for her: ". . . he who comes to Me I will by no means cast out."

Years later, her brother, Rev. Henry Elliott, was raising funds for a school for the children of poor clergymen. Charlotte wrote a poem, and it was printed and sold across England. The leaflet said: *Sold for the Benefit of St. Margaret's Hall, Brighton: Him That Cometh to Me I Will in No Wise Cast Out.* Underneath was Charlotte's poem— which has since become the most famous invitational hymn in history.

Charlotte lived to be 82 and wrote about 150 hymns, though she never enjoyed good health. As her loved ones sifted through her papers after her death, they found over a thousand letters she had kept in which people expressed their gratitude for the way this hymn had touched their lives.

Savior, Like a Shepherd Lead Us

Attr. to Dorothy A. Thrupp

William B. Bradbury

1. Sav - ior, like a Shepherd lead us; Much we need Thy ten-der care.
2. We are Thine; do Thou be - friend us; Be the Guard-ian of our way.
3. Thou hast prom-ised to re - ceive us, Poor and sin - ful tho' we be;
4. Ear - ly let us seek Thy fa - vor; Ear - ly let us do Thy will.

In Thy pleas - ant pas-tures feed us; For our use Thy folds pre - pare.
Keep Thy flock; from sin de - fend us; Seek us when we go a - stray.
Thou hast mer - cy to re - lieve us, Grace to cleanse,and power to free.
Bless - ed Lord and on - ly Sav - ior, With Thy love our bos-oms fill.

Bles - sed Je - sus, bless-ed Je-sus! Thou hast bought us; Thine we are.
Bless - ed Je - sus, bless - ed Je-sus! Hear, O hear us when we pray.
Bless - ed Je - sus, bless - ed Je-sus! We will ear - ly turn to Thee.
Bless - ed Je - sus, bless - ed Je-sus! Thou hast loved us; love us still.

Bless - ed Je - sus, bless - ed Je-sus! Thou hast bought us, Thine we are.
Bless - ed Je - sus, bless - ed Je-sus! Hear, O hear us when we pray.
Bless - ed Je - sus, bless - ed Je-sus! We will ear - ly turn to Thee.
Bless - ed Je - sus bless - ed Je-sus! Thou hast loved us; love us still.

Savior, Like a Shepherd Lead Us

1836

For the Lamb who is in the midst of the throne will shepherd them and lead them to living fountains of waters. And God will wipe away every tear from their eyes. Revelation 7:16, 17

T his hymn, originally for children, first appeared in an 1836 volume entitled *Hymns for the Young,* compiled by Dorothy A. Thrupp. Many hymnologists have attributed the words to Mrs. Thrupp, but her authorship is uncertain. One early hymnbook attributed it to Henry Francis Lyte; but that, too, is doubtful.

There's no doubt, however, about the composer of the music. It was the famous William Bradbury, one of the most prolific hymnists of the nineteenth century. A native of York, Maine, William moved to Boston at age fourteen to enroll in the Boston Academy of Music. There he joined Lowell Mason's choir at the Bowdoin Street Church.

Lowell Mason was a banker-turned-composer who became the first American to receive a Doctorate in Music from an American university. A dedicated Christian, he had written the tunes for such hymns as "Joy to the World!," "My Faith Looks Up to Thee," "Nearer, My God, to Thee," and "From Greenland's Icy Mountains." Mason was passionate about training children in sacred music.

Recognizing that young William Bradbury had an inborn talent, Mason sought to encourage him at every turn. Soon William was playing the organ under Mason's watchful eye, and earning a whopping $25 a year in the process.

William was so inspired by his mentor that he moved to New York City to do there what Mason had been doing in Boston—encouraging the Christian musical education of children. He organized and led children's singing conventions, encouraged music in the New York school system, and publishing Sunday school songbooks. During his lifetime, fifty-nine separate books appeared under his name.

Bradbury set in motion a great change in American church music. Prior to his work, most hymns were heavy, noble, and stately. William wanted to write lighter melodies that children could sing. His compositions were softer, full of movement, and easier for children to sing.

In so doing, William Bradbury helped usher in the era of gospel music. He may not have realized that adults would sing his hymns as readily as children would, but he paved the way for the likes of Fanny Crosby and Ira Sankey. Today Bradbury is remembered as the musical composer of such favorites as: "He Leadeth Me," "The Solid Rock," "Just As I Am," "Jesus Loves Me," "Sweet Hour of Prayer" and this one—"Savior, Like a Shepherd Lead Us."

Nearer, My God, to Thee

Sarah F. Adams

Lowell Mason

1. Near - er, my God, to Thee, Near - er to Thee,
2. Though like the wan - der - er, The sun gone down,
3. There let the way ap - pear, Steps un - to heav'n;
4. Then, with my wak - ing tho'ts Bright with Thy praise,
5. Or if, on joy - ful wing Cleav - ing the sky,

E'en though it be a cross That rais - eth me!
Dark - ness be o - ver me, My rest a stone;
All that Thou send - est me, In mer - cy giv'n;
Out of my ston - y griefs Beth - el I'll raise,
Sun, moon, and stars for - got, Up - ward I fly,

Still all my song shall be, Near - er, my God, to Thee;
Yet in my dreams I'd be, Near - er, my God, to Thee;
An - gels to beck - on me, Near - er, my God, to Thee;
So by my woes to be, Near - er, my God, to Thee;
Still all my song shall be, Near - er, my God, to Thee;

Near - er, my God, to Thee, Near - er to Thee!
Near - er, my God, to Thee, Near - er to Thee!
Near - er, my God, to Thee, Near - er to Thee!
Near - er, my God, to Thee, Near - er to Thee!
Near - er, my God, to Thee, Near - er to Thee!

Nearer, My God, to Thee

1840

Then he dreamed, and behold, a ladder was set up on the earth, and its top reached to heaven. Genesis 28:12

It was reported that the band aboard the *Titanic* gallantly played "Nearer, My God, to Thee" as the great liner sank to its watery grave on April 14, 1912. A Canadian survivor told of being comforted by its strains. Historians, however, have never been able to nail down the validity of the story.

Never mind. It's a great hymn anyway, written by a woman named Sarah Flower Adams. She was born in Harlow, England, in the winter of 1805. Her father was a newspaper editor and a man of prominence.

Sarah herself grew up enjoying the spotlight. She showed great interest in the stage and dreamed of being an actress. In 1834, she married William Bridges Adams, a civil engineer. The couple lived in London where Sarah could be near the great theaters. In 1837, she played "Lady MacBeth" in the Richmond Theater in London to rave reviews.

Her frail health hampered her career, however, and she found herself focusing more on her literary gifts. It's said that she wrote quickly, as if under compulsion; and seldom did editors find anything to change in her work. Among her compositions were hymns of praise to the Lord. Sarah's sister, Eliza, a gifted musician, often wrote the music for her hymns. The two were very close.

One day in 1841, their pastor, Rev. William Johnson Fox of London's South Place Unitarian Church, paid a visit. He was compiling a church hymnbook and he wanted to include some of their hymns. He further mentioned that he was frustrated at his inability to find a hymn to go along with the upcoming Sunday's message, which was from the story of Jacob at Bethel in Genesis 28:20–22.

Sarah offered to write a hymn based on those verses. For the rest of the week she poured over the passage, visualizing Jacob's sleeping with a stone for his pillow as he dreamed of a ladder reaching to heaven. The following Sunday, South Place Unitarian Church sang Sarah's "Nearer, My God, to Thee."

Eliza, who was suffering from tuberculosis, died in 1846. Sarah had faithfully cared for her sister during the illness, but by the time Eliza died, Sarah, too, was showing signs of consumption.

She passed away on August 14, 1848, at age 43.

Come, Christians, Join to Sing

Christian Henry Bateman

Traditional Spanish Melody
Arr. by Benjamin Carr

1. Come, Chris-tians, join to sing   Al - le - lu - ia! A - men!
2. Come, lift your hearts on high,   Al - le - lu - ia! A - men!
3. Praise yet our Christ a - gain,   Al - le - lu - ia! A - men!

Loud praise to Christ our King;   Al - le - lu - ia! A - men!
Let   prais - es   fill the sky;   Al - le - lu - ia! A - men!
Life shall not   end the strain;   Al - le - lu - ia! A - men!

Let all, with heart and voice,   Be - fore His throne re - joice;
He is our   Guide and Friend;   To us He'll con - des - cend;
On heav - en's bliss - ful shore His good - ness we'll a - dore,

Praise is His gra - cious choice: Al - le - lu - ia! A - men!
His love shall nev - er end: Al - le - lu - ia! A - men!
Sing - ing for - ev - er - more,   "Al - le - lu - ia! A - men!"

Come, Christians, Join to Sing

1843

Serve the LORD with gladness; Come before His presence with singing. Psalm 100:2

Many of our "adult" hymns were originally written for children. "Savior, Like a Shepherd Lead Us," is a good example. So is Isaac Watts' great hymn, "I Sing the Mighty Power of God," which first appeared in his *Divine and Moral Songs for Children.* The rousing "Onward, Christian Soldiers" was written for the youngsters of Horbury, England, to sing on a Monday morning in 1865 as they marched to a nearby village to establish a Sunday school. Even the great anthem, "All Creatures of Our God and King," by Saint Francis of Assisi, was first translated into English and set to music for a 1919 children's festival in Leeds, England.

Here's another instance: "Come, Christians, Join to Sing" first appeared in *Sacred Melodies for Children,* published in Edinburgh in 1843. The original words said, "Come, children, join to sing . . ."

Its author, Christian Henry Bateman, a pastor in Edinburgh, was committed to developing a Sunday school in which children sang the great truths of the Christian faith. Bateman had begun his ministry as a Moravian pastor, but moved to Edinburgh and became a Congregational minister and the pastor of Richmond Place Congregational Church, where he was serving when he wrote "Come, Christians, Join to Sing." He was later ordained in the Church of England and ministered in that communion until his retirement in 1884. He passed away five years later.

"Come, Christians, Join to Sing" originally had five stanzas, but Bateman reduced the hymn to its present form in the 1854 edition of his hymnal, *Sacred Melodies for Sabbath Schools and Families.* This book became one of the best-selling songbooks in Scottish history, selling more than six million copies by 1881 and becoming the standard hymnbook for Scottish Sunday schools for a generation.

The tune, MADRID, was a popular Spanish folk melody arranged for this hymn by Benjamin Carr, who was born in London in 1769, and died in Philadelphia in 1831. In England, Carr was a well-known singer with the London Ancient Concerts. Immigrating to America, he joined his father and brother in a music publishing enterprise, with stores in Philadelphia, New York, and Baltimore. He also served as a church organist and music director in Philadelphia for many years. Benjamin Carr is best known as the first American publisher of "Yankee Doodle"—and for arranging the music to "Come, Christians, Join to Sing."

Come, Ye Thankful People, Come

Henry Alford

George J. Elvey

1. Come, ye thank-ful peo-ple, come; Raise the song of har-vest home.
2. All the world is God's own field, Fruit un-to His praise to yield;
3. For the Lord our God shall come, And shall take His har-vest home;
4. Ev-en so, Lord, quick-ly come To Thy fi-nal har-vest home;

All is safe-ly gath-ered in, Ere the win-ter storms be-gin.
Wheat and tares to-geth-er sown, Un-to joy or sor-row grown;
From His field shall in that day All of-fens-es purge a-way;
Gath-er, Thou, Thy peo-ple in, Free from sor-row, free from sin;

God, our Mak-er, doth pro-vide For our wants to be sup-plied;
First the blade and then the ear, Then the full corn shall ap-pear.
Give His an-gels charge at last In the fire the tares to cast,
There for-ev-er pu-ri-fied, In Thy pres-ence to a-bide.

Come to God's own tem-ple, come; Raise the song of har-vest home.
Lord of har-vest grant that we Whole-some grain and pure may be.
But the fruit-ful ears to store In His gar-ner ev-er-more.
Come, with all Thine an-gels, come; Raise the glo-rious har-vest home.

Come, Ye Thankful People, Come

1844

Let us come before His presence with thanksgiving; Let us shout joyfully to Him with psalms. Psalm 95:2

Consider this definition of a gravesite for a Christian: "An Inn of a Pilgrim Traveling to Jerusalem." That's what Henry Alford wrote for his tombstone.

He was born October 7, 1810, in the Bloomsbury area of London, and even from childhood showed remarkable promise. At six, he wrote a biography of the apostle Paul. When he was ten he wrote a pamphlet titled, "Looking unto Jesus: the Believers' Support under Trials and Afflictions."

When sixteen, Henry penned a note in his Bible describing his rededication to Christ: "I do this day in the presence of God and my own soul renew my covenant with God and solemnly determine henceforth to become his and to do his work as far as in me lies."

This committed young man made a mark on Cambridge University as he studied there for the ministry. One of his deans said, "He was morally the bravest man I ever knew. His perfect purity of mind and singleness of purpose seemed to give him a confidence and unobtrusive self-respect which never failed him."

When he was ordained, Henry wrote in his journal: "I went up to town and received the Holy Orders of a Priest; may I be a temple of chastity and holiness, fit and clean. . . . O my beloved Redeemer, my dear Brother and Master, hear my prayer."

Henry was a powerful preacher and a brilliant scholar. He served in the village of Wymeswold for eighteen years before accepting the pastorate of a large London church in 1853. In 1857, he was appointed Dean of Canterbury, an office he held until his rather sudden death on January 12, 1871.

Henry Alford is remembered for his scholarly books, including his classic *Greek New Testament*, the fruit of eighteen years of labor. His two-volume set of psalms and hymns was published in 1844, while he was laboring among his flock in the little farming village of Wymeswold, where he was beloved. He visited every home, loved every soul, taught the Bible simply, and helped the people render thanksgiving.

This hymn, "Come, Ye Thankful People, Come" was written for the English Harvest Festival, the British version of the American Thanksgiving holiday.

Sweet Hour of Prayer

Attr. to William W. Walford

William B. Bradbury

1. Sweet hour of prayer, Sweet hour of prayer, That calls me from a world of care,
2. Sweet hour of prayer, Sweet hour of prayer, Thy wings shall my pe - ti - tion bear
3. Sweet hour of prayer, Sweet hour of prayer, May I Thy con - so - la - tion share,

And bids me at my Fa - ther's throne Make all my wants and wish - es known.
To Him whose truth and faith - ful - ness En - gage the wait - ing soul to bless;
'Til from Mount Pis - gah's loft - y height, I view my home and take my flight.

In sea - sons of dis - tress and grief My soul has of - ten found re - lief,
And since He bids me seek His face, Be - lieve His word, and trust His grace,
This robe of flesh I'll drop, and rise To seize the ev - er - last - ing prize;

And oft es - caped the temp - ter's snare, By Thy re - turn, sweet hour of prayer.
I'll cast on Him my ev - 'ry care, And wait for Thee, sweet hour of prayer.
And shout while pass - ing through the air, Fare - well, fare - well, sweet hour of prayer.

Sweet Hour of Prayer

1845

Hear my cry, O God; Attend to my prayer. Psalm 61:1

weet Hour of Prayer" first appeared in *The New York Observer* on September 13, 1845, accompanied by this explanatory note by a Rev. Thomas Salmon, a British minister recently immigrated to America:

At Coleshill, Warwickshire, England, I became acquainted with W. W. Walford, the blind preacher, a man of obscure birth and connections and no education, but of strong mind and most retentive memory. In the pulpit he never failed to select a lesson well adapted to his subject, giving chapter and verse with unerring precision and scarcely ever misplacing a word in his repetition of the Psalms, every part of the New Testament, the prophecies, and some of the histories, so as to have the reputation of "knowing the whole Bible by heart." He actually sat in the chimney corner, employing his mind in composing a sermon or two for Sabbath delivery. . . . On one occasion, paying him a visit, he repeated two or three pieces he had composed, and having no friend at home to commit them to paper, he had laid them up in the storehouse within. "How will this do?" asked he, as he repeated the following lines . . . ?" I rapidly copied the lines with my pencil as he uttered them, and sent them for insertion in the Observer.

No one, however, has ever found a trace of a blind preacher named W. W. Walford in Coleshill, England. There was a Congregational minister named William Walford who wrote a book about prayer containing striking similarities to this poem, and some believe he was the author. But he was neither blind nor uneducated, and the authorship of this hymn remains a mystery.

There's yet another mystery—a deeper one—connected with this hymn. It's the question Jesus asked Simon Peter in Gethsemane: "What? Could you not watch with Me one hour?" If an hour spent with the Lord is so sweet, why do we race through our day prayerless, then squeeze all our requests into a two-minute segment at bedtime? If prayer is so powerful, why do we neglect it so consistently? An oft-omitted verse to this hymn says:

> *Sweet hour of prayer! Sweet hour of prayer! The joys I feel, the bliss I share,*
> *Of those whose anxious spirits burn with strong desires for thy return!*
> *With such I hasten to the place where God my Savior shows His face,*
> *And gladly take my station there, and wait for thee, sweet hour of prayer!*

I Heard the Voice of Jesus Say

Horatius Bonar

John B. Dykes

1. I heard the voice of Je-sus say, "Come un-to Me and rest;
2. I heard the voice of Je-sus say, "Be-hold, I free-ly give
3. I heard the voice of Je-sus say, "I am this dark world's Light;

Lay down, thou wea-ry one, lay down Thy head up-on My breast."
The liv-ing wa-ter; thirst-y one, stoop down, and drink, and live."
Look un-to Me, thy morn shall rise, and all thy day be bright."

I came to Je-sus as I was, wea-ry and worn and sad;
I came to Je-sus, and I drank of that life-giv-ing stream;
I looked to Je-sus, and I found in Him my Star, my Sun;

I found in Him a rest-ing place, and He has made me glad.
My thirst was quenched, my soul re-vived, and now I live in Him.
And in that light of life I'll walk, till trav-el-ing days are done.

I Heard the Voice
of Jesus Say
1846

Come to Me, all you who labor and are heavy laden, and I will give you rest.
Matthew 11:28

Anyone can work with adults, but it takes a special person to communicate with children. Among the early hymnists, none connected with youngsters better than Horatius Bonar, "the prince of Scottish hymnists."

Horatius was born just before Christmas in 1808, one of eleven children. Two of his siblings—John and Andrew—also became outstanding preachers. After studying for the ministry at the University of Edinburgh and serving an internship at Leith, Horatius was ordained and began pastoring in Kelso. Later he moved to Edinburgh where he became one of Scotland's most famous pulpiteers.

He began writing hymns while at Kelso, and many of them were especially for children. Later, in his church in Edinburgh where only the Scottish version of the Psalms were sung, only the children were allowed to sing his hymns. On one occasion in the adult services, two of his church leaders stormed out in protest when a hymn was announced. But the children never protested. They loved his visits to Sunday School when he would lead them in exuberant singing.

Horatius wrote "I Heard the Voice of Jesus Say" for his Sunday School children in 1846. On the page containing the words, he doodled four faces and the head of a man wearing a hat. He based his three verses on three wonderful promises of Jesus in Matthew 11:28, John 4:14, and John 8:12. The first half of each stanza echoes our Lord's promise, and the last half of each stanza frames our response.

Where did his love for children come from? He and his wife had lost five of their children in rapid succession. But God gave him hundreds of children in his Sunday Schools. And that's not all . . .

Many years later, a surviving Bonar daughter was widowed and returned home to live with her parents. She had five young children. Writing to a friend, Horatius said, "God took five children from life some years ago, and He has given me another five to bring up for Him in my old age."

Horatius was nearly 80 when he preached in his church for the last time. Among his last requests was that no biography of him be written. He wanted all the glory to be Christ's alone.

Abide with Me

Henry F. Lyte

W. H. Monk

1. A - bide with me! Fast falls the e - ven - tide.
2. Swift to its close ebbs out life's lit - tle day.
3. I need Thy pres - ence Ev - ery pass - ing hour.
4. I fear no foe, With Thee at hand to bless;

The dark - ness deep - ens; Lord, with me a - bide!
Earth's joys grow dim; Its glo - ries pass a - way.
What but Thy grace Can foil the temp - ter's power?
Ills have no weight, And tears no bit - ter - ness.

When oth - er help - ers fail And com - forts flee,
Change and de - cay In all a - round I see;
Who, like Thy - self, My guide and stay can be?
Where is death's sting? Where, grave, thy vic - to - ry?

Help of the help - less, O a - bide with me!
O Thou, who chang - est not, a - bide with me!
Through cloud and sun - shine, Lord, a - bide with me.
I tri - umph still, If Thou a - bide with me.

Abide with Me

<u>1847</u>

If you abide in Me, and My words abide in you, you will ask what you desire, and it shall be done for you. John 15:7

Henry Francis Lyte, vicar in the fishing village of Lower Brixham, Devonshire, England, ministered faithfully for twenty-three years to his seafaring people.

Though a humble couple, he and his wife, Anne, lived in an elegant estate, Berry Head. It had reportedly been provided by King William IV, who had been impressed with Henry's ministry. At water's edge, its coastal views were among the most beautiful on the British Isles. Henry laid out walking trails through the estate's forty-one acres and enjoyed the tranquility of the house and grounds. There he wrote most of his sermons, poems, and hymns.

But Henry's lung condition hung over the home like a blackening cloud. Lower Brixham suffered damp winters, and while in his early fifties Henry realized his lung disorder had deteriorated into tuberculosis. On September 4, 1847, age 54, he entered his pulpit with difficulty and preached what was to be his last sermon. He had planned a therapeutic holiday in Italy. "I must put everything in order before I leave," he said, "because I have no idea how long I will be away."

That afternoon he walked along the coast in pensive prayer then retired to his room, emerging an hour later with a written copy of "Abide With Me." Some accounts indicate he wrote the poem during that hour; others say that he discovered it in the bottom of his desk as he packed for his trip to Italy, and that it had been written a quarter century earlier. Probably both stories are true. It is likely that, finding sketches of a poem he had previously started, he prayerfully revised and completed it that evening.

Shortly afterward, Henry embraced his family a final time and departed for Italy. Stopping in Avignon, France, he again revised "Abide With Me"—it was evidently much on his mind—and posted it to his wife. Arriving on the French Riviera, he checked into the Hotel de Angleterre in Nice, and there on November 20, 1847, his phthisic lungs finally gave out. Another English clergyman, a Rev. Manning of Chichester, who happened to be staying in the same hotel, attended him during his final hours. Henry's last words were, "Peace! Joy!"

When news of his death reached Brixham, the fishermen of the village asked Henry's son-in-law, also a minister, to hold a memorial service. It was on this occasion that "Abide With Me" was first sung.

O Holy Night

Placide Clappeau

Adolphe Charles Adam

Fall on your knees! O hear the an - gel voic - es! O night di - vine! O night when Christ was born, O night di - vine! O night, O night di - vine!

O Holy Night

1847

. . . The star which they had seen in the East went before them, till it came and stood over where the young Child was. Matthew 2:9

he words of "O Holy Night" were written in 1847 by a French wine merchant named Placide Clappeau, the mayor of Roquemaure, a town in the south of France. We know little about him except that he wrote poems as a hobby.

We know more about the man who composed the music, a Parisian named Adolphe Charles Adam. The son of a concert pianist, Adams was trained almost from infancy in music and piano. In his mid-twenties, he wrote his first opera and thereafter wrote two operas a year until his death at age fifty-two. Near the end of his life, he lost his savings in a failed business venture involving the French national opera, but the Paris Conservatory rescued him by appointing him professor of music.

It was John Dwight, son of Yale's president, Timothy Dwight ("I Love Thy Kingdom, Lord"), who discovered this French Carol, "Christian Midnight," and translated it into the English hymn, "O Holy Night."

After graduating from Harvard and Cambridge, John was ordained as minister of the Unitarian church in Northampton, but his pastoring experience wasn't happy. In 1841, George and Sophia Ripley founded a commune named Brook Farm "to prepare a society of liberal, intelligent, and cultivated persons, whose relations with each other would permit a more simple and wholesome life." John was hired as director of the Brook Farm School and began writing a regular column on music for the commune's publication.

Greatly influenced by the liberal views of Ralph Waldo Emerson, he became fascinated by the German culture, especially the symphonic music of Ludwig van Beethoven, and it was largely his influence that introduced Americans to Beethoven's genius.

When Brook Farm collapsed in 1847, John Dwight moved into a cooperative house in Boston and established a career in music journalism. He penned articles on music for major publications, and in 1852 he launched his own publication, *Dwight's Journal of Music.* He became America's first influential classical music critic. He was opinionated, sometime difficult, a great promoter of European classical music, and an early advocate of Transcendentalism.

How odd that a wine merchant, a penniless Parisian, and liberal clergyman should give Christianity one of its holiest hymns about the birth of Jesus Christ, Savior of the world.

All Things Bright and Beautiful

Cecil F. Alexander

17th Century English Melody

Unison All things bright and beau - ti - ful, All crea - tures great and small,

All things wise and won - der - ful, The Lord God made them all.

1. Each lit - tle flow'r that o - pens, Each lit - tle bird that sings,
2. The pur - ple - head - ed moun - tains, The riv - er run - ning by,
3. The cold wind in the win - ter, The pleas - ant sum - mer sun,
4. He gave us eyes to see them, And lips that we might tell

He made their glow-ing col - ors, He made their ti - ny wings.
The sun - set and the morn - ing, That bright - ens up the sky.
The ripe fruits in the gar - den, He made them ev - 'ry one.
How great is God Al - might - y, Who has made all things well.

All Things Bright and Beautiful

1848

Then God saw everything that He had made, and indeed it was very good. Genesis 1:31

One day, Mrs. Cecil Frances Alexander was working with one of her pupils in Sunday school—a little boy who happened to be her godson. He was struggling to understand the Apostles' Creed and certain portions of the catechism. Mrs. Alexander began to mull the possibility of converting the Apostles' Creed into songs for children, using simple little hymns to explain the phrases and truths of the Christian faith to little ones.

The Apostles' Creed begins: *I believe in God, the Father Almighty, Maker of heaven and earth, and in Jesus Christ, His only Son, our Lord.* For the phrase, "Maker of heaven and earth . . ." she wrote this lovely little song, "All Things Bright and Beautiful." She based the hymn on Genesis 1:31: "Then God saw everything that He had made, and indeed it was very good."

The Apostles' Creed goes on to say about Jesus Christ: ". . . who was conceived of the Holy Spirit, born of the Virgin Mary . . ." That spurred the writing of "Once in Royal David's City."

The next phrase, ". . . suffered under Pontius Pilate, was crucified, died, and was buried," became the basis for Mrs. Alexander's hymn, "There Is a Green Hill Far Away."

According to one account, the imagery Mrs. Alexander used for that hymn came about as she was driving into the city of Derry, Ireland, to do some shopping. Alongside the road near the old city walls was a little grass-covered hill. Somehow, this knoll helped her visualize Calvary, and from that came the inspiration for the hymn.

The Creed goes on to speak of the Second Coming of Christ, prompting Mrs. Alexander to write a lesser-known but still beautiful hymn entitled, "He Is Coming! He Is Coming!" which contrasts the Lord's First Coming as a babe with His return in power and glory.

These hymns were published in 1848 in Mrs. Alexander's book, *Hymns for Little Children.* It became one of the most successful hymn-publishing projects in history, going through over one hundred editions.

Cecil Frances Alexander published many other books and hymnals, including: *Verses from the Holy Scriptures* (1846), *Narrative Hymns for Village Schools* (1853), *Poems on Subjects in the Old Testament* (1854), *Hymns Descriptive and Devotional* (1858), and *The Legend of the Golden Prayer* (1859). But nothing has stood the test of time like the powerful combination of the Apostles' Creed with her own gift for song.

It Came upon the Midnight Clear

Edmund H. Sears

Richard Storrs Willis

1. It came up-on the mid-night clear, That glo-rious song of old;
2. Still thro' the clo-ven skies they come, With peace-ful wings un-furled;
3. For lo, the days are has-tening on, By proph-et bards fore-told;

From an-gels bend-ing near the earth To touch their harps of gold.
And still their heaven-ly mu-sic floats, O'er all the wear-y world.
When with the ev - er - cir-cling years, Comes round the age of gold.

"Peace on the earth good will to men, From heaven's all gra-cious King!"
A - bove its sad and low-ly plains, They bend on hov-ering wing;
When peace shall o - ver all the earth, Its an - cient splen-dors fling;

The world in sol - emn still-ness lay To hear the an-gels sing.
And ev - er o'er its Ba - bel sounds The bless-ed an-gels sing.
And the whole world give back the song Which now the an-gels sing.

It Came upon the Midnight Clear

1849

And suddenly there was with the angel a multitude of the heavenly host praising God and saying: "Glory to God in the highest, and on earth peace, goodwill toward men!" Luke 2:13–14

Edmund Hamilton Sears is the author of two Christmas carols that are mirror images of each other, written fifteen years apart.

He was born in Sandisfield, Massachusetts, on April 6, 1819, and attended Union College in Schenectady, then Harvard Divinity School. He was ordained in the Unitarian ministry and chose to devote himself to small towns in Massachusetts, where he had time to study, think, and write.

At 24, he wrote "Calm on the Listening Ear," a Christmas carol based on the song of the angels in Luke 2. It proved very similar to the more-famous carol he would later write. Having the same meter and theme, and it can be sung to the same tune:

> *Calm on the listening ear of night | Come heaven's melodious strains, |*
> *Where wild Judea stretches far | Her silver-mantled plains. |*
> *Celestial choirs, from courts above, | Shed sacred glories there, |*
> *And angels, with their sparkling lyres, | Make music on the air.*

Fifteen years later, he wrote its more famous twin. "It Came upon the Midnight Clear" is an unusual carol in that there is no mention of Christ, of the newborn Babe, or of the Savior's Mission. Sears, after all, was Unitarian. The author's only focus is the angelic request for peace on earth.

Notice again the date of the hymn. It was written as the clouds of civil strife were darkening the United States, setting the stage for the War Between the States. We can grasp the concern that drove Edmund to write this hymn by reading a stanza now usually omitted from most hymnals:

> *Yet with the woes of sin and strife| The world hath suffered long; |*
> *Beneath the angel-strain have rolled | Two thousand years of wrong; |*
> *And man, at war with man, hears not | The love song which they bring: |*
> *O hush the noise, ye men of strife, | And hear the angels sing!*

Edmund Sears became well-known because of his hymns and books. He was awarded a Doctor of Divinity degree in 1871, and took a preaching tour of England where he was met by large congregations. He died in Weston, Massachusetts, on January 16, 1876.

My God, How Wonderful Thou Art

Frederick W. Faber

Carl G. Gläser; arr. by Lowell Mason

1. My God, how won - der - ful Thou art, Thy
2. How dread are Thine e - ter - nal years, O
3. How won - der - ful, how beau - ti - ful The
4. O how I fear Thee, liv - ing God, With
5. Yet I may love Thee too, O Lord, Al -

maj - es - ty how bright! How beau - ti - ful Thy
ev - er - last - ing Lord, By pros - trate spir - its
sight of Thee must be. Thine end - less wis - dom,
deep - est ten - d'rest fears; And wor - ship Thee with
might - y as Thou art; For Thou hast stooped to

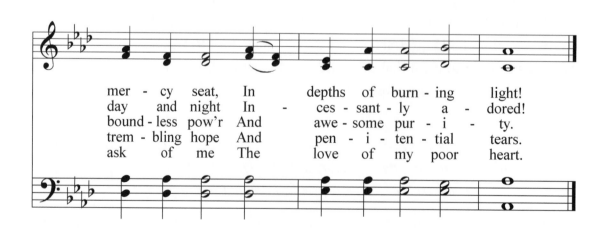

mer - cy seat, In depths of burn - ing light!
day and night In - ces - sant - ly a - dored!
bound - less pow'r And awe - some pur - i - ty.
trem - bling hope And pen - i - ten - tial tears.
ask of me The love of my poor heart.

My God, How Wonderful Thou Art

1849

Oh, that men would give thanks to the LORD for His goodness, And for His wonderful works to the children of men! Psalm 107:15

Frederick William Faber is a Roman Catholic whom Christians of every stripe and stamp love to read. A. W. Tozer, for example, was forever quoting his poetry and worshiping with his hymns. Faber was deeply devotional. His passion was to provide English Catholics with a body of hymns such as John Newton and William Cowper had given English Protestants in the *Olney Hymns*.

In the end, Faber provided all of Christianity with some of its richest songs, including "Faith of Our Fathers," "There's a Wideness to God's Mercy," and this song, "My God, How Wonderful Thou Art."

He was born on June 28, 1814, midway up the English coast in the village of Calverley, Yorkshire. His father was a Church of England pastor. During his college years at Balliol College at Oxford, Faber was torn between his Calvinistic roots and the reverent liturgy of Roman Catholicism. Following his studies, he was ordained an Anglican priest.

But these were the days of John Henry Newman, a British clergyman who had converted to Roman Catholicism. Under Newman's influence, the Church of England lost 250 of their best pastors to Roman Catholicism. This was known as the Oxford Movement. Faber couldn't shake Newman's influence, and, in 1846, he converted to Catholicism, was rebaptized, and took the name Wilfrid. He began ministering in and around the village of Cheadle in Staffordshire, and managed to convert the whole town, except, "the parson, the pew-opener, and two drunken men."

From 1849 until his death in 1863, he headed the Brompton Oratory in London. He was given a makeshift chapel in a former tavern, and there he established schools for the poor, conducted nightly services, and wrote his great hymns. He also authored a series of devotional books with titles like *All for Jesus* (1853), *The Foot of the Cross* (1858), and *The Precious Blood* (1860).

A lesser-known Faber hymn highlights the distinctive Christian doctrine of the deity of Jesus Christ—that Jesus was, is, and always will be God, proclaiming:

> *Jesus is God! O! could I now but compass earth and sea,*
> *To teach and tell the single truth, how happy should I be!*
> *O! had I but an angel's voice, I would proclaim so loud,*
> *Jesus, the good, the beautiful, is everlasting God.*

Faith of Our Fathers

Frederick W. Faber

Henri F. Hemy

1. Faith of our fa-thers, liv-ing still In spite of dun-geon,
2. Our fa-thers, chained in pris-ons dark, Were still in heart and
3. Faith of our fa-thers, we will love Both friend and foe in

fire and sword! O how our hearts beat high with joy
con - science free. How sweet would be their chil - dren's fate
all our strife; And preach Thee, too, as love knows how,

When-e'er we hear that glo - rious word! Faith of our fa - thers!
If they, like them could die for thee! Faith of our fa - thers!
By kind - ly words and vir - tuous life. Faith of our fa - thers!

Ho - ly faith! We will be true to Thee till death!
Ho - ly faith! We will be true to Thee till death!
Ho - ly faith! We will be true to Thee till death!

Faith of Our Fathers
1849

Now faith is the substance of things hoped for, the evidence of things not seen. For by it the elders obtained a good testimony. Hebrews 11:1, 2

Frederick William Faber was raised in an Anglican parsonage in Calverley, Yorkshire, England; but both his parents died when he was young. When he moved to Oxford University as a young man, he came under the influence of the great Roman Catholic, John Henry Newman, author of "Lead, Kindly Light." Following graduation, Faber entered the Anglican ministry, but his soul was troubled. He was drawn to the historic, reverent liturgy of the Catholic faith. On Sunday night, November 16, 1845, he announced to his congregation that he intended to leave the Church of England and be ordained as a Roman Catholic.

For the remainder of his short life—Faber died at fifty-nine—he endeavored to provide a body of hymns for English Catholics to sing. Perhaps his most enduring is "Faith of Our Fathers."

What most Protestants don't know is that Faber wrote this song to remind the Catholic Church of its martyrs during the days of the Protestant King Henry VIII and Queen Elizabeth I. "Good Queen Bess," for example, used fines, gallows, gibbets, racks, and whips against those who said Mass, honored the pope, or harbored a priest. Often in the middle of the night, thugs would burst into Catholic homes and drag them away to be scourged, fined, or seared with glowing irons. The dungeons were choked with victims.

Nicholas Owen was such a victim. Probably a builder by trade, Owen designed countless hiding places for endangered Catholics. He hid them in secret rooms, between the walls, and under the floors. He hid them in stone fences and in underground passages. He designed nooks and crannies that looked like anything but hiding places.

When Nicholas was at last betrayed, he was dragged to the Tower of London and his arms were fixed to iron rings. There he hung for hours, his body dangling. Weights added to his feet increased the suffering. The tortures continued until March 2, 1606, when "his bowels broke in a terrible way" and he passed to his reward.

It was for these Catholic heroes, martyred at the hands of so-called "Protestant" monarchs, that "Faith of Our Fathers" was originally written. Now, of course, this great hymn reminds us all of the noble sacrifices made by those in every branch of the Christian family who have passed on their faith to us ". . . in spite of dungeon, fire and sword."

In Heavenly Love Abiding

Anna L. Waring

Felix Mendelssohn

1. In heav'n-ly love a - bid - ing, No change my heart shall fear;
2. Wher - ev - er He may guide me, No want shall turn me back;
3. Green pas-tures are be - fore me, Which yet I have not seen;

And safe is such con - fid - ing, For noth-ing chang - es here.
My Shep-herd is be - side me, And noth-ing can I lack.
Bright skies will soon be o'er me, Where dark-est clouds have been.

The storm may roar with - out me, My heart may low be laid,
His wis - dom ev - er wak - eth; His sight is nev - er dim.
My hope I can-not mea - sure; My path to life is free;

But God is round a - bout me, And can I be dis - mayed?
He knows the way He tak - eth, And I will walk with Him.
My Sav - ior has my trea - sure, And He will walk with me.

In Heavenly Love Abiding

1850

Have I not commanded you? Be strong and of good courage; do not be afraid, nor be dismayed, for the LORD your God is with you wherever you go. Joshua 1:9

One of our most reassuring hymns is Anna L. Waring's, "In Heavenly Love Abiding." Anna was born into a Quaker family in Wales in 1823. As a teen, she joined the Church of England and was baptized in 1842. She was a lifelong student of the Hebrew language and daily read from the Book of Psalms in the original text. Anna's special burden was for those behind bars, and she devoted herself to prison ministry and to causes like the Discharged Prisoners' Aid Society.

In 1850, she published a little volume of nineteen hymns, among them this one—"In Heavenly Love Abiding"—which Anna called, "Safety in God."

Here's another, lesser-known Anna Waring hymn, based on Psalm 31:15: "My times are in Your hand."

Father, I know that all my life / Is portioned out for me, /
And the changes that are sure to come, / I do not fear to see; /
But I ask Thee for a present mind / Intent on pleasing Thee.

I ask Thee for a thoughtful love, / Through constant watching wise, /
To meet the glad with joyful smiles, / And to wipe the weeping eyes; /
And a heart at leisure from itself, / To soothe and sympathize.

I would not have the restless will / That hurries to and fro, /
Seeking for some great thing to do, / Or secret thing to know; /
I would be treated as a child, / And guided where I go.

Wherever in the world I am, / In whatsoe'er estate, /
I have a fellowship with hearts / To keep and cultivate; /
And a work of lowly love to do / For the Lord on whom I wait.

So I ask Thee for the daily strength, / To none that ask denied, /
And a mind to blend with outward life / While keeping at Thy side; /
Content to fill a little space, / If Thou be glorified.

Crown Him with Many Crowns

Matthew Bridges/Godfrey Thring

George J. Elvey

1. Crown Him with man-y crowns, The Lamb up - on His throne. Hark!
2. Crown Him the Lord of love: Be - hold His hands and side, Rich
3. Crown Him the Lord of life, Who tri - umphed o'er the grave. Who
4. Crown Him the Lord of heaven: One with the Fath - er known, One

how the heaven - ly an - them drowns All mu - sic but its own! A -
wounds, yet vi - si - ble a - bove, In beaut - y glo - ri - fied; No
rose vic - tor - ious to the strife, For those He came to save. His
with the Spir - it Through Him given From yon - der glor - ious throne. All

wake, my soul and sing Of Him who died for Thee; And
an - gel in the sky Can ful - ly bear that sight, But
glo - ries now we sing, Who died and rose on high. Who
hail, Re - deem - er, hail! For Thou hast died for me; Thy

hail Him as thy match - less King Through all e - ter - ni - ty.
down - ward bends His won - dering eye At mys - ter - ies so bright.
died e - ter - nal life to bring, And lives that death may die.
praise and glo - ry shall not fail Through-out e - ter - ni - ty.

Crown Him with Many Crowns

1851

. . . and on His head were many crowns . . . Revelation 19:12

T he original form of this hymn was written by Matthew Bridges and consisted of six eight-line stanzas. He thought of his hymn as a sermon in song, based on Revelation 19:12. ". . . and on His head were many crowns." He called his hymn, "The Song of the Seraphs." Matthew, who once wrote a book condemning Roman Catholics, ended up converting to Catholicism in 1848. He followed John Henry Newman out of the Church of England.

In 1874, Godfrey Thring, a staunch Anglican clergyman feared that some of Bridges' verses smacked too much of Catholic doctrine. Verse two, for example, said:

Crown Him the virgin's Son, the God incarnate born,
Whose arm those crimson trophies won which now His brow adorn;
Fruit of the mystic rose, as of that rose the stem;
The root whence mercy ever flows, the Babe of Bethlehem.

It seems odd to us now that such a verse would cause controversy, but in the end Godfrey wrote six new verses for the same song. "Crown Him with Many Crowns," therefore became a six-verse hymn that was written twice!

Over the years, these twelve stanzas have become intermingled in the hymnbooks, with editors mixing and matching the verses. Here are the first lines of all twelve verses, the first six by Bridges, the last six by Thring:

- Stanza 1: *Crown Him with many crowns, the Lamb upon His throne . . .*
- Stanza 2: *Crown Him the virgin's Son, the God incarnate born . . .*
- Stanza 3: *Crown Him the Lord of love, behold His hands and side . . .*
- Stanza 4: *Crown Him the Lord of peace, Whose power a scepter sways . . .*
- Stanza 5: *Crown Him the Lord of years, the Potentate of time,*
- Stanza 6: *Crown Him the Lord of Heaven, one with the Father known . . .*
- Stanza 7: *Crown Him with crowns of gold . . . .*
- Stanza 8: *Crown Him the Son of God, before the worlds began . . .*
- Stanza 9: *Crown Him the Lord of light . . . .*
- Stanza 10: *Crown Him the Lord of life, who triumphed over the grave . . .*
- Stanza 11: *Crown Him the Lord of lords, who over all doth reign . . . .*
- Stanza 12: *Crown Him the Lord of heaven, enthroned in worlds above . . .*

O Come, O Come, Emmanuel

Latin Hymn, 9th cent.
Translated by John M. Neale

Thomas Helmore

1. O come, O come, Em - man - u - el, And ran - som cap - tive
2. O come, thou Wis - dom from on high, Who or - derest all things
3. O come, De - sire of na - tions, bind All peo - ples in one
4. O come, thou Day - spring, come and cheer Our spir - its by Thine

Is - ra - el, That mourns in lone - ly ex - ile here
might - i - ly; To us the path of knowl - edge show
heart and mind. From dust Thou brought us forth to life;
ad - vent here; Dis - perse the gloom - y clouds of night,

Un - til the Son of God ap - pear.
And teach us in her ways to go. Re - joice! Re - joice! Em-
De - liv - er us from earth - ly strife.
And death's dark shad - ows put to flight.

man - u - el, Shall come to thee, O Is - ra - el!

O Come, O Come, Emmanuel

1851

Behold, the virgin shall be with child, and bear a Son, and they shall call His name Immanuel. Matthew 1:23

The origins of this plaintive carol date to medieval times. In the 800s, a series of Latin hymns were sung each day during Christmas Vespers from December 17 to 23. Each of these hymns began with the word "O," and were called the "Great" or "O" Antiphons (the word *antiphon* meaning psalm or anthem). These hymns were apparently restructured into verse form in the 1100s, and finally published in Latin in 1710. In the mid-1800s, they were discovered by an English minister named John Mason Neale, who wove together segments of them to produce the first draft of "O Come, O Come, Emmanuel," which was published in 1851. Neale's original version said, "Draw nigh, draw nigh, Emmanuel."

Neale is a man worth knowing. He was born in London on January 24, 1818, the son of an evangelical Anglican clergyman. He attended Cambridge University and proved to be a brilliant student and prize-winning poet. While there, Neale was influenced by the Oxford Movement and became attracted to Roman Catholicism. In 1841, he was ordained into the Anglican ministry; but his poor health and Catholic leanings prevented him from gaining a parish ministry.

He was appointed instead as the director of Sackville College, a home for old men. (Sackville College, started by Robert Sackville, Earl of Dorset, in the early 1600s as a home for the elderly, is still going strong today in East Grinstead, Sussex.) This was the perfect job for Neale, for he was a compassionate man with a great heart for the needy, but he was also a scholar needing time for research and writing.

As a high church traditionalist, Neale disliked the hymns of Isaac Watts and longed to return Christianity to the liturgical dignity of church history. He was an outspoken advocate of returning church buildings to their former glory. He campaigned, for example, against certain types of stoves that spoiled the tastefulness and charm of English churches. He also worked hard to translate ancient Greek and Latin hymns into English.

In today's hymnals, we find Neale and Watts side-by-side, the old differences having been forgotten. We owe a debt of gratitude to John Mason Neale every time we sing one of his Christmas carols: "Good King Wenceslas," "O Come, O Come, Emmanuel," "Good Christian Men, Rejoice," and his Palm Sunday hymn, "All Glory, Laud, and Honor."

Good King Wenceslas

John M. Neale

Swedish Carol

1. Good King Wen-ces-las looked out on the Feast of Ste-phen,
2. "Hith-er, page, and stand by me, if you know it, tell-ing,
3. "Bring me food and bring me wine, bring me pine logs hith-er,
4. "Sire, the night is dark-er now, and the wind blows stron-ger,
5. In his mas-ter's steps he trod, where the snow lay dint-ed;

When the snow lay round a-bout, deep and crisp and e-ven.
Yon-der peas-ant, who is he? Where and what his dwell-ing?"
You and I will see him dine, when we bear them thith-er."
Fails my heart, I know not how; I can go no long-er."
Heat was in the ver-y sod which the saint had print-ed.

Bright-ly shone the moon that night, though the frost was cru-el,
"Sire, he lives a good league hence, un-der-neath the moun-tain,
Page and mon-arch, forth they went, forth they went to-geth-er,
"Mark my foot-steps, my good page, tread now in them bold-ly,
There-fore, Chris-tian men, be sure, wealth or rank pos-sess-ing,

When a poor man came in sight, gath-ering win-ter fu-el.
Right a-gainst the for-est fence, by Saint Ag-nes' foun-tain."
Through the cold wind's wild la-ment and the bit-ter weath-er.
You shall find the win-ter's rage freeze your blood less cold-ly."
You who now will bless the poor shall your-selves find bless-ing.

Good King Wenceslas

1854

But when you give a feast, invite the poor, the maimed, the lame, the blind. And you will be blessed, because they cannot repay you; for you shall be repaid at the resurrection of the just." Luke 14:13–14

This story is about two men—a Bohemian Duke and an Anglican minister—who lived nearly a thousand years apart.

Wenceslas was born in Bohemia, in modern Czechoslovakia, in the early 900s. His father, the Czech ruler, Duke Ratislav, gave him a good education supervised by his godly grandmother. When his father died, Wenceslas, seeing his mother mishandle affairs of state, stepped in at age 18, seizing the reins of government. From the beginning, he proved a different sort of king. He sought good relations with surrounding nations, particularly with Germany. He took steps to reform the judicial system, reducing the number of death sentences and the arbitrary power of judges. He encouraged the building of churches and showed heartfelt concern for the poor. He reportedly cut firewood for orphans and widows, often carrying the provisions on his own shoulders through the snow.

Wenceslas' brief reign ended suddenly. His pagan and rebellious brother, Boleslav, murdered him on September 28, 929, as he left for church. His people venerated him as a martyr, and today Wenceslas is the patron saint of Czechoslovakia.

He would be hardly remembered, however, but for John Mason Neale, an Anglican minister with a passion for returning church architecture and music to their ancient grandeur. Neale helped establish a committee to investigate and restore dilapidated church buildings in Great Britain. He was particularly upset at the ugly stoves installed to heat churches in Victorian times.

Disliking the hymns of Isaac Watts, he also sought to return church music to its medieval roots. Neale worked hard to translate ancient Greek, Latin, and Syrian hymns into English. In so doing, he gave us the Christmas carols, "Good Christian Men Rejoice," (a fourteenth century text set to a fourteenth-century tune), and "O Come, O Come Emmanuel," (a ninth-century text set to a fifteenth-century tune). He also translated the Palm Sunday hymn "All Glory, Laud, and Honor."

Good King Wenceslas is not a translation, but an original poem written by Neal to honor a godly monarch's concern for the poor. Neale himself worked with the needy, serving as warden of a charitable residence for indigent old men.

John Neale's antiquated opinions were widely scorned in his own day, but we're still singing his songs.

Still, Still with Thee

Harriet B. Stowe

Felix Mendelssohn

1. Still, still with Thee, when pur - ple morn - ing break - eth,
2. A - lone with Thee, a - mid the my - stic sha - dows,
3. Still, still with Thee, as to each new - born morn - ing,
4. So shall it be at last, in that bright morn - ing,

When the bird wak - eth, and the shad - ows flee;
The sol - emn hush of na - ture new - ly born;
A fresh and sol - emn splen - dor still is given,
When the soul wak - eth and life's sha - dows flee;

Fair - er than morn - ing, love - li - er than day - light,
A - lone with Thee in breath - less ad - o - ra - tion,
So does this bless - èd con - scious-ness, a - wak - ing,
O in that hour, fair - er than day - light dawn - ing,

Dawns the sweet con - scious - ness, I am with Thee.
In the calm dew and fresh-ness of the morn.
Breathe each day near - ness un - to thee and heaven.
Shall rise the glo - rious thought, I am with Thee.

Still, Still with Thee

1855

How precious also are Your thoughts to me, O God! How great is the sum of them! If I should count them, they would be more in number than the sand; when I awake, I am still with You. Psalm 139:17–18

arriet Beecher Stowe, daughter of the famous Congregational pastor Lyman Beecher, is best known for her novel, *Uncle Tom's Cabin*, which sold 10,000 copies its first week of publication and contributed to the outbreak of the Civil War by arousing public sentiment against slavery.

Harriet was a remarkable woman. She raised seven children and managed a household while maintaining a career—which was unusual in those days—and taught in a college. She was also a social crusader. She wrote thirty books and countless articles and poems. After *Uncle Tom's Cabin* was published, she became an international celebrity in America and England. But her life was crowded with tragedy as well, including the drowning of her son while he was a freshman in college, the alcoholism and disappearance of another son, and the morphine addiction of a daughter who was given the medication as a pain-killer following childbirth.

How did she manage it all?

First, she had dedicated herself wholly to Christ at age 14, after listening to a sermon by her father. "As soon as my father came home and was seated in his study," she recalled, "I went up to him and fell in his arms, saying, 'Father, I have given myself to Jesus, and He has taken me.' I never shall forget the expression of his face as he looked down into my earnest childish eyes . . . 'Is that so?' he said, holding me silent to his heart as I felt the hot tears fall on my head."

Second, Harriet rose each morning at 4:30 to meet with the Lord before the day began. She enjoyed watching the sunrise, listening to the birds, and sensing the all-encompassing presence of God. It is this habit Harriet described in her best-known hymn, written while meditating on Psalm 139:17–18: "How precious also are Your thoughts to me, O God! How great is the sum of them. If I should count them, they would be more in number than the sand; When I awake, I am still with You."

Still, still with Thee, when purple morning breaketh,
When the bird waketh, and the shadows flee;
Fairer than morning, lovelier than daylight,
Dawns the sweet consciousness, I am with Thee.

Alone with Thee, amid the mystic shadows,
The solemn hush of nature newly born;
Alone with Thee in breathless adoration,
In the calm dew and freshness of the morn.

209

What a Friend We Have in Jesus

Joseph M. Scriven

Charles C. Converse

1. What a Friend we have in Je-sus, All our sins and griefs to bear!
2. Have we tri-als and temp-ta-tions? Is there trou-ble an-y-where?
3. Are we weak and heav-y-lad-en, Cum-bered with a load of care?

What a priv-i-lege to car-ry, Ev-ery-thing to God in prayer!
We should nev-er be dis-cour-aged; Take it to the Lord in prayer.
Pre-cious Sav-ior, still our ref-uge! Take it to the Lord in prayer.

Oh, what peace we of-ten for-feit, Oh, what need-less pain we bear.
Can we find a friend so faith-ful, Who will all our sor-rows share?
Do Thy friends de-spise, for-sake Thee? Take it to the Lord in prayer.

All be-cause we do not car-ry Ev-ery-thing to God in prayer!
Je-sus knows our ev-ery weak-ness; Take it to the Lord in prayer.
In His arms He'll take and shield Thee; Thou wilt find a so-lace there.

What a Friend We Have in Jesus

1855

... the peace of God, which surpasses all understanding, will guard your hearts and minds through Christ Jesus. Philippians 4:6–7

J oseph Scriven watched in shock as the body of his fiancée was pulled from the lake. Their wedding had been planned for the next day. Reeling from the tragedy, he made up his mind to immigrate to America. Packing up his belongings in Dublin, Ireland, he sailed for Canada, leaving his mother behind. He was about 25 years old.

Ten years later, in 1855, he received word that his mother was facing a crisis. Joseph wrote this poem and sent it to her. Mrs. Scriven evidently gave a copy to a friend who had it published anonymously, and it quickly became a popular hymn, though no one knew who had written it.

Meanwhile, Joseph fell in love again. But tragedy struck a second time when his bride, Eliza Catherine Roche, contracted tuberculosis and died in 1860 before their wedding could take place.

To escape his sorrow, Joseph poured himself into ministry, doing charity work for the Plymouth Brethren and preaching among the Baptists. He lived a simple, obscure life in Port Hope, Canada, cutting firewood for widows, giving away his clothes and money to those in need. He was described as "a man of short stature, with iron-gray hair, close-cropped beard, and light blue eyes that sparkled when he talked." Ira Sankey later wrote:

Until a short time before his death it was not known that he had a poetic gift. A neighbor, sitting up with him in his illness, happened upon a manuscript copy of "What a Friend We Have in Jesus." Reading it with great delight and questioning Mr. Scriven about it, he said that he had composed it for his mother, to comfort her in a time of special sorrow, not intending that anyone else should see it. Some time later, when another Port Hope neighbor asked him if it was true he composed the hymn, his reply was, "The Lord and I did it between us."

On October 10, 1896, Joseph became critically ill. In his delirium, he rose from his bed and staggered outdoors where he fell into a small creek and drowned at age 66. His grave was arranged so that his feet were opposite those of his lost love, Eliza Catherine Roche, that at the resurrection they might arise facing one another.

Children of the Heavenly Father

Carolina W. Sandell-Berg

Swedish Melody

1. Chil - dren of the heaven - ly Fa - ther, Safe - ly in His bos - om gath - er; Nest - ling bird nor star in heav - en Such a ref - uge e'er was giv - en.

2. God His own doth tend and nour - ish, In His ho - ly courts they flour - ish; From all e - vil things He spares them, In His might - y arms He bears them.

3. Nei - ther life nor death shall ev - er, From the Lord His chil - dren sev - er; Un - to them His grace He show - eth, And their sor - rows all He know - eth.

4. Though He giv - eth or He tak - eth, God His chil - dren ne'er for - sak - eth; His the lov - ing pur - pose sole - ly To pre - serve them pure and ho - ly.

Children of the Heavenly Father

1855

Behold what manner of love the Father has bestowed on us, that we should be called children of God! 1 John 3:1

This Scandinavian hymn was penned by Carolina (Lina) Sandell-Berg, the "Fanny Crosby of Sweden." She was born in a parsonage in Fröderyd, Sweden, on October 3, 1832, into a home full of music and literature. Lina (pronounced Lie-nah) was a "daddy's girl" in childhood, for her frail health often kept her indoors, in his study, when other children were outside playing.

When she was twelve, she fell ill and was paralyzed. Eventually Lina regained her health, and out of the experience came her first book of poems, published when she was a teenager. But another tragedy awaited her.

When she was twenty-six, she and her dad were traveling by boat outside the harbor of Göteborg when he fell overboard and drowned. Out of this experience came a flood of poems and hymns, including her classic, "Day by Day, and with Each Passing Moment."

Some hymn histories claim that "Children of the Heavenly Father" was one of the hymns written in response to her father's death; but it was first published in 1855, three years before this tragedy. This has prompted other historians to claim it was one of the poems she wrote as a teenager. All we know is that "Children of the Heavenly Father" first appeared in Lina's book, *Andeliga Dagg-Dropper* in 1855, when she was twenty-three.

The simple, lilting tune to "Children of Our Heavenly Father" is a Swedish folk melody called *"Tryggare Kan Ingen Vara,"* which translated, is: "No One Can Be Safer." Its origins are unknown, but "Sweden's Spiritual Troubadour," Oskar Ahnfelt, a Lutheran Pietist who helped introduce evangelical hymns to the Swedish Church, set many of Lina's poems to music. At the time, the state-sponsored church didn't allow simple pietistic hymns like "Children of the Heavenly Father." But Ahnfelt sang them anyway, traveling around with his ten-string guitar. When opposition arose, he was ordered to sing before King Karl XV. To the chagrin of church officials, the king loved Ahnfelt's simple melodies and tender hymns, saying, "You may sing them as much as you desire in both of my kingdoms."

He did, and many of his texts were written by Lina Sandell-Berg, who wrote about six hundred fifty hymns and poems during her lifetime. "Ahnfelt has sung my songs into the hearts of the people," she later said.

O How I Love Jesus

Frederick Whitfield

American Melody

1. There is a name I love to hear, I love to sing its worth;
2. It tells me of a Sav-ior's love, Who died to set me free;
3. It tells me what my Fa-ther hath, In store for ev-'ry day;
4. It tells of One whose lov-ing heart, Can feel my deep-est woe;

It sounds like mu - sic in my ear, The sweet - est Name on earth.
It tells me of His pre - cious blood, The sin - ner's per-fect plea.
And tho' I tread a dark-some path, Yields sun - shine all the way.
Who in each sor - row bears a part, That none can bear be - low.

O how I love Je - sus, O how I love Je - sus,

O how I love Je - sus; Be - cause He first loved me.

O How I Love Jesus

1855

We love Him because He first loved us. 1 John 4:19

rederick Whitfield was born on a cold January day in 1829, in tiny Threapwood, England, population about 250. He attended college in Dublin, Ireland, and devoted his life to pastoral ministry in the Church of England. His greatest legacy is this hymn about the name of Jesus, written when he was a student. Generations of Christians have loved "There Is a Name I Love to Hear" with its peppy refrain: *"O how I love Jesus, / O how I love Jesus, / O how I love Jesus, / because He first loved me."*

You might be interested to know that while Whitfield wrote the *verses* to this hymn, he didn't compose its famous chorus.

Both the simple words and the nimble tune of "O How I Love Jesus" are American inventions of unknown origin. They floated around like orphans, attaching themselves to various hymns in the nineteenth century. One hymnologist found forty-two occurrences of this chorus in early songbooks. Even such stately hymns as "Amazing Grace" and "Alas! And Did My Savior Bleed" were occasionally sung to this lighthearted melody, with "O How I Love Jesus" used as the refrain.

But when "O How I Love Jesus" was finally wedded to Whitfield's "There Is a Name I Love to Hear," it was a marriage made in heaven. We've been singing it ever since. Some of Whitfield's original verses have fallen by the wayside, which is too bad; every verse tells us what the Name of Jesus can do in our lives:

It tells me what my Father hath / in store for every day,
And though I tread a darksome path, / yields sunshine all the way.

It tells of One whose loving heart / can feel my deepest woe;
Who in each sorrow bears a part / that none can bear below.

It bids my trembling heart rejoice; / it dries each rising tear.
It tells me, in a "still small voice," / to trust and never fear.

This Name shall shed its fragrance still / along this thorny road,
Shall sweetly smooth the rugged hill / that leads me up to God.

And there with all the blood-bought throng, / from sin and sorrow free,
I'll sing the new eternal song / of Jesus' love for me.

Angels We Have Heard on High

French Carol

French Melody

1. An - gels we have heard on high Sweet - ly sing - ing o'er the plains,
2. Shep - herds, why this ju - bi - lee? Why your joy - ous strains pro - long?
3. Come to Beth - le - hem and see Him whose birth the an - gels sing;

And the moun - tains in re - ply Ech - o - ing their joy - ous strains.
What the glad - some tid - ings be, Which in - spire your heav'n - ly song?
Come a - dore on bend - ed knee, Christ the Lord, the new - born King.

Glo - - - - - - - - - - - - ri - a

in ex - cel - sis De - o! Glo - - - - - - - - - -

ri - a in ex - cel - sis De - o!

Angels We Have Heard on High

1855

And suddenly there was with the angel a multitude of the heavenly host praising God and saying: Glory to God in the highest, And on earth peace, goodwill toward men! Luke 2:13, 14

es Anges dans nos Campagnes" was a French carol dating from the 1700s, which appeared in several different versions. It was published in English in 1862, the words saying:

> *Angels we have heard on high | Sweetly singing o'er the plains,*
> *And the mountains in reply | Echoing their joyous strains.*
> Gloria, in excelsis Deo!

An older version had the title, "Harken All! What Holy Singing!" The words, translated into English, said:

> *Hearken, all! What holy singing | Now is sounding from the sky!*
> *'Tis a hymn with grandeur ringing, | Sung by voices clear and high.*
> Gloria, in excelsis Deo!

Still another primitive version speaks from the shepherds' vantage point, saying:

> *Shepherds in the field abiding, | Tell us when the seraph bright*
> *Greeted you with wondrous tiding, | What you saw and heard that night.*
> Gloria, in excelsis Deo!

Hymns are usually authored by human beings like us, but in this case obscure verses by unknown French poets were coupled with a refrain that was literally composed by angels in heaven: *Gloria, in excelsis Deo.* That's the Latin wording for the angelic anthem, "Glory to God in the highest!" It comes from Luke 2:14 in the Vulgate, the Latin version of the Bible. The Latin word *Gloria* means *Glory,* and *in excelsis* is the phrase for *in the highest.* Our English words *excel* and *excellent* come from the same root, meaning *to rise* or *to ascend* or *to be high.* The Latin word *Deo* means *God.*

This was the song proclaimed by the angels over Shepherds' Field the night Christ was born. The musical score stretches out and emphasizes the words in a way that is uniquely fun to sing and deeply stirring, as we lift our voices to proclaim: Jesus has come! Hope has arrived on earth! A Savior is born! Glory to God on High! *Gloria, in excelsis Deo!*

More Love to Thee, O Christ

Elizabeth P. Prentiss

William H. Doane

1. More love to Thee, O Christ, More love to Thee!
2. Once earth-ly joy I craved, Sought peace and rest.
3. Then shall my lat-est breath Whis-per Thy praise.

Hear Thou the prayer, I make on bend-ed knee.
Now Thee a-lone I seek; Give what is best.
This be the part-ing cry My heart shall raise;

This is my ear-nest plea: More love, O Christ to Thee;
This all my prayer shall be: More love, O Christ to Thee;
This still my prayer shall be: More love, O Christ to Thee;

More love to Thee, More love to Thee!
More love to Thee, More love to Thee!
More love to Thee, More love to Thee!

More Love to Thee, O Christ

1856

It is good for me that I have been afflicted, that I may learn Your statutes. Psalm 119:71

here's a little-known verse about sickness in the Bible, found in Isaiah 38:17. King Hezekiah, after the terrible illness that nearly cost his life, said, "Indeed it was for my own peace that I had great bitterness." Other translations put it:

- *It was for my own good that I had such hard times*—CEV
- *Surely it was for my benefit that I suffered such anguish*—NIV
- *It was for my welfare that I had great bitterness*—NRSV

Elizabeth Payson was born in Portland, Maine, on October 26, 1818. Her father, Edward Payson, was a famous Congregational minister, so revered that a thousand children were reportedly named for him. His writings and sermons are popular to this day.

In 1845, Elizabeth, a school teacher at the time, married a Presbyterian minister, George Lewis Prentiss, and the couple moved to New York where George began teaching at Union Theological Seminary. Elizabeth enjoyed writing, and her books, *Stepping Heavenward* and *The Flower of the Family*, became best-sellers.

Her health, however, was frail, and she suffered chronic insomnia. One day in 1856, following the deaths of two of her children, her health faltered and anxiety overwhelmed her. Inspired by the hymn "Nearer My God, To Thee," Elizabeth worked on a poem-prayer to the Lord. The words came easily at first, but by the end her creative energy evaporated, and she left the poem unfinished.

Thirteen years later, while rummaging through a stack of old papers, Elizabeth found this unfinished poem. As she re-read it, it didn't impress her as being very good. But when George insisted she finish it, she dutifully scribbled an ending in pencil. He printed a few copies, one of which landed on the desk of musician William Howard Doane in Cincinnati, who set the verses to music and published it in his *Songs of Devotion*.

"To love Christ more," Elizabeth once said, "is the deepest need, the constant cry of my soul . . . . Out in the woods and on my bed and out driving, when I am happy and busy, and when I am sad and idle, the whisper keeps going up for more love, more love, more love!"

219

Little Brown Church in the Vale

William S. Pitts

William S. Pitts

1. There's a church in the val-ley by the wild-wood, No love - li - er
2. There close by the side of that loved one, To the trees where the
3. How sweet on a clear Sab-bath morn - ing, To list to the
4. From the church in the val-ley by the wild-wood, When day fades a -

spot in the dale; No place is so dear to my child - hood
wild flow - ers bloom; Where the fare-well hymn will be chant - ed,
clear ring - ing bell; Its tones so sweet-ly are call - ing,
way in - to night. I would fain from this spot of my child - hood,

No spot is so dear To my child - hood

Fine

As the lit - tle brown church In the vale.
I shall rest by her side in the tomb. Oh, come, come, come, come
Oh, come to the church In the vale.
Wing my way to the man - sions of light.

As the lit - tle brown church in the vale.

D.S. al Fine

Come to the church in the wild - wood, Oh, come to the church in the vale;

Little Brown Church in the Vale

1857

Remember the Sabbath day, to keep it holy. Exodus 20:8

T he Little Brown Church in the Vale sits in a beautiful park alongside Highway 218 in the town of Bradford, near Nashua, in northern Iowa. But it wasn't there when the song was written.

A New York native named William Pitts, about twenty-seven, was traveling by stagecoach from his home in Wisconsin to Fredericksburg, Iowa, to see his girlfriend. It was a bright afternoon in 1857. When the stagecoach made a pit stop in Bradford, Pitts took a stroll among the trees to stretch his legs. The gently sloping hills formed a slight valley, and the Cedar River flowed peacefully by. That grove of trees, it seemed to Pitts, would be the perfect setting for a church.

Unable to erase the scene from his mind, Pitts returned home and composed the words and music to "Little Brown Church in the Vale." Nothing came of his song, however, and he filed it away.

Five years later, Pitts, now married to his sweetheart, relocated to Iowa to be near his elderly in-laws and to teach music at Bradford Academy. Imagine his surprise when he saw a church building sitting in the very spot he had previously envisioned it. Christians in the community, growing tired of meeting in abandoned stores, had determined to build a church. The Civil War was raging and times were hard; but by 1862, the building was up. It had to be painted using the cheapest color—which was brown.

When Pitts saw the little brown church in the vale, he rushed home and found "Little Brown Church in the Vale," packed among his papers. He sang his hymn at the building's dedication in 1864. Soon afterward, he sold his manuscript to a publisher in Chicago for $25. He used the money to enroll in Rush Medical College, and William spent the rest of his life as the town physician in Fredericksburg, Iowa, about fourteen miles from Bradford.

Today the Little Brown Church boasts a membership of about 100, but it's best known for the hundreds of weddings and thousands of tourists who flock there each year to see the church in the valley by the wildwood, the little brown church in the vale.

We Three Kings of Orient Are

John H. Hopkins, Jr.   John H. Hopkins, Jr.

1. We three kings of O - ri - ent are, Bear-ing gifts we trav - erse a - far;
2. Born a King on Beth-le-hem's plain, Gold I bring to crown Him a - gain;
3. Frank-in - cense to of - fer have I, In-cense owns a De - i - ty nigh;
4. Myrrh is mine, its bit - ter per - fume, Breathes a life of gath - er-ing gloom;
5. Glo - rious now be - hold Him a - rise, King and God and Sac - ri - fice;

Field and foun-tain, moor and moun-tain, Fol-low-ing yon - der star.
King for - ev - er, ceas - ing nev - er, O - ver us all to reign.
Prayer and prais - ing, all men rais - ing, Wor-ship Him, God on high.
Sor - rowing, sigh - ing, bleed-ing, dy - ing, Sealed in the stone cold tomb.
Al - le - lu - ia, al - le - lu - ia! Earth to heav'n re - plies.

O star of won-der, star of night, Star with roy - al beau-ty bright;

West-ward lead-ing, still pro - ceed-ing, Guide us to Thy per - fect light.

We Three Kings
of Orient Are
1857

Now after Jesus was born in Bethlehem of Judea in the days of Herod the king, behold, wise men from the East came to Jerusalem . . . Matthew 2:1

S
trange but true: A visit from St. Nicholas paved the way for "We Three Kings." It happened like this. After the War of 1812, Anglicans in America decided to establish their own seminary for training Episcopalian ministers. The proposal was first made in 1814; and in 1817, the Episcopalian General Convention voted to locate the school in New York City. But where in New York?

Clement Clarke Moore, son of New York's Episcopalian Bishop, was an up-and-coming land developer. He had recently become well-known because of a poem he had written, which began:

> *'Twas the night before Christmas, when all through the house*
> *not a creature was stirring, not even a mouse. . . .*

The popularity of his poem (reportedly written following a sleigh ride home from Greenwich Village) made his name a household word. The fame and increased income made him a more generous and sought-after layman.

Moore owned a large estate in the undeveloped northern regions of Manhattan. He referred to it as "a quiet, rural retreat on the picturesque banks of the Hudson." Hearing that the Episcopalians needed land for their seminary, he offered a portion of his estate, and thus was born General Theological Seminary. Moore, also a linguist and Hebrew scholar, became one of General's first professors, teaching biblical languages.

Some years later, a reporter named John H. Hopkins, Jr., enrolled in this seminary. Born in Pittsburgh, Hopkins had matriculated at the University of Vermont before moving to New York to pursue legal studies. But he fell in love with the Lord's work, enrolled in General, and graduated from the seminary in 1850. In 1855, he was hired as the school's first instructor of church music.

Hopkins wrote "We Three Kings" as part of a Christmas pageant produced by General Theological Seminary in 1857. In 1863 it was published in his *Carols, Hymns, and Songs*. This hymnal went through three editions by 1882, establishing Hopkins as a leader in Episcopalian hymnody. He wrote other hymns, but most have fallen into obscurity. "We Three Kings" was his crowning achievement, made possible, in a way, through the generosity of another poet whose most famous work ends:

> *But I heard him exclaim, 'ere he drove out of sight,*
> *Merry Christmas to all, and to all a good night!*

Stand Up, Stand Up for Jesus

George Duffield, Jr.

George J. Webb

1. Stand up, stand up for Je - sus, Ye sol - diers of the cross;
2. Stand up, stand up for Je - sus, The trum - pet call o - bey;
3. Stand up, stand up for Je - sus, Stand in His strength a - lone;
4. Stand up, stand up for Je - sus, The strife will not be long,

Lift high His roy - al ban - ner, It must not suf - fer loss;
Forth to the might - y con - flict In this His glo - rious day.
The arm of flesh will fail you, Ye dare not trust your own.
This day, the noise of bat - tle, The next, the vic - tor's song.

From vic - t'ry un - to vic - t'ry His ar - my shall He lead,
Ye that are men, now serve Him A - gainst un - num - bered foes;
Put on the Gos - pel a - rmor, Each piece put on with prayer;
To Him that o - ver - com - eth, A crown of life shall be;

Till ev - 'ry foe is van - quished And Christ is Lord in - deed.
Let cou - rage rise with dan - ger, And strength to strength op - pose.
Where du - ty calls, or dan - ger, Be nev - er want - ing there.
He with the King of Glo - ry Shall reign e - ter - nal - ly.

Stand Up, Stand Up for Jesus

1858

Stand therefore, having girded your waist with truth, having put on the breastplate of righteousness. Ephesians 6:14

Dudley Tyng served as his father's assistant at Philadelphia's Church of the Epiphany and was elected its pastor when his father retired in 1854. He was only 29 when he succeeded his father at this large Episcopal church, and at first it seemed a great fit. But the honeymoon ended when Dudley began vigorously preaching against slavery. Loud complaints rose from the more conservative members, resulting in Dudley's resignation in 1856.

He and his followers organized the Church of the Covenant elsewhere in the city, and his reputation grew. He began noontime Bible studies at the YMCA, and his ministry reached far beyond his own church walls. Dudley had a burden for leading husbands and fathers to Christ, and he helped organize a great rally to reach men.

On Tuesday, March 30, 1858, five thousand men gathered. As Dudley looked over the sea of faces he felt overwhelmed. "I would rather this right arm were amputated at the trunk than that I should come short of my duty to you in delivering God's message," he told the crowd.

Over a thousand men were converted that day.

Two weeks later Dudley was visiting in the countryside, watching a corn-thrasher in the barn. His hand moved too close to the machine and his sleeve was snared. His arm was ripped from its socket, the main artery severed. Four days later his right arm was amputated close to the shoulder. When it appeared he was dying, Dudley told his aged father: "Stand up for Jesus, father, and tell my brethren of the ministry to stand up for Jesus."

Rev. George Duffield of Philadelphia's Temple Presbyterian Church was deeply stirred by Dudley's funeral, and the following Sunday he preached from Ephesians 6:14 about standing firm for Christ. He read a poem he had written, inspired by Dudley's words:

> *Stand up, stand up for Jesus, / Ye soldiers of the cross; /*
> *Lift high His royal banner, / It must not suffer loss.*

The editor of a hymnal heard the poem, found appropriate music, and published it. "Stand Up, Stand Up for Jesus" soon became one of America's favorite hymns, extending Dudley's dying words to millions.

Praise Ye the Triune God

Elizabeth R. Charles

Friedrich F. Flemming

1. Praise ye the Fa - ther! For His lov - ing kind - ness,
2. Praise ye the Sa - vior! Great is His com - pas - sion,
3. Praise ye the Spir - it! Com - fort - er of Is - rael,

ten - der - ly cares He For His err - ing
gra - cious - ly cares He for His cho - sen
sent of the Fa - ther and the Son to

chil - dren; Praise Him, ye an - gels, praise Him in the
peo - ple; young men and maid - ens, ye old men and
bless us; praise to the Fa - ther, Son and Ho - ly

heav - ens, praise ye Je - ho - - - vah!
chil - dren, praise ye the Sav - - - ior!
Spir - it, praise ye the tri - une God!

Praise Ye the Triune God

1858

Go therefore and make disciples of all the nations, baptizing them in the name of the Father and of the Son and of the Holy Spirit. Matthew 28:19

Elizabeth Rundle Charles was blessed with an idyllic childhood in a picturesque village on the southwestern tip of England. Her father, John Rundle, was a banker and a Member of Parliament. Her mother, Joana, provided a well-ordered home where the hymns of Watts and Wesley were often sung. Elizabeth was an only child, but a brood of cousins lived nearby; together they were educated by governesses, and Elizabeth was well-trained in the liberal arts and foreign languages.

As a teenager, she began realizing that a Christian environment wasn't enough. She needed Christ Himself. One sunny afternoon after talking with a Swiss friend, César Malan, Elizabeth gave her heart to the Lord Jesus. She was eighteen. "For the first time I seemed to forget and lose myself altogether," she wrote. "I began to see that the work of our Redemption is not ours but God's, that Christ has borne away our sins. . . . The Spirit bore witness with my spirit that I was His child. I loved Him because He first loved me! For hours I was conscious of nothing but the absorbing joy. *My Father! I am Thy child!*" (italics hers).

Out of this experience she wrote one of her best-known hymns, "Come and Rejoice with Me," which she called "Eureka," meaning "I have found Him!"

Five years later, Elizabeth married Andrew Charles and they settled down in Hampstead, where Charles was part-owner in a factory. There she ministered among the poor around the factory, engaged in benevolent work, and wrote books and poems. This great hymn, "Praise Ye the Triune God" was published when she was about thirty. Every stanza is a verse of praise to one of the members of the Godhead—Father, Son, and Holy Spirit. It is unusual in that the lyrics do not rhyme.

Elizabeth's father later faced bankruptcy and her husband died, leaving her a widow at forty. She assumed financial care of her parents, and God provided through royalties from her fifty or so books. So great was her skill as a poet, novelist, devotional writer, linguist, musician, and painter that she became one of the best-known women in England during the nineteenth century—to which she would simply say: "Praise Ye the Triune God."*

---

*I am indebted to Virginia Davis of www.hiddenpearls.com for her willingness to share with me her original research on the extraordinary life of Elizabeth Rundle Charles.

Eternal Father, Strong to Save

William Whiting

John B. Dykes

1. E - ter - nal Fa - ther, strong to save, Whose arm hath bound the rest - less wave, Who bid'st the might - y o - cean deep Its own ap - point - ed lim - its keep; Oh, hear us when we cry to Thee, For those in per - il on the sea!

2. O Christ! Whose voice the wa - ters heard And hushed their rag - ing at Thy Word, Who walk - edst on the foam - ing deep, And calm a - midst its rage didst sleep; Oh, hear us when we cry to Thee, For those in per - il on the sea!

3. Most Ho - ly Spir - it! Who didst brood Up - on the cha - os dark and rude, And bid its an - gry tu - mult cease, And give, for wild con - fu - sion, peace; Oh, hear us when we cry to Thee, For those in per - il on the sea!

4. O Trin - i - ty of love and power! Our fam - 'ly shield in dan - ger's hour; From rock and tem - pest, fire and foe, Pro - tect us where - so - ev'r we go; Thus ev - er - more shall rise to Thee Glad hymns of praise from land and sea.

Eternal Father, Strong to Save

1860

Behold, He who keeps Israel shall neither slumber nor sleep. Psalm 121:4

salm 121 has been called the "Traveler's Psalm" because it requests God's watch-care over the comings and goings of His people: "The LORD shall preserve your going out and your coming in from this time forth, and even forevermore."

Nineteenth century hymnbooks usually had an entire collection of hymns echoing prayers for God's protection of travelers, especially for sailors. *Hymns for Christian Melody*, for example, published in 1832 by Rev. David Marks contains 24 hymns under the section: "Mariners." An 1857 hymnal published by the Freewill Baptist Printing Establishment in Dover, New Hampshire, devotes pages 928 to 943 to hymns for sailors.

The most famous mariners' hymn, "Eternal Father, Strong to Save," was written in 1869. It is called the "Navy Hymn" because of its association with the Naval Academy in Annapolis. It was Franklin Roosevelt's favorite hymn and was sung at his funeral. In November of 1963, its solemn strains accompanied the casket of John F. Kennedy as it was carried up the steps of the U.S. Capitol to lie in state.

The deeply moving melody was written by the famous composer, John B. Dykes, who named it MELITA after the island where Paul was shipwrecked in Acts 27.

Little is known about the author of the words, William Whiting of London. He was Master of an Anglican school for musicians, and he wrote several hymns; but only "Eternal Father, Strong to Save," is widely sung today. William reportedly wrote this hymn as a prayer for a friend who was preparing to sail to America:

> *Eternal Father, strong to save, | Whose arm hath bound the restless wave, |*
> *Who biddest the mighty ocean deep | Its own appointed limits keep; |*
> *Oh, hear us when we cry to Thee, | For those in peril on the sea!*

There follows a verse addressed to the Son, and one to the Holy Spirit. Then a closing verse requests traveling mercies from the Trinity. In more recent years, other verses have been added by various writers:

- *Lord, guard and guide the men who fly | Though the great spaces in the sky . . .*
- *Eternal Father, Lord of hosts, | Watch over the men who guard our coasts . . .*
- *God, Who dost still the restless foam, | Protect the ones we love at home . . .*
- *O Father, King of earth and sea, | We dedicate this ship to Thee . . .*

Jesus Loves Me

Anna B. Warner

William B. Bradbury

1. Je-sus loves me! this I know, For the Bi-ble tells me so;
2. Je-sus loves me! He who died, Heav-en's gate to o-pen wide;
3. Je-sus take this heart of mine, Make it pure and whol-ly Thine;
4. Je-sus loves me! He will stay, Close be-side me all the way;

Lit-tle ones to Him be-long, They are weak, but He is strong.
He will wash a-way my sin, Let His lit-tle child come in.
Thou has bled and died for me, I will hence-forth live for Thee.
He's pre-pared a home for me, And some-day His face I'll see.

Yes, Je-sus loves me, Yes, Je-sus loves me,

Yes, Je-sus loves me, The Bi-ble tells me so.

Jesus Loves Me

1860

That Christ may dwell in your hearts through faith; that you, being rooted and grounded in love, may be able to comprehend with all the saints what is the width and length and depth and height—to know the love of Christ which passes knowledge; that you may be filled with all the fullness of God. Ephesians 3:17–19

Anna and Susan Warner lived in a lovely townhouse in New York City where their father, Henry Whiting Warner, was a successful lawyer. But the "Panic of 1837" wrecked the family's finances, forcing them to move into a ramshackle Revolutionary War-era home on Constitution Island on the Hudson, right across from the Military Academy at West Point.

Needing to contribute to the family income, Anna and Susan began writing poems and stories for publication. Anna wrote "Robinson Crusoe's Farmyard," and Susan wrote, "The Wide, Wide World." The girls thus launched parallel literary careers which resulted in 106 publications, eighteen of them co-authored.

One of their most successful joint projects was a novel titled *Say and Seal* in which a little boy named Johnny Fox is dying. His Sunday School teacher, John Linden, comforts him by taking him in his arms, rocking him, and making up a little song: "Jesus loves me, this I know, for the Bible tells me so. . . ."

The novel became a best-seller, second only to *Uncle Tom's Cabin;* and when hymnwriter William Bradbury read the words of John Linden's little song (written by Anna), he composed a childlike musical score to go along with them. "Jesus Loves Me," soon became the best-known children's hymn on earth.

Despite their success, the Warner sisters never seemed able to recover from the staggering financial reverses of 1836. Years later a friend wrote, "One day when sitting with Miss Anna in the old living room she took from one of the cases a shell so delicate that it looked like lace work and holding it in her hand, with eyes dimmed with tears, she said, 'There was a time when I was very perplexed, bills were unpaid, necessities must be had, and someone sent me this exquisite thing. As I held it I realized that if God could make this beautiful home for a little creature. He would take care of me.'"

For forty years, Susan and Anna conducted Bible classes for cadets at West Point, and both were buried with full military honors. They are the only civilians buried in the military cemetery at West Point. To this day, their home on Constitution Island is maintained by West Point as a museum to their memory.

I Gave My Life for Thee

I Gave My Life for Thee

1860

For even the Son of Man did not come to be served, but to serve, and to give His life a ransom for many. Mark 10:45

Who said there's no place for the arts in Christianity?

In the early 1700s, there lived in Germany a young nobleman named Nikolaus Ludwig von Zinzendorf. His father had died when he was six weeks old, and Nikolaus was raised on a huge estate by three women—his mother, his grandmother, and his aunt, all of them devout Christians.

After graduating from the university at Wittenberg, the young count embarked on a grand tour of Europe. It was in the art museum at Düsseldorf that he had a life-altering experience with Christ. Housed in the museum was a painting by Domenico Feti entitled *Ecce Homo* ("Behold the Man"). It was a portrait of the thorn-crowned Christ gazing at the viewer. Beneath the painting were the words, "I have done this for you; what have you done for me?" Zinzendorf said to himself, "I have loved Him for a long time, but I have never actually done anything for Him. From now on I will do whatever He leads me to do."

As a result of that decision, Zinzendorf became one of the most influential leaders in Christian history, initiating the great Moravian missions movement which gave rise to global Protestant missions. He also wrote the great hymn, "Jesus, Thy Blood and Righteousness."

Many years later, on January 10, 1858, another young Christian visited the Düsseldorf art museum. Frances Havergal, about 17, was tired and sat down opposite the same painting. As she studied the picture and read the accompanying inscription, a few words of a hymn came to mind. Frances jotted them down. Later, back in England, she worked on her poem some more, but grew discouraged with it and threw it in the fire. Somehow it fell out of the grate. Several months later, Frances showed it to her father who was so moved that he wrote a tune for the words (although the tune most frequently used in American churches is by Philip Bliss). In 1860, it was published:

> *I gave my life for thee,*
> *My precious blood I shed,*
> *That thou might'st ransomed be,*
> *And quickened from the dead;*
> *I gave, I gave my life for thee,*
> *What hast thou given for me?*

Battle Hymn of the Republic

Julia Ward Howe American Melody

1. Mine eyes have seen the glo - ry Of the com - ing of the Lord;
2. I have seen Him in the watch-fires Of a hun-dred cir - cling camps;
3. He has sound - ed forth the trum - pet That shall nev - er sound re - treat;
4. In the beau - ty of the lil - ies, Christ was born a - cross the sea,

He is tramp-ling out the vin - tage Where the grapes of wrath are stored;
They have build - ed Him an al - tar In the eve - ning dews and damps;
He is sift - ing out the hearts of men Be - fore His judg - ment seat;
With a glo - ry in His bos - om That trans - fig - ures you and me;

He hath loosed the fate - ful light - ning Of His ter - ri - ble swift sword;
I can read His righ - teous sen - tence By the dim and flar - ing lamps;
O be swift, my soul, to an - swer Him! Be ju - bi - lant, my feet!
As He died to make men ho - ly, Let us live to make men free,

His truth is march - ing on.
His day is march - ing on.
Our God is march - ing on.
While God is march - ing on.

Battle Hymn of the Republic

1861

Who is this King of glory? The LORD strong and mighty, the Lord mighty in battle.
Psalm 24:8

After the September 11, 2001 attacks on the Pentagon and the World Trade Center, a national service of prayer and remembrance was conducted at Washington's National Cathedral. America's most powerful leaders prayed together, listened to brief sermons by evangelist Billy Graham and others, then joined voices to sing the defiant anthem, "Battle Hymn of the Republic." Its words seemed to perfectly signal America's intention to battle the forces of terror in the world.

"Battle Hymn of the Republic" was written by Julia Ward Howe, a leader in women's rights and an ardent foe of slavery. Julia, who came from a wealthy New York family, was married to prominent Boston philanthropist and humanitarian, Dr. S. G. Howe. They were both crusaders for progressive political and moral issues of the day.

In 1861, during the darkest days of the Civil War, the Howes visited Washington, and Julia toured a nearby Union Army Camp on the Potomac in Virginia. There she heard soldiers singing a tribute to John Brown, who had been hanged in 1859 for attempting to lead an insurrection of slaves at Harper's Ferry: "John Brown's Body Lies a-mold'ring in the Grave." The music was rousing, but the words needed improvement. Julia's pastor, who accompanied her, asked her to consider writing new and better verses. That night, after the Howes retired to their room at the Willard Hotel, the words came.

> I went to bed and slept as usual, but awoke the next morning in the gray of the early dawn, and to my astonishment found that the wished-for lines were arranging themselves in my brain. I lay quite still until the last verse had completed itself in my thoughts, then hastily arose, saying to myself, I shall lose this if I don't write it down immediately. I searched for an old sheet of paper and an old stub of a pen which I had had the night before, and began to scrawl the lines almost without looking, as I learned to do by often scratching down verses in the darkened room when my little children were sleeping. Having completed this, I lay down again and fell asleep, but not before feeling that something of importance had happened to me.

Julia gave her song to a friend who worked at *The Atlantic Monthly*. The magazine published it in February, 1862, sending her a check for five dollars.

He Leadeth Me

Joseph H. Gilmore

William B. Bradbury

1. He lead-eth me, O bless-ed thought! O words with heaven-ly com-fort fraught!
2. Some-times 'mid scenes of deep-est gloom, Some-times where E-den's bow-ers bloom,
3. Lord, I would clasp Thy hand in mine, Nor ev-er mur-mur nor re-pine;
4. And when my task on earth is done, When by Thy grace the vic-t'ry's won,

What-e'er I do, where-e'er I be, Still 'tis God's hand that lead-eth me.
By wa-ters still, o'er trou-bled sea, Still 'tis His hand that lead-eth me!
Con-tent what-ev-er lot I see, Since 'tis my God that lead-eth me.
E'en death's cold wave I will not flee, Since God through Jor-dan lead-eth me.

He lead-eth me, He lead-eth me, By His own hand He lead-eth me;

His faith-ful fol-lower I would be, For by His hand He lead-eth me.

He Leadeth Me

1862

. . . He leads me in the paths of righteousness for His name's sake. Psalm 23:3b

On autumn nights as we sleep peacefully in our beds, millions of songbirds travel under cover of darkness, heading south. Somehow, they know their way. God has given them a state-of-the-art internal guidance system.

We're more valuable than many sparrows. If God guides His creation, will He not also guide His children? The Psalmist thought so, saying, "He leadeth me . . . He leadeth me . . ." (Psalm 23:2–3).

Dr. Joseph H. Gilmore, son of a Governor of New Hampshire, gave this account of writing his famous hymn on this theme:

As a young man recently graduated . . . , I was supplying for a couple of Sundays the pulpit of the First Baptist Church in Philadelphia. At the mid-week service, on the 26th of March, 1862, I set out to give the people an exposition of the Twenty-third Psalm, which I had given before on three or four occasions, but this time I did not get further than the words "He Leadeth Me." Those words took hold of me as they had never done before, and I saw in them a significance . . . of which I had never dreamed.

It was the darkest hour of the Civil War. I did not refer to that fact—that is, I don't think I did—but it may subconsciously have led me to realize that God's leadership is the one significant fact in human experience, that it makes no difference how we are led, or whither we are led, so long as we are sure God is leading us.

At the close of the meeting a few of us in the parlor of my host, Deacon Watson, kept on talking about the thought I had emphasized; and then and there, on a blank page of the brief from which I had intended to speak, I penciled the hymn, talking and writing at the same time, then handed it to my wife and thought no more about it. She sent it to *The Watchman and Reflector*, a paper published in Boston, where it was first printed. I did not know until 1865 that my hymn had been set to music by William B. Bradbury. I went to Rochester to preach as a candidate before the Second Baptist Church. Going into their chapel . . . I picked up a hymnal to see what they were singing, and opened it at my own hymn, "He Leadeth Me."

Revive Us Again

William P. Mackay

John J. Husband

1. We praise Thee, O God, For the Son of Thy love;
2. We praise Thee, O God, For Thy Spir - it of light,
3. All glo - ry and praise To the Lamb that was slain,
4. Re - vive us a - gain; Fill each heart with Thy love;

For Je - sus, who died And is now gone a - bove.
Who has shown us our Sav - ior And scat - tered our night.
Who has borne all our sins And hath cleansed ev - ery stain.
May each soul be re - kin - dled With fire from a - bove.

Hal - le - lu - jah! Thine the glo - ry! Hal - le - lu - jah! A - men!

Hal - le - lu - jah! Thine the glo - ry! Re - vive us a - gain.

Revive Us Again

1863

Will You not revive us again, that Your people may rejoice in You? Psalm 85:6

In his own words, here is the testimony of Scottish doctor, W. P. Mackay, author of "Revive Us Again."

My dear mother . . . had been a godly, pious woman, quite often telling me of the Savior, and many times I had been a witness to her wrestling in prayer for my soul's salvation. But nothing had made a deep impression on me. The older I grew the more wicked I became. . . .

One day a seriously injured (laborer) . . . was brought into the hospital. The case was hopeless. . . . He seemed to realize his condition, for he was fully conscious, and asked me how long he would last. . . . I gave him my opinion in as cautious a manner as I could. . . .

"Have you any relatives whom we could notify?" I continued.

The patient shook his head. . . . His only wish was to see his landlady, because he owed her a small sum, and also wished to bid her farewell. He also requested his landlady send him, "The Book . . ."

I went to see him on my regular visits at least once a day. What struck me most was the quiet, almost happy expression constantly on his face. . . . After the man died, some things about the deceased's affairs were to be attended to in my presence.

"What shall we do with this?" asked the nurse, holding up a book in her hand.

"What kind of book is it?" I asked.

"The Bible of the poor man. . . . As long as he was able to read it, he did so, and when he was unable to do so anymore, he kept it under his bed cover."

I took the Bible and—could I trust my eyes? It was my own Bible! The Bible which my mother had given me when I left my parents' home, and which later, when short of money, I sold for a small amount. My name was still in it, written in my mother's hand. . . .

With a deep sense of shame I looked upon . . . the precious Book. It had given comfort and refreshing to the unfortunate man in his last hours. It had been a guide to him into eternal life, so that he had been enabled to die in peace and happiness. And this Book, the last gift of my mother, I had actually sold for a ridiculous price. . . .

Be it sufficient to say that the regained possession of my Bible was the cause of my conversion.

For the Beauty of the Earth

Folliott S. Pierpoint

Conrad Kocher

1. For the beau - ty of the earth, For the glo - ry
2. For the won - der of each hour Of the day and
3. For the joy of hu - man love, Broth - er, sist - er,
4. For Thy Church that ev - er - more Lift - eth ho - ly
5. For Thy - self, best gift di - vine, To our race so

of the skies, For the love which from our birth
of the night, Hill and vale and tree and flower,
par - ent, child; Friends on earth and friends a - bove;
hands a - bove, Of - fering up on ev - ery shore
free - ly given; For that great, great love of Thine,

O - ver and a - round us lies;
Sun and moon and stars of light:
For all gen - tle thoughts and mild:
Her pure sac - ri - fice of love:
Peace on earth and joy in heaven:

Lord of all, to Thee we raise This our hymn of grate-ful praise.

For the Beauty of the Earth

1864

Therefore You are great, O LORD God. For there is none like You, nor is there any God besides You, according to all that we have heard with our ears. 2 Samuel 7:22

olliot Sandford Pierpoint—that's the unlikely name of the author of this great hymn. Folliot was born October 7, 1835, in Bath, England. After graduating from Cambridge, he taught at Somersetshire College in his home area of Bath.

One day when he was 29, Folliot found himself walking in the countryside on a beautiful Spring day. He saw the ocean of green, the blue dome of heaven, and the winding Avon River cutting through the flowery landscape. Overwhelmed with God's creative brilliance, he wrote this poem. He intended it primarily for Communion services in the Anglican Church, but when it jumped the Atlantic, it quickly became associated with the American Thanksgiving holiday.

In Folliot's original version, each verse ended with: "Christ, Our God, to Thee we raise / This our sacrifice of praise." That line was eventually changed to, "Lord of all, to Thee we raise / This our hymn of grateful praise."

Little else is known about Folliot Sandford Pierpoint. He resigned from his position at Somersetshire, and apparently moved from place to place, teaching some, writing hymns, and publishing his poetry. He died in 1917.

"For the Beauty of the Earth" is one of only a few songs devoted purely to giving thanks. One of the strange things about the "attitude of gratitude" is that we tend to exhibit it in reverse proportion to the number of blessings received. The more we have, the less thankful we are.

Among the lessons Viktor Frankl learned in the Nazi death-camp, Auschwitz, was to take time to be thankful and to count your blessings. He wrote that prisoners in the camp dreamed at night about certain things more than others. Bread, cakes, and nice warm baths—the very things we take for granted every day.

Ralph Waldo Emerson observed that if the constellations appeared only once in a thousand years, imagine what an exciting event it would be. But because they're there every night, we barely give them a look.

One of the evidences of the Holy Spirit's work in our lives is a gradual reversal of that twisted pattern. God wants to make us people who exhibit a thankfulness in proper proportion to the gifts and blessings we've received.

Why not take time to sing this hymn to the Lord right now?

My Jesus, I Love Thee

My Jesus, I Love Thee

1864

We love Him because He first loved us. 1 John 4:19

The young people of today are utterly dissolute and disorderly," fumed grumpy old Martin Luther in the sixteenth century. The philosopher Plato agreed. "The youth are rebellious, pleasure-seeking, and irresponsible," he wrote. "They have no respect for their elders." Socrates complained, "Children now love luxury. They have bad manners, contempt for authority. They show disrespect for elders, and love chatter."

A 6000-year-old Egyptian tomb bears this inscription: "We live in a decadent age. Young people no longer respect their parents. They are rude and impatient. They inhabit taverns and have no self-control."

The next time you think the "modern generation" is going from bad to worse, remember that God always has a rich handful of teenage heroes ready to change the world. In Bible times, we read of Joseph the dreamer, Daniel in Babylon, David the giant-killer, and the virgin Mary (likely still a teen).

As a teenager, Charles Spurgeon preached to great crowds, but when they referred to his youthfulness, he replied, "Never mind my age. Think of the Lord Jesus Christ and His preciousness."

In our own day, we've been deeply moved by young people like 17-year old Cassie Bernall of Littleton, Colorado, who was shot for her faith during the Columbine tragedy.

Some of our greatest hymns were also written by young adults. Isaac Watts wrote most of his most memorable hymns at about the age of nineteen. When poet John Milton was fifteen, he wrote the well-known, "Let Us with a Gladsome Mind." The hymn, "Work for the Night Is Coming," was written by an eighteen-year-old. And this hymn of deep devotion, "My Jesus, I Love Thee," was written by William Ralph Featherston at age sixteen. Sixteen!

Featherston was born July 23, 1846, in Montreal. He died in the same city 26 years later. His family attended the Wesleyan Methodist Church, and it seems likely that William wrote this hymn as a poem celebrating his conversion to Christ. Reportedly, he sent it to an aunt living in California, and somehow it was published as an anonymous hymn in a British hymnal in 1864.

Little else is known about the origin of the hymn or its author, but that's all right. It's enough just to know that God can change the world through anyone—regardless of age—who will say, "My Jesus, I love Thee, I know Thou art mine. For Thee, all the follies of sin I resign."

Shall We Gather at the River?

Robert Lowry

Robert Lowry

1. Shall we gath-er at the riv - er, Where bright an - gel feet have trod;
2. On the mar-gin of the riv - er, Wash - ing up its sil - ver spray,
3. Ere we reach the shin-ing riv - er, Lay we ev - ery bur - den down;
4. Soon we'll reach the shin-ing riv - er, Soon our pil-grim-age will cease,

With its crys-tal tide for - ev - er Flow-ing by the throne of God?
We will walk and wor-ship ev - er, All the hap-py gold - en day.
Grace our spir-its will de - liv - er, And pro - vide a robe and crown.
Soon our hap-py hearts will quiv - er With the mel - o - dy of peace.

Yes, we'll gath - er at the riv - er, The beau - ti-ful, the beau-ti-ful riv - er;

Gath-er with the saints at the riv - er That flows by the throne of God.

Shall We Gather at the River?

1864

And he showed me a pure river of water of life, clear as crystal, proceeding from the throne of God and of the Lamb. Revelation 22:1

Often called the "Good Doctor," Robert Lowry was a cheerful man with a big beard and a quick mind. He pastored Baptist churches in the Eastern U.S. during the mid-1800s. One friend said, "Very few men had greater ability in painting pictures from imagination. He could thrill an audience with his vivid descriptions, inspiring them with the same thoughts that inspired him."

But he is best remembered for his hymns. Even in childhood he had composed tunes, and as he became acquainted with leaders in America hymnology—many of them based in New York—he realized he could reach more people through his songs than through his sermons.

He set many of Fanny Crosby's hymns to music, including the classic, "All the Way My Savior Leads Me." And he wrote both words and music to the popular gospel song: "What can wash away my sins? / Nothing but the blood of Jesus."

The doctor's best known hymn is "Shall We Gather at the River?" Though often used at baptisms, it's actually a song about heaven. It came to Lowry on a mid-summer's day in New York, when, in the sweltering heat, he began musing about the cool, crystal river that flows through the city of God as described in Revelation 22.

One afternoon in July, 1864, when I was pastor at Hanson Place Baptist Church, Brooklyn, the weather was oppressively hot, and I was lying on a lounge in a state of physical exhaustion. I felt almost incapable of bodily exertion, and my imagination began to take itself wings. Visions of the future passed before me with startling vividness. The imagery of the apocalypse took the form of a tableau. Brightest of all were the throne, the heavenly river, and the gathering of the saints. My soul seemed to take new life from that celestial outlook. I began to wonder why the hymn writers had said so much about the "river of death" and so little about the "pure water of life, clear as crystal, proceeding out of the throne of God and the Lamb." As I mused, the words began to construct themselves. They came first as a question of Christian inquiry, "Shall we gather?" Then they broke out in a chorus, "Yes, we'll gather." On this question and answer the hymn developed itself. The music came with the hymn.

Thou Didst Leave Thy Throne

Emily E. S. Elliott

Timothy R. Matthews

1. Thou didst leave Thy throne and Thy king - ly crown When Thou
2. Heav - en's arch - es rang when the an - gels sang, Pro -
3. The fox - es found rest, and the birds their nest In the
4. Thou cam - est, O Lord, with the liv - ing word That should
5. When the heavens shall ring and the an - gels sing At Thy

cam - est to earth for me, But in Beth - le - hem's home was there
claim - ing Thy roy - al de - cree, But of low - ly birth didst Thou
shade of the for - est tree; But Thy couch was the sod, O Thou
set Thy peo - ple free; But with mock - ing scorn and with
com - ing to vic - tor - y, Let Thy voice call me home, say - ing,

found no room For Thy ho - ly na - tiv - i - ty. O come to my
come to earth And in great hu - mil - i - ty. O come to my
Son of God, In the des - erts of Gal - i - lee. O come to my
crown of thorn They bore Thee to Cal - va - ry. O come to my
"Yet there is room, There is room at My side for thee." And my heart shall re-

heart, Lord Je - sus: There is room in my heart for Thee!
heart, Lord Je - sus. There is room in my heart for Thee!
heart, Lord Je - sus. There is room in my heart for Thee!
heart, Lord Je - sus. There is room in my heart for Thee!
joice, Lord Je - sus, When Thou com - est and call - est me.

Thou Didst Leave Thy Throne

1864

And she brought forth her firstborn Son, and wrapped Him in swaddling cloths, and laid Him in a manger, because there was no room for them in the inn. Luke 2:7

mily Elliott was born south of London in the little holiday town of Brighton on the English Channel in 1836. Her father, Edward Elliott, was pastor of St. Mark's Church there. His invalid aunt—Charlotte Elliott, well-known hymnist and the author of the invitational hymn, "Just as I Am"—lived nearby.

While working with children in the church choir and the local parish school, Emily, in her late twenties, wanted to use the Christmas season to teach them about the entire life and mission of the Savior. As she studied Luke 2:7, she wrote this hymn. The first and second verses speak of our Lord's birth, but the third verse describes His life as an itinerate preacher. The next stanza describes His death on Calvary, and the last verse proclaims His Second Coming.

Emily had her hymn privately printed, and it was first performed in her father's church during the Christmas season of 1864. Six years later, she included it in a magazine she edited called "Church Missionary Juvenile Instructor."

Several years later, Emily inserted this carol into her book of poems and hymns entitled *Chimes for Daily Service.* "Thou Didst Leave Thy Throne" first appeared in the United States in *The Sunday School Hymnal,* published in Boston in 1871.

Emily devoted her life to Sunday school work, to ministering to the down-and-out in Brighton's rescue missions, and to sharing the message of Christ through poems, hymns, and the printed page. Another of her carols was widely used for many years during the Christmas season, though it isn't well-known today. The words are ideally suited for the children Emily so loved. This carol, too, encompasses our Lord's entire life and mission:

> *There came a little Child to earth long ago;*
> *And the angels of God proclaimed His birth, high and low.*
>
> *Out on the night, so calm and still, their song was heard;*
> *For they knew that the Child on Bethlehem's hill was Christ the Lord.*
>
> *In mortal weakness, want and pain, He came to die,*
> *That the children of earth might in glory reign with Him on high.*
>
> *And evermore in robes so fair and undefiled,*
> *Those ransomed children His praise declare, who was a Child.*

I Heard the Bells on Christmas Day

Henry Wadsworth Longfellow

Jean Baptiste Calkin

1. I heard the bells on Christ - mas day Their
2. And thought how, as the day had come, The
3. And in de - spair I bowed my head: "There
4. Then pealed the bells more loud and deep: "God
5. Till ring - ing, sing - ing on its way, The

old fa - mil - iar car - ols play, And wild and sweet the
bel - fries of all Chris - ten - dom Had rolled a - long th'un -
is no peace on earth," I said, "For hate is strong, and
is not dead, nor doth He sleep; The wrong shall fail, the
world re - volved from night to day, A voice, a chime, a

words re - peat, Of peace on earth, good - will to men.
bro - ken song Of peace on earth, good - will to men.
mocks the song Of peace on earth, good - will to men."
right pre - vail, With peace on earth, good - will to men."
chant sub - lime, Of peace on earth, good - will to men!

I Heard the Bells on Christmas Day

1864

Behold, He who keeps Israel shall neither slumber nor sleep. Psalm 121:4

The famous Longfellow brothers were born and raised in Portland, Maine, in the 1800s. Henry Wadsworth was born in 1807, and younger brother Samuel arrived in 1819. Henry became a Harvard professor of literature and one of America's greatest writers, and Samuel became a Unitarian minister and a hymnist.

While Henry was publishing his books, however, dark clouds were gathering over his life and over all America. In 1861, his wife tragically died when her dress caught fire in their home in Cambridge, Massachusetts. That same year, the Civil War broke out, tearing the nation apart. Two years later, during the fiercest days of the conflict, Henry's son, Charley, seventeen, ran away from home and hopped aboard a train to join President Lincoln's army.

Charley proved a brave and popular soldier. He saw action at the Battle of Chancellorsville in 1863, but in early June he contracted typhoid fever and malaria and was sent home to recover. He missed the Battle of Gettysburg, but by August, Charley was well enough to return to the field. On November 27, during the battle of New Hope Church in Virginia, he was shot through the left shoulder. The bullet nicked his spine and came close to paralyzing him. He was carried into the church and later taken to Washington to recuperate.

Receiving the news on December 1, 1863, Henry left immediately for Washington. He found his son well enough to travel and they headed back to Cambridge, arriving home on December 8. For weeks Henry sat by his son's bedside, slowly nursing his boy back to health.

On Christmas Day, December 25, 1863, Henry gave vent to his feelings in this plaintive carol that can only be understood against the backdrop of war. Two stanzas now omitted from most hymnals speak of the cannons thundering in the South and of hatred tearing apart "the hearth-stones of a continent." The poet feels like dropping his head in despair, but then he hears the Christmas bells. Their triumphant pealing reminds him that "God is not dead, nor doth He sleep."

The Sunday school children of the Unitarian Church of the Disciples in Boston first sang this song during that year's Christmas celebration. How wonderful that such a song should emerge from the bloody clouds of the War Between the States.

For All the Saints

William W. How

Ralph Vaughan Williams

1. For all the saints Who from their la - bors rest,
2. Thou wast their Rock, their fort - ress and their might;
3. O blest com - mu - nion, fel - low - ship di - vine!
4. And when the strife is fierce, the war - fare long,
5. From earth's wide bounds and o - cean's far - thest coast,

Who Thee by faith be - fore the world con - fessed, Thy
Thou, Lord, their Cap - tain in the well - fought fight;
We fee - bly strug - gle; they in glo - ry shine. Yet
Steals on the ear the dis - tant tri - umph song, And
Through gates of pearl streams in the count - less host,

name, O Je - sus, be for - ev - er blest.
Thou in the dark - ness drear, their one true light.
all are one in Thee, for all are Thine.
hearts are brave a - gain and arms are strong.
Sing - ing to Fa - ther, Son and Ho - ly Ghost.

Al - - le - lu - ia! Al - le - lu - ia!

For All the Saints

1864

But the saints of the Most High shall receive the kingdom, and possess the kingdom forever, even forever and ever. Daniel 7:18

William Walsham How was born into a wealthy British home just before Christmas in 1823. His father was a lawyer and his grandfather a preacher. William attended Oxford to study law, but after graduation he entered the Anglican ministry. He proved very capable and was offered the Bishopric of Manchester; but he turned it down without even telling his family of the offer. He also refused the Bishopric of Durham, England, with its large salary and prestige. He wanted to serve in humbler places.

In 1851, he became a country parson in the rural parish of Whittington near the Welsh border. He labored there for twenty-eight years, during which time he wrote most of his nearly sixty hymns. In 1879, he moved to London and began working tirelessly among the poor as an assisting (suffragen) Bishop.

He was called the "Omnibus Bishop" for he refused to ride in the private coach afforded bishops. He preferred public transportation. He was also called "the Poor Man's Bishop" because of his concern for the poverty-stricken of Victorian London.

William tended toward liberalism in his theology and was influenced by the intellectual trends of his day, including the theory of evolution. His son once said, "My father considered evolution to be the wonderful way in which 'the Lord formed man out of the dust of the ground.'"

Nevertheless, William was a passionate soul-winner and an evangelical hymnist. He once said a minister "should be a man pure, holy, and spotless in his life; a man of much prayer; in character meek, lowly . . . devoting his days and nights to lightening the burdens of humanity." And he said about his poems: "A good hymn should be like a good prayer—simple, real, earnest, and reverent."

In 1897, How was asked to write the national hymn for the British Empire's observance of Queen Victoria's Jubilee, but he had little time to enjoy the honor. He died on August 10 that year while vacationing in Ireland.

One of William's greatest hymns is "For All the Saints," originally titled "Saints Day Hymn—Cloud of Witnesses—Hebrews 12:1." It was written for All Saints' Day (November 1) and is often used as a processional in church services on that day due to its majestic tune. It was first published in 1864 in Earl Nelson's *Hymns for Saint's Days and Other Hymns*.

We Give Thee But Thine Own

William W. How

Lowell Mason and George J. Webb

1. We give Thee but Thine own, What-
2. May we Thy boun-ties thus As
3. To com-fort and to bless, To
4. And we be-lieve Thy word, Though

e'er the gift may be. All that we have is
stew-ards true re-ceive. And glad-ly, as Thou
find a balm for woe, To tend the lone and
dim our faith may be. What-ev-er task we

Thine a-lone, A trust, O Lord, from Thee.
bless-est us, To Thee our first-fruits give.
fa-ther-less, Is an-gels' work be-low.
do, O Lord, We do it un-to Thee.

We Give Thee But Thine Own

1864

. . . We thank You And praise Your glorious name. . . . For all things come from You, And of Your own we have given You. 1 Chronicles 29:13, 14

A recent newspaper report said that if American Christians would simply give the biblical tithe to the Lord, an additional $143 billion dollars would flow annually into His worldwide work. Despite being the most affluent generation in history, only a fraction of believers tithe from their income to the ministry of the gospel.

Perhaps it's because they don't understand 1 Chronicles 29:14. When King David was planning the temple in Jerusalem, he gave liberally of his wealth and asked his people to do the same. When the money came in, David was ecstatic: "But who am I, and who are my people," he exclaimed, "that we should be able to offer so willingly as this? For all things come from You, and of Your own we have given You."

William How, a nineteenth-century English bishop, put David's words into verse form in this great stewardship hymn:

> *We give Thee but Thine own, whate'er the gift may be;*
> *All that we have is Thine alone, a trust, O Lord, from Thee.*

How had a burning desire to minister to the masses of London. This was the era of the Industrial Revolution, when multitudes had left the tranquility of the English countryside to work in the burgeoning factories and dockyards of London's East Side. It was the stuff of a Dickens' novel. Endless slums. Child labor. Long hours. Poverty. Alcoholism. Squalor. William How was called the "Poor Man's Bishop" as he visited, counseled, preached, evangelized, and provided for the needs of the desperate. His concern is seen in a frequently omitted stanza of this hymn:

> *To comfort and to bless, to find a balm for woe,*
> *To tend the lone and fatherless is angels' work below.*

If only we would realize that when we give to God we're only giving from what He has already given us. Someone said, "It isn't whether we're going to give ten percent of *our* income to God. It's whether we're going to keep ninety percent of *His* money for ourselves."

Coming to Christ, we give Him all we are and have, and we become His stewards. "So let each one give as he purposes in his heart," says 1 Corinthians 8:9, "not grudgingly or of necessity; for God loves a cheerful giver."

253

Day by Day

Karolina Sandell-Berg

Oskar Ahnfelt

1. Day by day and with each pass-ing mo-ment, Strength I find to meet my tri-als here;
2. Ev - 'ry day the Lord Him-self is near me With a spe - cial mer - cy for each hour;
3. Help me then in ev - 'ry trib - u - la - tion, So to trust Your prom - is-es, O Lord;

Trust-ing in my Fa - ther's wise be - stow-ment, I've no cause for wor - ry or for fear.
All my cares He fain would bear and cheer me, He whose name is Coun - se - lor and Pow'r.
That I lose not faith's sweet con - so - la - tion, Of - fered me with - in Your ho - ly Word.

He whose heart is kind be-yond all mea-sure, Give un - to each day what He deems best;
The pro - tec - tion of His child and trea-sure, Is a charge that on Him-self He laid;
Help me, Lord, when toil and trou-ble meet-ing, E'er to take, as from a Fa-ther's hand,

Lov - ing -ly, its part of pain and plea-sure, Min-gling toil with peace and rest.
"As your days, your strength shall be in mea-sure," This the pledge to me He made.
One by one, the days, the mo-ments fleet-ing, Till I reach the prom - ised land.

Day by Day

1865

The LORD is my light and my salvation; whom shall I fear? The LORD is the strength of my life; of whom shall I be afraid? Psalm 27:1

This is a Scandinavian hymn, written by the "Fanny Crosby of Sweden," Karolina W. Sandell-Berg.

Lina was born in Frvderyd on October 3, 1832, the daughter of Jonas Sandell, pastor of the village's Lutheran church. Though frail in body, she had a strong spirit, feasting on the artistic, literary, and religious influences of her home life.

But tragedy struck when she was twenty-six. Lina and her father were enjoying a boat trip on the east coast of Sweden near Gothenburg when the ship suddenly lurched. Before her eyes, Rev. Sandell pitched overboard and drowned. Returning home alone, Lina began processing her grief through the Scriptures and expressing her faith in poetry. Fourteen poems were published that year, 1858, one of which is sung to this day:

> *Children of the heavenly Father | Safely in His bosom gather; |*
> *Nestling bird nor star in heaven | Such a refuge e'er was given.*

Seven years later, her best-known hymn, "Day by Day," was published. In it, Lina spoke from personal experience about the daily strength the Lord provides for His struggling children.

> *Day by day, and with each passing moment, | Strength I find, to meet my trials here; |*
> *Trusting in my Father's wise bestowment, | I've no cause for worry or for fear.*

If you need strength for a particular trial, take this grand old hymn into the day with you, and claim some of the wonderful promises God has given:

- *The LORD is my strength and song, and He has become my salvation*—Exodus 15:2
- *As your days, so shall your strength be*—Deuteronomy 33:25
- *Do not sorrow, for the joy of the Lord is your strength*—Nehemiah 8:10
- *God is our refuge and strength, a very present help in trouble*—Psalm 46:1
- *Those who wait on the Lord shall renew their strength*—Isaiah 40:31
- *My grace is sufficient for thee: for my strength is made perfect in weakness*—2 Corinthians 12:9
- *I can do all things through Christ who strengthens me*—Philippians 4:13

Jesus Paid It All

Elvina M. Hall

John T. Grape

1. I hear the Sav - ior say, "Thy strength in - deed is small;
2. Lord, now in - deed I find, Thy power and Thine a - lone;
3. For noth - ing good have I, Where - by Thy grace to claim;
4. And when be - fore the throne, I stand in Him com - plete;

Child of weak - ness watch and pray, Find in Me thine all in all."
Can change the lep - er's spots And melt the heart of stone.
I'll wash my gar - ments white, In the blood of Cal - vary's Lamb.
"Je - sus died my soul to save," My lips shall still re - peat.

Je - sus paid it all, all to Him I owe;

Sin had left a crim - son stain, He washed it white as snow.

Jesus Paid It All

1865

Not with the blood of goats and calves, but with His own blood He entered the Most Holy Place once for all, having obtained eternal redemption. Hebrews 9:12

It was Sunday morning at Monument Street Methodist Church in Baltimore. Rev. George Schrick was droning on in a lengthy prayer while, up in the choir loft, Elvina Hall's mind was wandering. She thumbed quietly through the hymnbook, then began doodling on the flyleaf. By and by, these words came to her, which she scribbled on the front flap of her hymnal:

I hear my Savior say | Thy strength indeed is small, |
Thou hast naught My debt to pay, | Find in Me thy all in all.

Yea, nothing good have I, | Whereby Thy grace to claim; |
I'll wash my garments white | In the blood of Calvary's Lamb.

And now complete in Him, | My robe His righteousness, |
Close sheltered 'neath His side, | I am divinely blest,

When from my dying bed | My ransomed soul shall rise, |
Jesus paid it all | Shall rend the vaulted skies.

Elvina's poem fell into the hands of John T. Grape, a coal merchant and the church organist at Monument Street Methodist Church. As it happened, the church was being renovated, and the small organ had been taken to Grape's house for safekeeping. There he composed the music to "Jesus Paid It All."

Through the years, the words of this hymn have been edited and altered, but its great theme of redemption has remained untouched.

༄

The colorful preacher, Rowland Hill, was once preaching to a crowd of people when the wealthy aristocrat, Lady Ann Erskine, drove up in her coach. Seeing her, Rev. Hill changed his sermon.

"I have something for sale," he suddenly declared. "Yes, I have something for sale. It is the soul of Lady Ann Erskine. Is there anyone here that will bid for her soul? Ah, do I hear a bid? Who bids? Satan bids. Satan, what will you give for her soul? 'I will give riches, honor, and pleasure.' But stop, do I hear another bid? Yes, Jesus Christ bids. Jesus, what will You give for her soul? 'I will give eternal life.' Lady Ann Erskine, you have heard the two bids—which will you take?"

Lady Erskine, realizing Christ had purchased her soul with His life's blood on the Cross, took Him.

Now the Day Is Over

Sabine Baring-Gould

Joseph Barnby

1. Now the day is o - ver,
2. Je - sus, give the wear - y
3. Grant to lit - tle chil - dren
4. Through the long night watch - es
5. When the morn - ing wak - ens,

Night is draw - ing nigh, Shad - ows of the
Calm and sweet re - pose; With Thy ten - derest
Vi - sions bright of Thee; Guard the sail - ors
May Thine an - gels spread Their white wings a -
Then may I a - rise Pure, and fresh, and

eve - ning Steal a - cross the sky.
bless - ing May mine eye - lids close.
toss - ing On the deep, blue sea.
bove me, Watch - ing round my bed.
sin - less In Thy ho - ly eyes.

Now the Day Is Over

<u>1865</u>

When you lie down, you will not be afraid; Yes, you will lie down and your sleep will be sweet. Proverbs 3:24

Highly productive people have one thing in common—they know how to plunge into their work. Basketball star Jerry West said, "You can't get much done in life if you only work on the days when you feel good."

That was the attitude of British pastor Sabine Baring-Gould, author of "Onward Christian Soldiers." In addition to shepherding his village church, teaching in the local college, dabbling in archaeology, publishing travelogues, and writing hymns, he wrote fiction. For many years he published a new novel annually. His novels have recently been republished in England and are finding a new generation of fans.

He also wrote "Lives of the Saints," "Curious Myths of the Middle Ages," and, "The Book of Werewolves: Being an Account of Terrible Superstition."

He is primarily remembered in southwest England for his work as a collector of local folk songs. For years, he traveled through the west of England, visiting old people and recording the songs they remembered from childhood. In 1889, he published a remarkable book, "Songs of the West" which established him as an authority in the field of British folk music.

No one really knows how many other books and publications he penned. It was an astonishing number—at one time, he was responsible for more books in the British Museum Library than any other author.

The ensuing income allowed him to travel, explore, compose poetry, raise a family of fifteen children, restore his vast family estate, rebuild the old village church, and pursue his multitude of hobbies.

Sabine Baring-Gould declared that he often did his best work when he felt least inclined to apply himself to the task. Rather than waiting for inspiration, he plunged into his work and plodded on until it was finished. "The secret is simply that I stick to a task when I begin it," he said. "It would never do to wait from day to day for some moments that might seem favorable for work."

Did his massive workload shorten his life? No, he lived to be ninety, and was buried in his own churchyard across the street from his estate.

"Now the Day is Over" is a fitting epitaph for this prodigious man. It was written for a vesper service in 1865, based on Proverbs 3:24, and is one of Church history's classic "bedtime prayers."

Onward Christian Soldiers

Sabine Baring-Gould

Arthur S. Sullivan

1. On-ward, Chris-tian sol - diers, March-ing as to war, With the cross of
2. At the sign of tri - umph, Sa-tan's host doth flee; On, then, Chris-tian

Je - sus Go-ing on be - fore! Christ, the roy - al Mas - ter, Leads a-
sol - diers, On to vic-to - ry! Hell's foun-da-tions quiv - er At the

gainst the foe; For-ward in - to bat - tle, See His ban-ners go!
shouts of praise; Broth-ers, lift your voi - ces, Loud your an-thems raise!

On - ward, Chris - tian sol - diers, March - ing as to war,

With the cross of Je - sus Go - ing on be - fore!

Onward Christian Soldiers

<u>1865</u>

You will not need to fight in this battle. Position yourselves, stand still and see the salvation of the LORD, Who is with you . . . 2 Chronicles 20:17

R ev. Sabine Baring-Gould was born in Exeter in 1834. His father, an officer with the East India Company, had a disabling carriage accident and decided that if he couldn't work, he could at least travel. As a result, little Sabine was dragged from one end of Europe to the other, year after year. It gave him an unsettled childhood, spotty schooling, and a wanderlust he never outgrew. He later managed to scrape through Cambridge, but for the most part he is remembered as a brilliant, self-taught scholar. That helps explain why he developed certain eccentric habits. When he taught school, for example, he kept a pet bat on his shoulder.

From Sabine's original mind flowed an endless number of books, articles, poems, hymns, and tracts. This particular hymn, "Onward Christian Soldiers," was written on a Whitsunday's evening in the mid-1860s.

Whitsunday is better known as Pentecost Sunday. It got its "nickname" because it became a popular day for new Christians to be baptized. The baptismal candidates marched to the rivers or fonts wearing robes of white. Thus it came to be called "White Sunday" or Whitsunday.

It was on this day in 1865, in the little town of Horbury, England, that Sabine stayed up late searching through hymnbooks for a martial-type hymn for children. The next day, Monday, all the village children were marching to the neighboring town for a Sunday School rally. Sabine wanted to give them a "marching song" for the trip. Searching his hymnals and finding nothing, he began scribbling on a piece of paper, playing with words, dashing off lines until he had written a hymn of his own just for the occasion:

> *Onward, Christian soldiers, | Marching as to war, |*
> *With the cross of Jesus | Going on before.*

"It was written in great haste," he later said, "and I am afraid some of the rhymes are faulty. Certainly, nothing has surprised me more than its popularity."

Perhaps you've noticed that several of our greatest "adult" hymns were originally written or translated for children. See, for example, the stories behind "All Creatures of Our God and King," "I Sing the Mighty Power of God," "I Heard the Voice of Jesus Say," and "O Little Town of Bethlehem." Add "Onward, Christian Soldiers" to that list, and visualize this eccentric preacher, singing in step, marching alongside the children—perhaps with a pet bat on his shoulder.

Rejoice, Ye Pure in Heart

Edward H. Plumptre

Arthur H. Messiter

Rejoice, Ye Pure in Heart

1865

Rejoice in the Lord always. Again I will say, rejoice! Philippians 4:4

Edward H. Plumptre was a Christian intellectual. Born in London in 1821, he became a well-known Anglican scholar, author, theologian, and preacher. For many years he served as chaplain of King's College, where he also taught pastoral theology and New Testament exegesis. He wrote books on the classics, history, theology, biblical criticism, and biography. He served on the Old Testament Company for the Revision of the Authorized Version of the Holy Scriptures, and for the last ten years of his life (1881-1891), he was the dean of Wells Cathedral.

Edward was also a poet. In May, 1865, he was preparing for the annual choir festival in the majestic, towering cathedral of Peterborough, England. Needing a long and celebratory processional to give the participating choirs time to proceed down the aisles, he focused his thoughts on two passages of Scripture:

- Psalm 20:5: *We will rejoice in your salvation, and in the name of our God we will set up our banners!*
- Philippians 4:4: *Rejoice in the Lord always. Again I will say, rejoice!*

Inspired by those verses, Edward, 44, began writing:

Rejoice ye pure in heart; / Rejoice, give thanks, and sing; /
Your glorious banner wave on high, / The cross of Christ your King. /
Rejoice, Rejoice, Rejoice, give thanks, and sing!

Edward composed eleven stanzas in all. Most hymnals today use only stanzas 1, 2, 7, and 10. Here are some of the omitted verses:

Yes onward, onward still / With hymn, and chant and song, /
Through gate, and porch and columned aisle, / The hallowed pathways throng. /
Rejoice, Rejoice, Rejoice, give thanks, and sing!

Your clear hosannas raise; / And alleluias loud; /
Whilst answering echoes upward float, / Like wreaths of incense cloud. /
Rejoice, Rejoice, Rejoice, give thanks, and sing!

Praise Him Who reigns on high, / The Lord Whom we adore, /
The Father, Son and Holy Ghost, / One God forevermore. /
Rejoice, Rejoice, Rejoice, give thanks, and sing!

What Child Is This?

William C. Dix

English Melody

1. What child is this, who laid to rest, on Mary's lap is sleeping?
2. Why lies He in such mean es-tate, where ox and ass are feed-ing?
3. So bring Him in-cense, gold, and myrrh; come peas-ant, king to own Him.

Whom an-gels greet with an-thems sweet, while shep-herds watch are keep-ing?
Good Chris-tian, fear; for sin-ners here the si-lent Word is plead-ing.
The King of kings, sal-va-tion brings, let lov-ing hearts en-throne Him.

This, this is Christ the King, whom shep-herds guard and an-gels sing;
Nails, spear, shall pierce Him thro', the cross be borne, for me, for you.
Raise, raise the song on high, The vir-gin sings her lul-la-by.

Haste, haste to bring Him laud, the Babe, the Son of Mar-y.
Hail, hail the Word made flesh, the Babe, the Son of Mar-y.
Joy, joy for Christ is born, the Babe, the Son of Mar-y.

What Child Is This?

1865

. . . When the angels had gone away from them into heaven, that the shepherds said to one another, "Let us now go to Bethlehem . . ." Luke 2:15

eelings of sadness come over me whenever I hear this deeply moving carol. It is, after all, set in the key of E minor, the "saddest of all keys." Yet triumphant joy dispels the sadness as we exclaim: "This, this is Christ the King, whom shepherds guard and angels sing."

The melancholic melody is a famous old British tune called "Greensleeves," originally a ballad about a man pining for his lost love, the fair Lady Greensleeves. Tradition says it was composed by King Henry VIII for Anne Boleyn. That's unlikely, but we do know that Henry's daughter, Queen Elizabeth I, danced to the tune.

Shakespeare referred to it twice in his play, *The Merry Wives of Windsor*. In Act V, for example, Falstaff said, "Let the sky rain potatoes; let it thunder to the tune of 'Green Sleeves.'"

It was licensed to two different printers in 1580, and soon thereafter was being used with religious texts. Its first association with Christmas came in 1642, in a book titled *New Christmas Carols*, in which it was used with the poem "The Old Year Now Away Has Fled." The last verse says: *Come, give's more liquor when I doe call, / I'll drink to each one in this hall . . . And God send us a happy new yeare!*

For nearly 150 years, however, "Greensleeves" has been most identified with "What Child Is This?" The words of this carol are taken from a longer poem written by an insurance agent named William Chatterton Dix, born in Bristol, England, in 1837. His father was a surgeon who wanted his son to follow his footsteps. But having no interest in medicine, William left Bristol Grammar School, moved to Glasgow, and sold insurance.

His greatest love was his prose and poetry for Christ. He wrote two devotional books, a book for children, and scores of hymns, two of which remain popular Christmas carols: "What Child Is This?" and "As with Gladness Men of Old."

All of Dix's hymns should be more widely sung today, for they are masterpieces of poetry, filled with rich scriptural truth. Here's the way he begins his exultant hymn, "Alleluia!"

Alleluia! Sing to Jesus! His the scepter, His the throne.
Alleluia! His the triumph, His the victory alone.

Ring the Bells of Heaven

William O. Cushing

George F. Root

1. Ring the bells of heav-en! There is joy to-day, For a soul re-
2. Ring the bells of heav-en! There is joy to-day, For the wan-d'rer
3. Ring the bells of heav-en! Spread the feast to-day! An-gels swell the

turn-ing from the wild! See! the Fa-ther meets Him out up-on the way,
now is rec - on - ciled; Yes, a soul is res - cued from His sin-ful way,
glad tri - um-phant strain! Tell the joy - ful ti - dings, bear it far a -way!

Wel-com-ing His wea-ry, wan-d'ring child.
And is born a - new a ran-somed child.
For a pre-cious soul is born a - gain.

Glo-ry! Glo-ry! How the

an - gels sing! Glo-ry! Glo-ry! How the loud harps ring! 'Tis the ran-somed

ar - my, like a might-y sea, Peal-ing forth the an-them of the free.

Ring the Bells of Heaven
1866

. . . I say to you, there is joy in the presence of the angels of God over one sinner who repents. Luke 15:10

Civil War musician George Root wrote a song entitled, "Glory! Glory! (The Little Octoroon)." The word "octoroon" was a term defining a person of one-eighth African ancestry. In Root's song, a little octoroon named Rosa was sitting with her mother on a Southern plantation at the close of day when they heard the sounds of Northern troops in the distance. The mother, a slave, knew that this might be Rosa's one and only chance for freedom. With heart-tugging courage, she told little Rosa to "Fly, my precious darling to the Union camp; / I will keep the hounds and hunters here. / Go right through the forest though 'tis dark and damp, / God will keep you, dear one, never fear." The chorus said:

> *Glory! glory! How the Freedmen sang!*
> *Glory! glory! How the old woods rang!*
> *'Twas the loyal army sweeping to the sea,*
> *Flinging out the banner of the Free!*

Some time later, Christian hymnist William Cushing, hearing it, determined to claim the tune for gospel music. In his autobiography, *Story of a Musical Life*, he wrote:

"The melody ran in my head all day long, chiming and flowing in its sweet musical cadence. I wished greatly that I might secure the tune for use in Sunday school and for other Christian purposes. When I heard the bells of heaven ringing of some sinner that had returned . . . the word(s) 'Ring the Bells of Heaven' at once flowed down into the waiting melody."

As Cushing wrote it, the chorus said:

> *Glory! Glory! How the angels sing:*
> *Glory! Glory! How the loud harps ring!*
> *'Tis the ransomed army, like a mighty sea,*
> *Pealing forth the anthem of the free.*

George Root, who also wrote gospel songs, was pleased with the changes and published "Ring the Bells of Heaven" in 1866 in one of his own music books, *Chapel Gems for Sunday School*.

This was the second of Root's Civil War songs to be "Christianized." The first was "Tramp! Tramp! Tramp!" which became the noted children's song, "Jesus Loves the Little Children."

The Church's One Foundation

Samuel J. Stone

Samuel S. Wesley

1. The Church's one foun-da-tion Is Je-sus Christ her Lord,
2. She is from ev-'ry na-tion, Yet one o'er all the earth,
3. 'Mid toil and trib-u-la-tion, And tu-mult of her war,
4. Yet she on earth hath un-ion With God the Three in One,

She is His new cre-a-tion By wa-ter and the word;
Her char-ter of sal-va-tion, One Lord, one faith, one birth;
She waits the con-sum-ma-tion Of peace for-ev-er-more;
And mys-tic sweet com-mu-nion With those whose rest is won;

From heav'n He came and sought her To be His ho-ly bride;
One ho-ly name she bless-es, Par-takes one ho-ly food,
Till with the vi-sion glo-rious Her long-ing eyes are blest,
With all her sons and daugh-ters, who by the Mas-ter's hand

With His own blood He bought her, And for her life He died.
And to one hope she press-es, With ev-'ry grace en-dued.
And the great Church vic-to-rious Shall be the Church at rest.
Led through the death-ly wa-ters, Re-pose in Ed-en land.

The Church's One Foundation

1866

For no other foundation can anyone lay than that which is laid, which is Jesus Christ. 1 Corinthians 3:11

This great hymn emerged from a ragged and wearing controversy that threatened to tear asunder the Church of England. In the mid-1800s, the liberal views of German theologians drifted like a poisonous fog over Anglicans worldwide. In South Africa, Bishop John William Colenso, influenced by the German "higher critics," questioned whether Moses had really written the first five books of the Bible. He also took liberal views toward Paul's Book of Romans, denying the doctrine of eternal punishment. Colenso had been a tireless missionary bishop, serving the Zulu people in northeastern South Africa with laudable passion, but his emerging liberalism sent shock waves among evangelical Anglican leaders.

In 1853, Bishop Robert Gray of Capetown, defending the historic faith, removed Colenso from his post. Colenso fought the order and was reinstated by a London court of law. The resulting conflict shook the Anglican Church to its foundations.

One man on the side of evangelical truth was Samuel Stone, the curate at Windsor in the shadow of Windsor Castle. In 1866, he wrote twelve hymns based on the twelve articles of the Apostles' Creed. "The Church's One Foundation" was based on the ninth article of the creed, which says: "I believe in the holy catholic (universal) church: the communion of saints."

The next year, Anglican bishops from around the world assembled for a theological enclave that became known as the first Lambeth Conference. The tone of the proceedings was set by Stone's hymn, "The Church's One Foundation," which had been set to music by Samuel Wesley, the grandson of Charles Wesley. It became the processional for that conference, and has been one of the church's best-loved hymns ever since. Not all the verses, however, are sung today. Here is a stanza you may never have sung, but which helps us understand the passion of Samuel Stone as he wrote in defense of the integrity of Christ's holy church:

> *Though with a scornful wonder men see her sore oppressed,*
> *By schisms rent asunder, by heresies distressed:*
> *Yet saints their watch are keeping, their cry goes up, "How long?"*
> *And soon the night of weeping shall be the morn of song!*

I Love to Tell the Story

I Love to Tell the Story

1866

Then they will see the Son of Man coming in the clouds with great power and glory.
Mark 13:26

Villiam Wilberforce, the Christian statesman and abolitionist, led a fierce campaign in nineteenth-century England to eradicate slavery from the British Empire. The geographical center of the campaign was a wealthy neighborhood in the south of London known as Clapham, where a group of Anglican evangelicals lived. The "Clapham Sect" also advocated prison reform, education for children, and the expansion of missionary efforts overseas. Though lampooned for their efforts, they changed the world.

Arabella Katherine Hankey was born into this environment in 1834. Her father was a banker in Clapham and a leader in the Clapham Group. Early in life, Kate became involved in religious work. As a young girl, she taught Sunday school; and when she was eighteen she organized a Bible study for factory girls in London. (This Bible study was never large, but the girls became close and fifty years later, five of them met together at Kate's funeral.) When her brother fell ill in Africa, Kate traveled there to bring him home. That trip sparked a passion for foreign missions, and in later life Kate devoted all proceeds from her writing to missionary work.

During the winter of 1865–1866, Kate, thirty, became seriously ill. The doctors warned her to abandon her Christian activities and remain in bed for a full year. To occupy her time, Kate wrote a poem of one hundred stanzas entitled "The Old, Old Story." She began the first section, "The Story Wanted," on January 29, 1866. Later that year, she wrote a second section entitled, "The Story Told."

The following year, at the international convention of the Young Men's Christian Association, Major General Russell ended his powerful sermon by quoting from Kate's poem. It left the audience breathless. Songwriter William Doane, in the crowd that day, put a portion of Kate's poem to music, giving birth to the hymn, "Tell Me the Old, Old Story."

Another composer, William G. Fischer, set a second portion of Kate's poem to a musical score he named HANKEY, and thus we have this hymn, "I Love to Tell the Story." It was first published in an American hymnbook in 1869, and was later popularized around the world in the great evangelistic campaigns of D. L. Moody and Ira Sankey.

The Cleansing Wave

Phoebe W. Palmer

Phoebe P. Knapp

1. O now I see the crim - son wave, The foun-tain deep and wide;
2. I see the new cre - a - tion rise, I hear the speak-ing blood;
3. I rise to walk in heav'n's own light, A - bove the world and sin;
4. A - maz-ing grace! 'tis heav'n be - low, To feel the blood ap - plied;

Je - sus, my Lord, might - y to save, Points to His wound - ed side.
It speaks! pol - lut - ed na - ture dies, Sinks 'neath the crim - son flood.
With heart made pure and gar-ments white, And Christ en-throned with - in.
And Je - sus, on - ly Je - sus know, My Je - sus cru - ci - fied.

The cleans-ing stream I see, I see! I plunge, and Oh, it cleans-eth me;

Oh praise the Lord, it cleans-eth me, It cleans-eth me, yes, cleans-eth me.

The Cleansing Wave

1867

. . . He was crucified in weakness, yet He lives by the power of God . . . we also are weak in Him, but we shall live with Him by the power of God toward you.
2 Corinthians 13:4

The cleansing stream I see! I see! I plunge, and oh, it cleanses me!" says this exuberant hymn about the soul-cleansing blood of Jesus. It was written by an unusual mother/daughter team, Phoebe Palmer and Phoebe Knapp.

The mother, Phoebe Palmer, was born in New York City in 1807. At age twenty, she married Walter C. Palmer, a physician, and several years later during a revival at New York's Allen Street Methodist Church, Phoebe and Walter knelt in prayer and pledged their lives to promoting holiness.

Soon Phoebe was leading a women's prayer meeting in her home. Before long, men were slipping in to enjoy Phoebe's teaching, including bishops, theologians, and ministers. Phoebe and Walter began traveling throughout the area, preaching and promoting revival. Though Phoebe spoke to great crowds, she insisted she wasn't "preaching" but "giving exhortations." The articles and books flowing from her pen magnified her impact, and she is now considered the "Mother of the Holiness Movement in the United States." It was this woman who wrote the words to "The Cleansing Wave."

Her daughter, Phoebe Knapp, composed the lively tune. Phoebe Palmer Knapp grew up in an atmosphere of revival. At age 16, she married a man who would later become an executive of the Metropolitan Life Insurance Company. They lived lives of high society, often entertaining the most famous people of their day. Their vast wealth allowed Phoebe to focus on her first love—Christian music. The Knapp Mansion had one of the nation's finest music rooms, and Phoebe even had a large pipe organ installed in her home.

One of her closest friends was the blind hymnist, Fanny Crosby. One day when Fanny was visiting, Phoebe went to the piano and played a melody she had written and asked Fanny what the tune seemed to say. The little hymnist replied, "Blessed Assurance, Jesus Is Mine." Fanny composed the words at once, and a great hymn was born.

Incidentally, Phoebe Knapp may have been one of the first hymnists to hear her own song on a phonograph. In February 1909, Thomas Edison's National Phonograph Company of Orange, New Jersey, released a wax cylinder recording of "Blessed Assurance," sung by the Edison Mixed Quartette. It's likely that Phoebe heard the original recording prior to her death.

Safe in the Arms of Jesus

Fanny J. Crosby

William H. Doane

1. Safe in the arms of Je - sus,   safe on His gen-tle   breast,
2. Safe in the arms of Je - sus,   safe from cor-rod-ing   care,
3. Je - sus, my heart's dear Ref - uge,   Je - sus has died for   me;

There by His love o'er - shad - ed,   sweet - ly my soul shall   rest.
Safe from the world's temp - ta - tions,   sin   can-not harm me   there.
Firm   on the Rock of A - ges,   ev - er my trust shall   be.

Hark! 'tis the voice of   an - gels,   borne in   a   song to   me.
Free   from the blight of   sor - row,   free   from my doubts and   fears;
Here   let me wait with   pa - tience,   wait   till the night is   o'er;

O - ver the fields of   glo - ry,   o - ver the jas - per   sea.
On - ly   a   few more   tri - als,   on - ly   a   few more   tears!
Wait till I   see the   morn - ing   break on the gold - en   shore.

Safe in the Arms of Jesus

1868

And He took them up in His arms, laid His hands on them, and blessed them.
Mark 10:16

n March 5, 1858, Fanny Crosby, the blind hymnist and America's "Queen of Gospel Songs," quietly married Alexander Van Alsteine. A year later, the couple suffered a tragedy that shook the deepest regions of Fanny's heart.

She gave birth to a child—no one knows if it was a boy or a girl. In later years, she never spoke about it except to say in her oral biography, "God gave us a tender babe," and "soon the angels came down and took our infant up to God and His throne."

One of Fanny's relatives, Florence Paine, lived with the poet for six years and could never get her to talk about this. The child's death seemed to have devastated her, and she privately bore the sadness all her life.

Years later, on April 30, 1868, musician Howard Doane knocked on the door of Fanny's apartment in Manhattan. "I have exactly forty minutes," he said, "before I must meet a train for Cincinnati. I have a tune for you. See if it says anything to you. Perhaps you can commit it to memory and then compose a poem to match it." He then hummed the tune.

Fanny clapped her hands and said, "Why, that says, 'Safe in the arms of Jesus!'" She retreated to the other room of her tiny apartment, knelt on the floor, and asked God to give her the words quickly. Within half an hour, she had composed the poem in her mind and dictated it to Doane, who dashed off to catch his train.

During her lifetime, "Safe in the Arms of Jesus" was among the most widely sung of Fanny's hymns, and she considered it in a class by itself. She claimed it was written for the bereaved, especially for mothers who had lost children. Often when comforting a grief-stricken mother, she would say, "Remember, my dear, your darling cherub is safe in the arms of Jesus." Rev. John Hall of New York's Fifth Avenue Presbyterian Church told Fanny that her hymn had given more "peace and satisfaction to mothers who have lost their children than any other hymn I have ever known."

It isn't hard to understand why.

Safe in the arms of Jesus, safe on His gentle breast;
There by His love o'ershaded, sweetly my soul shall rest.

O Little Town of Bethlehem

O Little Town of Bethlehem

1868

. . . Bethlehem . . . though you are little among the thousands of Judah, yet out of you shall come forth to Me the One to be Ruler in Israel . . . Micah 5:2

At nearly six feet six, weighing three hundred pounds, Phillips Brooks cast a long shadow. He was a native Bostonian, the ninth generation of distinguished Puritan stock, who entered the Episcopalian ministry and pastored with great power in Philadelphia and in Boston. His sermons were topical rather than expositional, and he's been criticized for thinness of doctrine. Nonetheless he's considered one of America's greatest preachers. His delivery came in lightning bursts; he felt he had more to say than time in which to say it.

While at Philadelphia's Holy Trinity Church, Phillips, 30, visited the Holy Land. On December 24, 1865, traveling by horseback from Jerusalem, he attended a five-hour Christmas Eve service at the Church of the Nativity in Bethlehem. He was deeply moved. "I remember standing in the old church in Bethlehem," he later said, "close to the spot where Jesus was born, when the whole church was ringing hour after hour with splendid hymns of praise to God, how again and again it seemed as if I could hear voices I knew well, telling each other of the *Wonderful Night* of the Savior's birth."

Three years later, as he prepared for the Christmas season of 1867, he wanted to compose an original Christmas hymn for the children to sing during their annual program. Recalling his magical night in Bethlehem, he wrote a little hymn of five stanzas and handed the words to his organist, Lewis Redner, saying, "Lewis, why not write a new tune for my poem. If it is a good tune, I will name it 'St. Lewis' after you."

Lewis struggled with his assignment, complaining of no inspiration. Finally, on the night before the Christmas program, he awoke with the music ringing in his soul. He jotted down the melody, then went back to sleep. The next day, a group of six Sunday school teachers and thirty-six children sang "O Little Town of Bethlehem."

Brooks was so pleased with the tune that he did indeed name it for his organist, changing the spelling to St. Louis, so as not to embarrass him. The fourth stanza, usually omitted from our hymnbooks, says:

> *Where children pure and happy pray to the blessèd Child,*
> *Where misery cries out to Thee, Son of the mother mild;*
> *Where charity stands watching and faith holds wide the door,*
> *The dark night wakes, the glory breaks, and Christmas comes once more.*

The King of Love My Shepherd Is

Henry W. Baker

John B. Dykes

1. The King of love my Shepherd is, Whose
2. Where streams of living water flow My
3. Perverse and foolish oft I strayed But
4. In death's dark vale I fear no ill With
5. And so through all the length of days, Thy

goodness faileth never; I nothing lack if
ransomed soul He leadeth; And where the verdant
yet in love He sought me. And on His shoulder
Thee, dear Lord beside me; Thy rod and staff my
goodness faileth never. Good Shepherd, may I

I am His, And He is mine forever.
pastures grow, With food celestial feedeth.
gently laid, And home rejoicing brought me.
comfort still, Thy cross before to guide me.
sing Thy praise, Within Thy house forever.

The King of Love My Shepherd Is

1868

Yea, though I walk through the valley of the shadow of death, I will fear no evil;
For You are with me; Your rod and Your staff, they comfort me. Psalm 23:4

This is among the most beautiful of all the renditions of the Twenty-third Psalm. It was written by Henry Williams Baker, born in London on May 27, 1821, the oldest son of a Vice Admiral in the British Navy. Henry attended Trinity College, Cambridge, and was ordained in 1844 at age 24. After serving as an assistant pastor for several years, he became the vicar of Monkland, Herefordshire, in 1851. That same year, upon his father's death, he was knighted and became a baronet.

For years Henry worked on a book of hymns that would reflect the grandeur of majestic worship. The first edition was published in 1861, entitled *Hymns Ancient and Modern*. On the British Isles, it was known by its initials: *H. A. and M.* Because Henry had labored so earnestly over every hymn, editing and changing and deleting words, some called it *Hymns Asked for and Mutilated*. But it became the leading hymnbook in the Anglican church, going through many revisions and selling over 150 million copies. "The King of Love" didn't appear until the 1868 revision, in the appendix.

When Henry passed away in 1877, his friend, John Ellerton, reported that his last words were from this great hymn:

> *Perverse and foolish oft I stayed, / But yet in love He sought me, /*
> *And on His shoulder gently laid, / And home, rejoicing, brought me.*

Henry wrote many other, lesser-known hymns. One of the finest is his morning hymn, to be recommended for all upon arising:

> *My Father, for another night of quiet sleep and rest,*
> *For all the joy of morning light, Thy holy Name be blest.*

> *Now with the newborn day I give myself anew to Thee,*
> *That as Thou willest I may live, and what Thou willest be.*

> *Whate'er I do, things great or small, whate'er I speak or frame,*
> *Thy glory may I seek in all, do all in Jesus' Name.*

> *My Father, for His sake, I pray thy child accept and bless;*
> *And lead me by Thy grace today in paths of righteousness.*

The Ninety and Nine

Elizabeth C. Clephane

Ira D. Sankey

1. There were nine-ty and nine that safe-ly lay In the shel-ter of the
2. Lord, Thou hast here Thy nine-ty and nine; Are they not e-nough for
3. But none of the ran-somed ev-er knew How deep were the wa-ters
4. Lord, whence are those blood drops all the way, That mark out the moun-tain's
5. But all thro' the moun-tains, thun-der riv'n, And up from the rock-y

fold, But one was out on the hills a-way, Far off from the gates of
Thee? But the Shep-herd made an-swer: "This of mine has wan-dered a-way from
crossed; Nor how dark was the night That the Lord passed thro' Ere He found His sheep that was
track? They were shed for one who had gone a-stray Ere the Shep-herd could bring Him
steep, There a-rose a glad cry to the gate of heav'n; "Re-joice! I have found my

gold, A-way on the moun-tains wild and bare, A-way from the ten-der
Me, And al-though the road be rough and steep, I go to the des-ert to
lost. Out in the des-ert He heard its cry Sick and help-less, and
back. Lord whence are Thy hands so rent and torn? They're pierced to-night by
sheep!" And the an-gels ech-oed a-round the throne, Re-joice for the Lord brings

Shep-herd's care, A-way from the ten-der Shep-herd's care.
find My sheep, I go to the des-ert to find My sheep."
read-y to die, Sick and help-less, and read-y to die.
man-y a thorn, They're pierced to-night by man-y a thorn.
back His own, Re-joice for the Lord brings back His own.

The Ninety and Nine
1868

And if he should find it, assuredly, I say to you, he rejoices more over that sheep than over the ninety-nine that did not go astray. Matthew 18:13

Evangelist D. L. Moody enlisted Ira Sankey as the song leader and soloist at his great campaigns. The two became a renowned duo; but unfortunately, within a few years Sankey's magnificent voice was ruined by overuse. Later in life, exhausted and facing blindness, he was invited by Dr. J. H. Kellogg (of Kellogg's cereal fame) to Battle Creek, Michigan, for convalescence. There Sankey finished a long-anticipated book of hymn stories. But a fire at the sanitarium destroyed his manuscript and all his notes. He rewrote the book as well as memory would allow, and there we find the story of the "The Ninety and Nine."

In 1874, Moody and Sankey had just finished a series of meetings in Glasgow. At the station en route to Edinburgh, Sankey picked up a penny newspaper, hoping for news from America. Aboard the train, he perused the paper, finding in it a poem by a woman named Elizabeth C. Clephane.

Sankey wrote:

I called Mr. Moody's attention to it, and he asked me to read it to him. This I proceeded to do with all the vim and energy at my command. After I finished I looked at Moody to see what the effect had been, only to discover he had not heard a word, so absorbed was he in a letter he had received. I cut out the poem and placed it in my musical scrapbook.

At the meeting on the second day, the subject was the Good Shepherd. At the conclusion Moody turned to me with the question: "Have you a solo appropriate for this subject with which to close?" I was troubled to know what to do. At this moment I seemed to hear a voice saying: "Sing the hymn you found on the train!" But I thought this impossible, as no music had been written for it. Placing the newspaper slip on the organ, I lifted my heart in prayer, struck the key of A flat, and began to sing.

Note by note the tune was given, which has not been changed from that day to this. Mr. Moody was greatly moved. He came to where I was seated and said, 'Sankey, where did you get this hymn? I've never heard the like of it in my life.' Moved to tears, I replied, 'Mr. Moody, that's the hymn I read to you yesterday on the train, which you did not hear.'

Sweet By and By

Sanford F. Bennett   Joseph P. Webster

1. There's a land that is fair-er than day, And by faith we can
2. We shall sing on that beau-ti-ful shore The me-lo-di-ous
3. To our boun-ti-ful Fa-ther a-bove We will of-fer our

see it a-far; For the Fa-ther waits o-ver the way, To pre-
songs of the blest, And our spir-its shall sor-row no more, Not a
trib-ute of praise, For the glo-ri-ous gift of His love And the

pare us a dwell-ing place there.   In the sweet   by and
sigh for the bless-ing of rest.
bless-ings that hal-low our days.

by   We shall meet on that beau-ti-ful shore.   In the

sweet   by and by,   We shall meet on that beau-ti-ful shore.

Sweet By and By

1868

In My Father's house are many mansions; if it were not so, I would have told you.
I go to prepare a place for you. John 14:2

In 1868, a pharmacist named Sanford Fillmore Bennett, 31, was filling prescriptions and handling sales at his apothecary in Elkhorn, Wisconsin. His friend Joseph Webster entered the store. Joseph was a local musician, vocalist, violinist, and amateur composer who suffered from periods of depression. The two men had occasionally collaborated on hymns and songs, Sanford writing the words and Joseph the music.

On this particular day, Joseph was unusually blue and his face was long. Looking up, Sanford asked, "What is the matter now?"

"It's no matter," Joseph replied, "it will be all right by and by."

An idea for a hymn hit Sanford like a flash of sunlight. Sitting at his desk, he began writing as fast as he could. The words came almost instantly. Two customers entered the drugstore, but no attempt was made to assist them—Sanford was too absorbed in his poem—so they sallied over to the stove and visited with Joseph. Finally, Sanford rose and joined them, handing a sheet of paper to his friend.

"Here is your prescription, Joe," he said. "I hope it works." Webster read the words aloud:

> *There's a land that is fairer than day,*
> *And by faith we can see it afar;*
> *For the Father waits over the way,*
> *To prepare us a dwelling place there.*
> *In the sweet by and by,*
> *We shall meet on that beautiful shore.*
> *In the sweet by and by,*
> *We shall meet on that beautiful shore.*

Instantly a tune suggested itself, and Joseph jotted down some notes. Picking up his fiddle, he played his melody over a time or two, then said to the others, "We four make a good male quartet. Let's try the new song and see how it sounds."

As "Sweet By and By" was being sung for the first time, another customer, R. R. Crosby, entered the store. "Gentlemen," he said, "I never heard that song before but it is immortal."

He was right. For over a hundred years we've been singing an immortal hymn that was written in less than thirty minutes in a drugstore.

Whispering Hope

Alice Hawthorne

Alice Hawthorne

Duet

Soft as the voice of an an - gel, Breathing a les-son un - heard,

Hope with a gen - tle per - sua - sion Whis-pers her com-fort-ing word:

Wait till the dark - ness is o - ver, Wait till life's tem-pest is done,

Hope for the sun - shine to - mor - row, Aft - er the show - er is gone.

Whis - per-ing hope, O how wel - come thy voice,

Whis-per-ing hope, whis-per-ing hope, Wel-come thy voice, O how wel-come thy voice,

Mak - ing my heart in its sor - row re - joice.

Mak-ing my heart, Mak-ing my heart in its sor-row, its sor-row re - joice.

Whispering Hope
1868

This hope we have as an anchor of the soul, both sure and steadfast . . . Hebrews 6:19

T
he background of this hymn offers a few surprises, the first being the author's identity. Though published under the name "Alice Hawthorne," it was actually written by a man named Septimus Winner. Second, he's also the author of such classic folk tunes as "Oh Where, Oh Where Has My Little Dog Gone?" Third, he was once charged with treason against the government of the United States of America.

Septimus Winner was born into a musical family in 1827 in Philadelphia. He was the seventh child in the family, hence the name Septimus. His father was a violin maker and a crafter of instruments, and Septimus showed early signs of musical prowess. After attending Philadelphia's Central High School, Septimus joined one of his brothers in forming a music publishing business. By age twenty, he was also running his own music shop. Though largely self-taught, he became a popular music instructor in Philadelphia, giving lessons in violin, guitar, and banjo and performing with several of the city's bands and orchestras.

Septimus is best remembered, however, for his popular songs which he usually published under the name of Alice Hawthorne. They are known in American folk music history as "Hawthorne's Ballads." His most popular were "Listen to the Mocking Bird" (which he reportedly sold to another Philadelphia publisher for five dollars) and "Oh Where, Oh Where Has My Little Dog Gone?" written to a German tune.

Perhaps the most interesting moment of his life occurred in 1862, after Abraham Lincoln had fired General George B. McClellan for delays in following up and attacking the Confederate Army. There was great support for the popular McClellan, and his firing incensed Septimus. He instantly published a song entitled, "Give Us Back Our Old Commander: Little Mac, the People's Pride." It sold 80,000 copies in the first two days, leading to Winner's arrest for treason. He was released when he agreed to destroy all the remaining copies of the song.

Septimus Winner produced over two hundred instructional books for more than twenty-three instruments, and he wrote thousands of musical arrangements. He was inducted into the Songwriters Hall of Fame in 1970.

"Whispering Hope," published in 1868, was his last successful composition, and is based on Hebrews 6:19: "This hope we have as an anchor of the soul, both sure and steadfast, and which enters the Presence behind the veil."

Yield Not to Temptation

Horatio R. Palmer

Horatio R. Palmer

1. Yield not to temp - ta - tion, For yield - ing is sin;
2. Shun e - vil com - pan - ions, Bad lan - guage dis - dain;
3. To him that o'er - com - eth God giv - eth a crown;

Each vic - t'ry will help you Some oth - er to win;
God's name hold in rev - 'rence, Nor take it in vain;
Thro' faith we shall con - quer, Though of - ten cast down;

Fight man - ful - ly on - ward, Dark pas - sions sub - due;
Be thought-ful and ear - nest, Kind - heart - ed and true;
He who is our Sav - ior, Our strength will re - new;

Look ev - er to Je - sus, He will car - ry you through.
Look ev - er to Je - sus, He will car - ry you through.
Look ev - er to Je - sus, He will car - ry you through.

Yield Not to Temptation

1868

. . . He said to them, "Pray that you may not enter into temptation." Luke 22:40

Horatio Palmer was one of New York's favorite musicians. Born in the middle of the state in 1834, Horatio grew up in a musical family. He joined the church choir conducted by his father when he was only seven. As a young man, he traveled to Rushford, New York, south of Buffalo, to attend Rushford Academy, a newly established institution of higher learning. He stayed after his graduation to become music professor for ten years, serving also as the choir director for the local Baptist church.

After further training in Europe, Horatio moved to Chicago, where he wrote theory books, edited a musical journal, served on the staff of a church, and worked hard to develop choral unions and music festivals. He was also an enthusiastic promoter of the hymns of Clara Scott, author of "Open My Eyes That I Might See."

Moving back to New York in 1873, Palmer became dean of the summer school of music at Chautauqua, New York. He also organized a massive church choral union in New York City that eventually grew to twenty thousand singers. On one occasion, he filled Madison Square Garden as he led a four-thousand-voice choir in a concert of sacred music.

About "Yield Not to Temptation," Palmer said: "I am reverently thankful God gave me the song, and has used it as a power for good. The song is an inspiration. I was at work on the dry subject of 'Theory' when the complete idea flashed upon my mind. I laid aside the theoretical work and hurriedly penned both words and music as fast as I could write them."

All his life, Palmer worked with young people and this was one of several hymns he wrote on the subject of temptation. Another, lesser-known hymn, is entitled "Have Courage to Say No."

You're starting, my boy, on life's journey,
Along the grand highway of life;
You'll meet with a thousand temptations—
Each city with evil is rife.
This world is a stage of excitement,
There's danger wherever you go;
But if you are tempted to weakness,
Have courage, my boy, to say No!

Beneath the Cross of Jesus

Elizabeth C. Clephane

Frederick C. Maker

1. Be - neath the cross of Je - sus I fain would take my stand:
2. Up - on the cross of Je - sus Mine eyes at times can see
3. I take, O cross, thy shad - ow For my a - bid - ing place;

The shad - ow of a might - y Rock With - in a wea - ry land,
The ver - y dy - ing form of One Who suf - fered there for me;
I ask no oth - er sun - shine than The sun - shine of His face,

A home with - in the wil - der - ness, A rest up - on the way,
And from my strick - en heart with tears, Two won - ders I con - fess:
Con - tent to let the world go by, To know no gain nor loss,

From the burn - ing of the noon - tide heat And the bur - den of the day.
The won - ders of re - deem - ing love And my un - wor - thi - ness.
My sin - ful self, my on - ly shame, My glo - ry all the cross.

Beneath the Cross of Jesus
1868

For the message of the cross is . . . to us who are being saved . . . the power of God.
1 Corinthians 1:18

The author of this hymn, Elizabeth Clephane, was born in Edinburgh, where her father was Sheriff of Fife. One of her siblings later wrote: "My sister was a very quiet little child, shrinking from notice and was always absorbed in books. The loss of both her parents at an early age taught her sorrow. As she grew up she was recognized as the cleverest one of our family. She was first in her class and a favorite at school. Her love for poetry was a passion. Among the sick and suffering she won the name, 'My Sunbeam.'" (Elizabeth's own comment on her nickname is written into a line of this hymn: "I take, O Cross, thy shadow for my abiding place; / I ask no other sunshine than the sunshine of His face.")

At some point, Elizabeth's family moved to Melrose, southeast of Edinburgh, where she spent her remaining years. Though frail, she was a diligent Bible student, a sympathetic listener, and a worker among the poor. She and her sisters raised money for the unfortunate, on one occasion selling their horse and carriage for a needy family.

Elizabeth's poems were published in the Scottish magazine, *The Family Treasury*. This one, appearing after her death, was discovered by Ira Sankey and introduced in the great Moody/Sankey meetings in Britain. In his autobiography, Sankey stated: "The author of this hymn, Elizabeth Celphane, also wrote the widely known hymn, 'The Ninety and Nine,' and these two were her only hymns. The first time this hymn was sung is still fresh in my memory. The morning after I had composed the music, Rev. W. H. Aitkin was to speak at our mission in London. . . . Before the sermon, I sang 'Beneath the Cross of Jesus' as a solo; and as in the case of 'The Ninety and Nine,' much blessing came from its use for the first time. With eyes filled with tears and deeply moved, the preacher said to the audience: 'Dear friends, I had intended to speak to you this morning upon work for the Master, but this new hymn has made such an impression on my heart, and evidently upon your own, that I will defer my proposed address and speak to you on "The Cross of Jesus."'"

Sankey's tune has since been replaced in popular usage by St. Christopher, music composed for this hymn by Frederick C. Maker.

Pass Me Not, O Gentle Savior

Fanny J. Crosby

William H. Doane

1. Pass me not, O gen - tle Sav - ior; Hear my hum - ble cry!
2. Let me at Thy throne of mer - cy Find a sweet re - lief;
3. Trust-ing on - ly in Thy mer - it, Would I seek Thy face.
4. Thou, the Spring of all my com - fort, More than life to me!

While on oth - ers Thou art call - ing, Do not pass me by.
Kneel - ing there in deep con - tri - tion, Help my un - be - lief.
Heal my wound - ed, bro - ken spir - it, Save me by Thy grace.
Whom have I on earth be - side Thee? Whom in heaven but Thee?

Sav - ior, Sav - ior, hear my hum - ble cry!

While on oth - ers Thou art call - ing, Do not pass me by.

Pass Me Not, O Gentle Savior

1868

And it shall come to pass That whoever calls on the name of the LORD shall be saved. Acts 2:21

Born in Connecticut in 1832, William Doane grew up in a devout family and was converted to Christ in high school. At eighteen, he was hired by J. A. Fay & Co. of Norwich, Connecticut, one of America's largest woodworking machinery factories. Within ten years he had become the managing partner of the Cincinnati factory, and by his thirtieth birthday, he was the company's president.

That's when he suffered a heart attack and almost died. As he recovered, Doane felt his illness hadn't been caused by long hours or hard work. He determined that God was chastening him for not devoting more time to gospel music. He began writing music and publishing volumes of Sunday school songs. But he was frustrated because he didn't have quality poems. He needed a gifted and godly lyricist.

In 1867, while in New York on business, Doane visited his friend, Dr. W. C. Van Meter, director of Five Points Rescue Mission. Van Meter asked Doane to write a song for the mission's upcoming anniversary. The businessman said he'd be glad to write the music, but who would write the words?

Returning to his hotel room, Doane knelt and laid the need before the Lord. At once, there was a knock at the door. It was a messenger from the blind poet, Fanny Crosby, bearing this note: "Mr. Doane, I have never met you, but I feel impelled to send you this hymn. May God bless it."

The words of the poem began: "More like Jesus would I be, / Let my Savior dwell with me." Doane composed the music that night and it was used with great success as the anniversary hymn for the Five Points Mission.

Thus began a wonderful partnership that produced such "hits" as "I Am Thine, O Lord," "Near the Cross," "Rescue the Perishing," "Safe in the Arms of Jesus," "Savior, More Than Life to Me," "'Tis the Blessed Hour of Prayer," "Will Jesus Find Us Watching," "To God Be the Glory," and this hymn, "Pass Me Not."

In all, Doane wrote about two thousand tunes and published some forty collections of songs. For a quarter century, he also served as superintendent of the Sunday school of Cincinnati's Mount Auburn Baptist Church. After his death on Christmas Eve, 1915, Doane's vast estate went to his two daughters, who used much of it to fund Christian missionary and educational causes in the twentieth century.

Rescue the Perishing

Fanny J. Crosby

William H. Doane

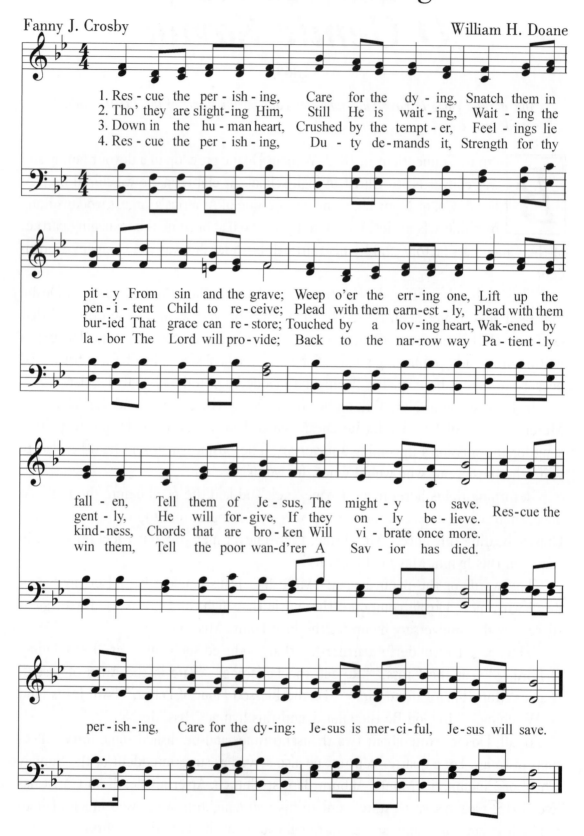

1. Res-cue the per-ish-ing, Care for the dy-ing, Snatch them in pit-y From sin and the grave; Weep o'er the err-ing one, Lift up the fall-en, Tell them of Je-sus, The might-y to save.

2. Tho' they are slight-ing Him, Still He is wait-ing, Wait-ing the pen-i-tent Child to re-ceive; Plead with them earn-est-ly, Plead with them gent-ly, He will for-give, If they on-ly be-lieve.

3. Down in the hu-man heart, Crushed by the tempt-er, Feel-ings lie bur-ied That grace can re-store; Touched by a lov-ing heart, Wak-ened by kind-ness, Chords that are bro-ken Will vi-brate once more.

4. Res-cue the per-ish-ing, Du-ty de-mands it, Strength for thy la-bor The Lord will pro-vide; Back to the nar-row way Pa-tient-ly win them, Tell the poor wan-d'rer A Sav-ior has died.

Res-cue the per-ish-ing, Care for the dy-ing; Je-sus is mer-ci-ful, Je-sus will save.

Rescue the Perishing

1869

But others save with fear, pulling them out of the fire . . . Jude 23

W hile visiting her friend, Howard Doane, in Cincinnati, Fanny Crosby, the blind hymnist, was asked to speak to a group of blue collar workers. Near the end of her address, she had an overwhelming sense that "some mother's boy" before her "must be rescued that night or not at all." She mentioned this to the crowd, pleading, "If there is a dear boy here tonight who has perchance wandered away from his mother's home and his mother's teaching, would he please come to me at the close of the service?"

Afterward a young man of about eighteen approached her. "Did you mean me?" he asked. "I promised my mother to meet her in heaven, but the way I have been living, I don't think that will be possible now." Fanny had the joy of leading him to Christ.

Returning to her room that night, all she could think about was the theme "rescue the perishing," and when she retired that night she had written the complete hymn. The next day, Howard Doane wrote the music, and it was published the following year in his *Songs of Devotion.*

Many years later, Fanny was speaking at the YMCA in Lynn, Massachusetts, and she recounted the story behind "Rescue the Perishing." After the service, a man approached her, his voice quivering. "Miss Crosby," he said, "I was that boy who told you more than thirty-five years ago that I had wandered from my mother's God. That evening you spoke, I sought and found peace, and I have tried to live a consistent Christian life ever since. If we never meet again on earth, we will meet up yonder." He turned and left, unable to say another word. But Fanny later described it as one of the most gratifying experiences of her life.

This song served as a prelude to Fanny Crosby's second career. About age sixty, she began working in downtown rescue missions, spending several days a week in lower Manhattan, witnessing to the down-and-out. Despite her fame as a hymnwriter, she chose to live in near poverty in New York's ghettos, for she felt a calling to minister to the needy. Just a few blocks from her little tenement apartment was the Bowery, a haunt for alcoholics and where every kind of vice flourished. There Fanny would go day after day to rescue the perishing.

293

Near the Cross

Fanny J. Crosby

William H. Doane

1. Je - sus, keep me near the cross, There a pre - cious foun - tain,
2. Near the cross, a trem - bling soul, Love and mer - cy found me;
3. Near the cross! O Lamb of God, Bring its scenes be - fore me;
4. Near the cross I'll watch and wait, Hop - ing, trust - ing ev - er,

Free to all, a heal - ing stream, Flows from Cal - vary's moun - tain.
There the bright and Morn - ing Star Shed its beams a - round me.
Help me walk from day to day, With its shad - ows o'er me.
'Til I reach the gold - en strand Just be - yond the riv - er.

In the cross, in the cross, Be my glo - ry ev - er,

'Til my rap - tured soul shall find Rest be - yond the riv - er.

Near the Cross

1869

And He, bearing His cross, went out to a place called the Place of a Skull, which is called in Hebrew, Golgotha. John 19:17

F anny Crosby was born in Putnam County, New York, in 1820, and was blinded in infancy through the malpractice of a doctor. In 1835, she enrolled in a school for the blind in New York City, staying there twelve years, first as a student then as a teacher. Her remarkable poetry brought widespread acclaim to the school, and she frequently recited her work for visiting dignitaries.

In 1850, Fanny, thirty, attended a revival meeting at New York's Thirtieth Street Methodist Church. During these services, she felt something was missing in her life. On two occasions during the meetings, she prayed with counselors, but without gaining assurance of a personal relationship with God. On November 20, 1850, as the altar call was given, Fanny went forward and found Christ as her Savior. The congregation was singing Isaac Watts' great hymn about the cross:

> *At the cross, at the cross where I first saw the light,*
> *And the burden of my heart rolled away,*
> *It was there by faith I received my sight,*
> *And now I am happy all the day.*

Shortly thereafter, Fanny turned her poetic skills to hymn writing, and many of her songs focused on the theme of the cross, such as "At the Cross, There's Room," "Blessed Cross," "Room at the Cross," "Save Me at the Cross," and this one, "Jesus Keep Me Near the Cross." It was composed after Cincinnati businessman William Doane gave her a melody he had written. Fanny, listening to it, felt it said, "Jesus, keep me near the cross," and she promptly wrote the words.

Fanny Crosby wrote approximately 8,000 hymns. We aren't surprised, then, to discover that many of her later hymns were little more than rewritten versions of earlier ones. In 1893, she and Phoebe Knapp published a gospel song similar to "Near the Cross." The 1893 hymn, entitled, "Nearer the Cross," said:

> *"Nearer the cross!" my heart can say I am coming nearer,*
> *Nearer the cross from day to day, I am coming nearer;*
> *Nearer the cross where Jesus died,*
> *Nearer the fountain's crimson tide,*
> *Nearer my Savior's wounded side,*
> *I am coming nearer, I am coming nearer.*

Christ for the World We Sing

Samuel Wolcott

Felice de Giardini

1. Christ for the world we sing! The world to Christ we bring, With lov - ing zeal; The poor, and them that mourn, The faint and ov - er - borne, Sin - sick and sor - row worn, Whom Christ doth heal.

2. Christ for the world we sing! The world to Christ we bring, With fer - vent prayer; The way - ward and the lost, By rest - less pas - sions tossed, Re - deemed at count - less cost, From dark de - spair.

3. Christ for the world we sing! The world to Christ we bring, With one ac - cord; With us the work to share, With us re - proach to dare, With us the cross to bear, For Christ our Lord.

4. Christ for the world we sing! The world to Christ we bring, With joy - ful song; The new - born souls whose days, Re - claimed from er - ror's ways, In - spired with hope and praise, To Christ be - long.

Christ for the World We Sing

1869

. . . "I will declare Your name to My brethren; In the midst of the assembly I will sing praise to You." Hebrews 2:12

Looking back on his teen years, George Williams described himself as a "careless, thoughtless, godless, swearing young fellow." But then he met Christ as Savior. "I cannot describe to you the joy and peace which flowed into my soul when first I saw that the Lord Jesus had died for my sins, and that they were all forgiven," he later wrote.

In June 1844, George, twenty, found a job as sales clerk at a drapery store in London. But his heart was torn by the masses of young men he saw living on the streets, in bars and brothels, occupied with gambling and fighting. On June 6, 1844, he began a program to win young men to Christ and to help them grow strong in body, mind, and soul. It was called the Young Men's Christian Association—the YMCA.

Williams' idea spread to America, and in 1869, Dr. Samuel Wolcott, pastor of Plymouth Congregational Church in Cleveland, Ohio, and a former missionary to Syria, hosted the local branch of the YMCA in his church. At the rally, he listened carefully to the speakers and noticed the banner over the pulpit that said, "Christ for the World and the World for Christ."

Wolcott had first attempted to write hymns at age fifty-six. Though he had "never put two rhymes together" and felt he could no more compose a hymn as perform a miracle, he felt strangely led to write a hymn of five stanzas. Imagine his surprise when his first hymn, "Father! I Own Thy Voice" was published.

He was trying to find a subject for his second hymn when the local chapter of the YMCA asked to use his church for their rally. That day in 1868, as Wolcott sat listening to the speakers and reading the banner over their heads, he received his inspiration. Walking home alone through the streets of Cleveland after the meeting, Dr. Wolcutt composed all four stanzas of "Christ for the World We Sing."

Samuel Wolcott went on to write over two hundred hymns, but this one—his second attempt—is the only one still in popular usage. It came about because of a London sales clerk who cared about the souls of lost young men, and of a local pastor in Cleveland who shared the burden of winning "Christ for the World and the World for Christ."

Jesus Loves Even Me

Philip P. Bliss

Philip P. Bliss

Jesus Loves Even Me

ABOUT 1870

Now hope does not disappoint, because the love of God has been poured out in our hearts by the Holy Spirit who was given to us. Romans 5:5

Philip Bliss was born in a Pennsylvania log cabin where his father led in daily prayer and where music was the primary entertainment. As a result, the lad found himself drawn to both the Lord Jesus and to music at an early age.

When he was ten, Philip sold vegetables door to door. Approaching an elegant home, he heard a sort of music he'd never heard before. Dropping his vegetables, he scaled the fence and slipped unseen into the parlor. A woman was playing something new and strange to Philip—a piano. He was enthralled. When she stopped, he exclaimed, "O lady, please play some more!"

Spinning on her stool, the alarmed woman saw the little urchin standing there. "Get out of here with your big, bare feet!" she cried. Philip beat a fast retreat, but the sounds of that piano stayed with him and deepened his desire to become a musician.

The next year, he left home to work in lumber camps, earning nine dollars a month as assistant cook. Later he became a log cutter and sawmill worker, but he never lost his burden for music.

In 1859, Philip married Lucy Young and spent a year working her father's farm. Lucy encouraged his dreams, and her grandmother provided funds for classes at a nearby music school. The next year, armed with a melodeon, Philip mounted his horse, Old Fanny, and began traveling place to place, teaching music and leading singing schools. In 1864, he sold his first song to a publishing company. Within a remarkably short time, he was one of America's foremost writers of gospel hymns. Among his songs: "Wonderful Words of Life," "Almost Persuaded," "Dare to Be a Daniel," "Hallelujah, What a Savior," "The Light of the World is Jesus," and "I Will Sing of My Redeemer."

In 1870, Philip joined the staff of the First Congregational Church in Chicago. One evening, very weary, Philip found inner refreshment while meditating on Romans 5:5: "The love of God has been poured out in our hearts by the Holy Spirit." Picking up pen and paper, he began writing: "I am so glad that my Father in heaven / tells of His love in the book He has given . . . ."

As he taught that song to his children the next Sunday, perhaps his mind went back to that elegant parlor where he wasn't welcome, and to the strains of music that had defined his life.

Take the Name of Jesus with You

Lydia Baxter

William H. Doane

1. Take the name of Je-sus with you, Child of sor-row and of woe.
2. Take the name of Je-sus ev - er As a shield from ev-ery snare;
3. At the name of Je-sus bow-ing, Fall-ing pros-trate at His feet;

It will joy and com-fort give you; Take it then wher-e'er you go.
If temp - ta - tions 'round you gath - er, Breathe that ho - ly name in prayer.
King of kings, we'll glad - ly crown Him When our jour-ney is com - plete.

Pre - cious name, O how sweet! Hope of earth and joy of heaven.

Pre - cious name, O how sweet! Hope of earth and joy of heaven.

Take the Name of Jesus with You

1870

Repent, and let every one of you be baptized in the name of Jesus Christ for the remission of sins . . . Acts 2:38

I have a very special armor," Lydia Baxter once told friends who asked her how she could be so radiant despite her health problems. "I have the name of Jesus. When the tempter tries to make me blue or despondent, I mention the name of Jesus, and he can't get through to me anymore."

Lydia, born in Petersburg, New York, on September 8, 1809, was converted alongside her sister under the preaching of a Baptist evangelist named Eben Tucker. She married Colonel John C. Baxter and moved to New York City, where she worked tirelessly for Christ until a severe illness left her bedridden. Her attitude, however, was so sunny that the Baxter home became a gathering place for Christian workers.

Lydia also wrote gospel songs. One of her favorites, "The Gate Ajar," spoke of Christ's leaving the gate open for us. The chorus said: "O depth of mercy! Can it be / That gate was left ajar for me?"

In his memoirs, song leader Ira Sankey wrote of how popular this song became during D. L. Moody's Great Britain Campaign of 1873–74. "It was sung at the watch-night service in 1873," Sankey said, "in the Free Assembly Hall of Edinburgh. A young woman—Maggie Lindsay, of Aberdeen, Scotland—was much impressed by the hymn, and those seated by her side heard her exclaim, 'O, heavenly Father, is it true that the gate is standing ajar for me? If it is so, I will go in.' That night she became a disciple of the Lord Jesus. . . . Scarcely a month later, on January 28, Maggie took a train for her home, but she never reached there alive. . . . A collision took place, (and) a number of passengers were killed. Maggie, all crushed and broken, was found in the wreck. In one of her hands was a copy of her favorite hymn, 'There Is a Gate That Stands Ajar.'"

"The Gate Ajar" is seldom sung now, but Lydia's other popular hymn has stood the test of time. "Take the Name of Jesus with You" sprang from Lydia's own study of the precious name of Jesus in the Bible. It was written four years before her death and published in 1871 by William Doane and Robert Lowry.

O Zion, Haste

Mary A. Thomson

James Walch

1. O Zi-on, haste, Thy mis-sion high ful-fill-ing, To tell to
2. Be-hold how man-y thou-sands still are ly-ing, Bound in the
3. Pro-claim to ev-ery peo-ple, tongue, and na-tion that God in
4. Give of Thy sons to bear the mes-sage glo-rious, Give of thy

all the world that God is light; That He who made all na-tions
dark-some pris-on house of sin. With none to tell them of the
whom they live and move is love; Tell how He stooped to save His
wealth to speed them on their way; Pour out Thy soul for them in

is not will-ing One soul should per-ish, lost in shades of night.
Sav-ior's dy-ing, Or of the life He died for them to win.
lost cre-a-tion, And died on earth that we might live a-bove.
prayer vic-to-rious, O Zi-on, haste to bring the bright-er day.

Pub-lish glad tid-ings, Tid-ings of peace,

Tid-ings of Je-sus, Re-demp-tion and re-lease.

O Zion, Haste

1871

"Behold, I lay in Zion a stumbling stone and rock of offense, And whoever believes on Him will not be put to shame." Romans 9:33

Untold numbers of missionaries have been sent off to the regions beyond by congregations singing this rousing Episcopalian missionary hymn that exhorts the church ("Zion") to hurry and fulfill its mission of telling "all the world that God is light." But few realize it was written by a worried mother sitting at the bedside of her dangerously ill son.

Mary Ann Fulkner, the author of "O Zion, Haste," was born in London in 1834, and her family immigrated to America when she was young. After marrying John Thomson, the first librarian of the Free Library in Philadelphia, she and her husband joined the Church of the Annunciation (Episcopalian) in Philadelphia, where they served many years.

Mary Ann, who enjoyed writing poetry, penned more than forty hymns, though only "O Zion, Haste" has lasted in the hymnals. This is what she had to say about writing her most famous hymn:

> *I wrote the greater part of the hymn, "O Sion, Haste," in the year 1868. I had written many hymns before, and one night, while I was sitting up with one of my children who was ill with typhoid fever, I thought I should like to write a missionary hymn to the tune of the hymn, 'Hark, Hark my Soul! Angelic Songs are Swelling,' as I was fond of that tune, but I could not then get the refrain I liked. I left the hymn unfinished and about three years later I finished it by writing the refrain which now forms a part of it."*

Most hymnals omit some of Thomson's original verses, one of which says:

> *'Tis Thine to save from peril of perdition*
> *The souls for whom the Lord His life laid down;*
> *Beware lest, slothful to fulfill thy mission,*
> *Thou lose one jewel that should deck His crown.*

The Rock That Is Higher Than I

Erastus Johnson

William G. Fischer

1. O some-times the shad-ows are deep, And rough seems the path to the goal,
2. O some-times how long seems the day, And some-times how wea-ry my feet;
3. O near to the Rock let me keep If bless-ings or sor-rows pre-vail,

And sor-rows, some-times how they sweep Like tem-pests down o-ver the soul!
But toil-ing in life's dust-y way, The Rock's bless-ed sha-dow, how sweet!
Or climb-ing the moun-tain way steep, Or walk-ing the sha-dow-y vale.

O then to the Rock let me fly, To the Rock that is high-er than I;

O then to the Rock let me fly, To the Rock that is high-er than I!

The Rock That Is Higher Than I

1871

. . . For they drank of that spiritual Rock that followed them, and that Rock was Christ. 1 Corinthians 10:4

rom the end of the earth I will cry to You, when my heart is overwhelmed," wrote King David in Psalm 61, "lead me to the rock that is higher than I." What a prayer to memorize and hold in reserve in our hearts. It's appropriate for all of life's situations, even financial disaster.

It was in such a crisis that Erastus Johnson wrote a hymn based on that verse: "The Rock That Is Higher Than I," with its resounding chorus: *On then to the Rock let me fly, | To the Rock that is higher than I.*

Erastus was born in a logging camp on the banks of the Penobscot River north of Bangor, Maine, in the spring of 1826. He wanted to enter the ministry, but his poor health and eyesight prevented his attending seminary. At age seventeen, he became a schoolteacher. In his mid-twenties, he followed his brothers to California in search of gold. After living in San Francisco several years, he returned East and settled down in Pittsburgh, farming and working in oil. In 1861, he attended a YMCA convention in nearby Carlisle, Pennsylvania, and it was there he wrote this hymn. His autobiography says:

There was a convention of the Y.M.C.A. at Carlisle, Pa., which I attended as a delegate, and John Wanamaker was president of the convention. About the second day there came a telegram from Philadelphia that the banking house of Jay Cook & Co. had failed, in which Mr. Wanamaker had $70,000 which to him at that time in life was a great amount to lose. Soon followed reports of other firms throughout the country, indicating a general panic. As a matter of course, it threw a pall of gloom over the convention, for nearly all its members were men of business. As an expression of the common feeling I wrote "The Rock That Is Higher Than I." Mr. Wm. Fisher of Philadelphia, the composer of many tunes for gospel hymns, was at the convention, and in conjunction with Brother William, led the singing. I gave the words to him and he set them to music, sang them, and they with the music immediately became popular in the convention, especially with Mr. Wanamaker, who several times called for it. And soon it found its way into many publications.

All for Jesus

Mary D. James

Source Unknown

1. All for Je - sus, all for Je - sus! All my be - ing's ran - somed powers:
2. Let my hands per - form His bid - ding, Let my feet run in His ways;
3. Since my eyes were fixed on Je - sus, I've lost sight of all be - side,
4. O what won - der! how a - maz - ing! Je - sus, glo - rious King of kings,

All my thoughts and words and do - ings, All my days and all my hours:
Let my eyes see Je - sus on - ly, Let my lips speak forth His praise:
So en - chained my spir - it's vi - sion, Look - ing at the Cru - ci - fied:
Deigns to call me His be - lov - ed, Lets me rest be - neath His wings:

All for Je - sus! all for Je - sus! All my days and all my hours;
All for Je - sus! all for Je - sus! Let my lips speak forth His praise;
All for Je - sus! all for Je - sus! Look - ing at the Cru - ci - fied;
All for Je - sus! all for Je - sus! Rest - ing now be - neath His wings;

All for Je - sus! all for Je - sus! All my days and all my hours.
All for Je - sus! all for Je - sus! Let my lips speak forth His praise.
All for Je - sus! all for Je - sus! Look - ing at the Cru - ci - fied.
All for Je - sus! all for Je - sus! Rest - ing now be - neath His wings.

All for Jesus

<u>1871</u>

Jesus said to him, "You shall love the LORD your God with all your heart, with all your soul, and with all your mind." Matthew 22:37

How sweetly does her life exhibit the beauty of holiness," someone said of Mary James, author of this hymn. "I think I never saw an individual more fully possessed by that love that thinketh no evil, than our beloved Sister James, yet as she professes the enjoyment of a state of holiness, she has her trials."

Mary was born in 1810, and began teaching Sunday school in her Methodist Episcopal Church when she was only thirteen. She had about a dozen girls in her class, and soon she was visiting them in their homes, often bearing gifts her mother had made. It was the beginning of a lifetime for Jesus.

As an adult, Mary's greatest love was traveling to Methodist camp meetings, especially in Ocean Park, New Jersey. There she led prayer meetings, engaged in personal counseling, taught Bible classes, organized workers, shared her testimony, and sometimes preached. She became a close associate of Methodist Holiness leader, Phoebe Palmer, author of "The Cleansing Wave."

Letter-writing was another arena for Mary's gifts, and she frequently penned letters of encouragement to young pastors just starting their ministries. She authored many articles and was a frequent contributor to popular Christian magazines of the day. Her habit was to rise early in the day and scribble down the essence of her freshest thoughts, laying them aside for additional work later.

Her writings included one book, a biography entitled *The Soul Winner: A Sketch of Edmund J. Yard,* published in 1883, the year of her death. (Her son, Rev. Joseph H. James published Mary's biography three years later.)

Occasionally Mary's scribblings would result in a hymn. In all, she wrote about fifty gospel songs, but only "All for Jesus" remains popular. It was written for her New Year's letter of 1871. Reviewing the previous year, Mary thanked God for the progress of her ministry. "I have written more, talked more, prayed more, and thought more of Jesus than in any previous year," she wrote, "and had more peace of mind, resulting from a stronger and more simple faith in Him." She attached this poem of consecration, "All for Jesus," as a commitment for the coming year.

Mary had a dozen more years of ministry before being laid to rest in a cemetery in Trenton, New Jersey. Inscribed on her gravestone are the simple words: "All for Jesus."

Jesus, Savior, Pilot Me

Edward Hopper

John E. Gould

1. Je - sus, Sav - ior, pi - lot me, O - ver
2. As a moth - er stills her child, Thou canst
3. When at last I near the shore, And the

life's tem - pes - tuous sea; Un - known waves be - fore me
hush the o - cean wild; Bois - t'rous waves o - bey Thy
fear - ful break - ers roar 'Twixt me and the peace - ful

roll, Hid - ing rocks and treach - 'rous shoal; Chart and
will When Thou say'st to them, "Be still!" Won - drous
rest, Then while lean - ing on Thy breast, May I

com - pass came from Thee- Je - sus, Sav - ior, pi - lot me!
Sov - 'reign of the sea, Je - sus, Sav - ior, pi - lot me!
hear Thee say to me, "Fear not, I will pi - lot thee!"

Jesus, Savior, Pilot Me

1871

"Why are you fearful, O you of little faith?" Then He arose and rebuked the winds and the sea, and there was a great calm. Matthew 8:26

Visitors to Manhattan should take time to visit the First Chinese Presbyterian Church at the corner of Henry Street and Market on the Lower East Side, not far from the Manhattan and Brooklyn Bridges. This grand old building is a Gothic historical landmark, the second oldest church building in New York City. Dutch Reformed Christians built it in 1819. When that group disbanded their church in 1864, the building was acquired by another congregation who chose an unusual name for their church: The Church of Sea and Land.

This was the busy harbor section of New York, with thousands of sailors filling the streets every day. The pastor of the Church of Sea and Land was Edward Hooper, a lifelong New Yorker and a graduate of both the University of the City of New York and Union Theological Seminary in the heart of Manhattan. After pastorates in Greenville, New York, and later in Long Island, Hopper returned to Manhattan to engage in pastoral and evangelistic work among the sailors. Hopper often composed hymns for his sailors, including one titled, "Wrecked and Struggling in Mid-Ocean."

On May 3, 1871, this poem-prayer, "Jesus, Savior, Pilot Me," appeared without attribution in *The Sailor's Magazine.*

In Philadelphia, an ailing composer named John Edgar Gould, saw a copy of this poem and, deeply moved, composed music for it the night before he sailed to Africa in an effort to regain his health. Gould died in Algiers four years later. But "Jesus, Savior, Pilot Me" developed a healthy following in churches across America, especially among those ministering to seafaring men. The sailors and parishioners at the Church of Sea and Land numbered this among their favorite hymns, dubbing it "The Sailor's Hymn," though they had no idea that their own pastor was its author. That fact remained hidden for years, until Hopper finally disclosed it at a special anniversary celebration of New York's Seamen's Friend Society.

On April 23, 1888, suffering from heart disease, Hooper sat in the easy chair of his study, preparing to write another hymn. At the top of the page he put its title—"Heaven"—then he slumped over dead. Among the papers found in his study was the original manuscript of "Jesus Savior, Pilot Me."

Almost Persuaded

Philip B. Bliss

Philip B. Bliss

1. "Al-most per-suad-ed" now to be-lieve;
2. "Al-most per-suad-ed," come, come to-day;
3. "Al-most per-suad-ed," har-vest is past!

"Al-most per-suad-ed" Christ to re-ceive:
"Al-most per-suad-ed," turn not a-way:
"Al-most per-suad-ed," doom comes at last!

Seems now some soul to say, "Go, Spir-it, go Thy way;
Je-sus in-vites you here, An-gels are lin-ger-ing near,
"Al-most" can-not a-vail, "Al-most" is but to fail!

Some more con-ven-ient day On Thee I'll call."
Prayers rise from hearts so dear, O wan-der-er, come.
Sad, sad, that bit-ter wail, "Al-most," but lost!

Almost Persuaded

1871

Then Agrippa said to Paul, "You almost persuade me to become a Christian." Acts 26:28

No one in the history of gospel music is more revered than Philip P. Bliss, a gifted young musician who died tragically at age thirty-five in a train disaster. Interestingly, just a year before his death, this hymn—which he wrote—had a profound influence in his decision to give himself to full-time gospel ministry.

Philip, his wife Lucy, and their two small children lived in Chicago where Philip worked for a publishing company, writing sacred and secular songs. He was considered a rising star on the American music scene. As time allowed, he also volunteered as a soloist and song leader in evangelist meetings.

One day he was assisting a preacher named Rev. Brundage. During the sermon, the evangelist quoted Acts 26:28 and declared: "He who is almost persuaded is almost saved, and to be almost saved is to be entirely lost!" Struck by those words, Philip penned this hymn, "Almost Persuaded."

Shortly afterward, Philip received a letter from evangelist D. L. Moody, urging him to "sing the gospel" by becoming a fulltime evangelistic song leader. As they prayed over the decision, Philip and Lucy were understandably cautious, for it would mean the end of a stable, regular income. It would cost Bliss's career in secular music and entail a nomadic lifestyle of itinerate evangelism. "I am willing," Lucy wrote, "that Mr. Bliss should do anything that we can be sure is the Lord's will, and I can trust the Lord to provide for us, but I don't want him to take such a step simply on Mr. Moody's will."

Shortly afterward, evangelist Daniel Whittle requested Philip's help with evangelistic rallies in Waukegan, Illinois. The meetings started slowly, but on March 26, 1871, as Philip sang his new hymn, "Almost Persuaded," an unusual power swept over the crowd. Lucy wrote, "In different parts of the house, sinners arose as he sang, presenting themselves for prayer, and souls that night rejoiced in Christ. Our hearts were very full, and a great responsibility was upon us."

The next day, Philip made a formal commitment to the Lord to leave all secular concerns and engage himself in fulltime ministry. In the year left to him, Philip Bliss exerted a lasting influence on gospel music, singing multitudes into the Kingdom and writing many of the hymns we love today.

I Need Thee Every Hour

Annie S. Hawks; Robert Lowry, Refrain

Robert Lowry

1. I need Thee ev-'ry hour, Most gra - cious Lord;
2. I need Thee ev-'ry hour, Stay Thou near by;
3. I need Thee ev-'ry hour In joy or pain;
4. I need Thee ev-'ry hour, Most Ho - ly One.

No ten - der voice like Thine Can peace af - ford.
Temp - ta - tions lose their power When Thou art nigh.
Come quick - ly and a - bide Or life is vain.
Oh, make me Thine in - deed, Thou bless - ed Son!

I need Thee, O I need Thee; Ev - 'ry hour I need Thee;

O bless me now, my Sav - ior, I come to Thee!

I Need Thee Every Hour

1872

Not that we are sufficient of ourselves to think of anything as being from ourselves, but our sufficiency is from God. 2 Corinthians 3:5

In his book, *The Practice of the Presence of God*, Brother Lawrence claimed to be as close to God while working in the kitchen as when praying the chapel. The Lord, after all, is *always* near us, thus wherever we are is holy ground. That was the experience of Annie Hawks, a housewife and mother of three in Brooklyn, New York.

As a child, Annie Sherwood had dabbled in poetry, her first verse being published when she was fourteen. In 1857, she married Charles Hawks and they established their home in Brooklyn, joining Dr. Robert Lowry's Hanson Place Baptist Church.* With the good doctor's encouragement, she began writing Sunday school songs for children, and he set many of them to music.

"I Need Thee Every Hour" was written on a bright June morning in 1872. Annie later wrote, "One day as a young wife and mother of 37 years of age, I was busy with my regular household tasks. Suddenly, I became so filled with the sense of nearness to the Master that, wondering how one could live without Him, either in joy or pain, these words, 'I Need Thee Every Hour,' were ushered into my mind, the thought at once taking full possession of me."

The next Sunday, Annie handed these words to Dr. Lowry, who wrote the tune and chorus while seated at the little organ in the living room of his Brooklyn parsonage. Later that year, it was sung for the first time at the National Baptist Sunday School Association meeting in Cincinnati, Ohio, and published in a hymnbook the following year.

When Annie's husband died sixteen years later, she found that her own hymn was among her greatest comforts. "I did not understand at first why this hymn had touched the great throbbing heart of humanity," Annie wrote. "It was not until long after, when the shadow fell over my way, the shadow of a great loss, that I understood something of the comforting power in the words which I had been permitted to give out to others in my hour of sweet serenity and peace."

Some time after Charles' death, Annie moved to Bennington, Vermont, to live with her daughter and son-in-law. All in all, she wrote over four hundred hymns during her eighty-three years, though only this one is still widely sung.

---

*See story of "Shall We Gather at the River."

Lord, Speak to Me

Frances Ridley Havergal

Robert Schumann

1. Lord, speak to me, that I may speak
2. O teach me, Lord, that I may teach
3. O fill me with Thy full - ness, Lord,
4. O use me, Lord, use e - ven me,

In liv - ing ech - oes of Thy tone;
The pre - cious things Thou dost im - part;
Un - til my ver - y heart o'er - flow
Just as Thou wilt, and when, and where,

As Thou hast sought, so let me seek Thine
And wing my words that they may reach The
In kin - dling thought and glow - ing word, Thy
Un - til Thy bless - ed face I see Thy

err - ing chil - dren lost and lone.
hid - den depths of many a heart.
love to tell, Thy praise to show.
rest, Thy joy, Thy glo - ry share.

Lord, Speak to Me

1872

. . . that in it I may speak boldly, as I ought to speak. Ephesians 6:20

rances Ridley Havergal came by her love of hymnology naturally. Her father, Rev. William Henry Havergal, was an Anglican clergyman who devoted his life to improving the music of the Church of England, writing over 100 hymns himself.

Frances, born in the rectory at Astley, Worcestershire, on December 14, 1836, was a delightful child who began reading and memorizing the Bible at age four. By age seven, she was already writing poems. At age nine, her family moved to the rectory of St. Nicholas, Worcester, and there she had her own room. "Dear child," her mother told her, "you have your own little bedroom now, it ought to be a little Bethel."

"I could not then make head or tail of what she meant," Frances later wrote, "and often wondered, till some months later, when reading in Genesis, I came to the chapter; and then I understood it. Having that small room to myself developed me much as a child; it was mine, and to me it was the coziest little nest in the world."

A deep sadness fell on her at age eleven, however, when her mother became ill. Calling Frances to her bedside, she said, "You are my youngest little girl, and I feel more anxious about you than the rest. I do pray for the Holy Spirit to lead and guide you. And remember, nothing but the precious blood of Christ can make you clean and lovely in God's sight."

"Oh, mamma, I am sure you will get better and go to church again."

"No, dear child; the church mamma is going to is the general assembly and the church of the Firstborn in heaven. How glorious to know I shall soon see my Savior face to face! Now go and play and sing some of your little hymns for me."

When her mother died shortly afterward, Frances crept again and again into the room when no one was near, drawing aside the curtain, looking at the stilled form. But she never forgot her mother's last words to her, and soon thereafter she gained assurance of her salvation.

Frances Ridley Havergal went on to become a deeply spiritual writer of hymns and devotional books. This hymn, originally entitled "A Worker's Prayer," was written on April 28, 1872, at Winterdyne, Bewdley, England, for the use of lay helpers in the church.

Nobody Knows the Trouble I've Seen

African-American spiritual

African-American spiritual

No-bo-dy knows the trou-ble I've seen; No-bo-dy knows but Je-sus.

No-bo-dy knows the trou-ble I've seen; Glo-ry hal-le-lu-jah.

1. Some - times I'm up; some - times I'm down; Oh yes, Lord.
2. Al - though You see me goin' a - long, Oh yes, Lord,
3. What makes old Sa - tan hate me so? Oh yes, Lord;

Some - times I'm al - most to the ground; Oh yes, Lord.
I have my trou - bles here be - low; Oh yes, Lord.
He got me once and let me go; Oh yes, Lord

Nobody Knows the Trouble I've Seen

1872

"Let not your heart be troubled; you believe in God, believe also in Me." John 14:1

F isk University in Nashville, Tennessee, opened its doors in 1866, at the close of the Civil War. It was one of the schools established for liberated slaves by the American Missionary Association. As students and professors arrived on campus, they found themselves living in abandoned Union Army hospital barracks built on the site of old slave pens.

Among the arriving professors was a New York Yankee, a white man named White. As music instructor, George White taught his students classical cantatas and patriotic songs, but he was particularly intrigued by the old plantation melodies and slave songs he overheard in the dorms and among the students between classes. White had trouble coaxing his students to sing him those songs; it seemed a particularly private type of hand-me-down music. There were no written scores or words—just plaintive strains passed voice to voice between the generations.

Within a few years, the old buildings at Fisk started rotting. The university found itself in crisis, without even money to buy food for its four hundred students. Regretfully, the Missionary Association decided to close the school. When White approached the trustees suggesting a series of fund-raising concerts, the board refused (they called his scheme "a wild goose chase"). White decided to try it anyway. "I'm depending on God, not you," he told the board.

Selecting nine students (most of them former slaves), White and his wife sold their jewelry and personal belongings to finance the first tour. On October 6, 1871, the singers boarded a train in Nashville for the Midwest. It was a hard trip, and at times the young people had to relinquish their seats to white folks. Other times they were evicted from trains or hotels. Sometimes the little group, braving threats, insults, obscenities, and indignities, sang in nearly empty halls and churches.

At the National Council of Congregational Churches meeting in Oberlin, Ohio, some of the delegates protested giving time to the "colored students from Fisk University." The problem was the pressing nature of denominational business. Their slate was full, and the delegates didn't want interruptions in their business sessions. But George White wouldn't be denied, and finally the Fisk students sang one song during a recess as the delegates were milling around in little groups and leaving the building.

What happened next changed the course of American music.

Continued in the next story . . .

Swing Low, Sweet Chariot

African-American spiritual

African-American spiritual

Swing low, sweet char - i - ot, Com - in' for to car-ry me home;

Swing low, sweet char - i - ot, Com - in' for to car-ry me home.

1. I looked o - ver Jor - dan and what did I see, Com - in' for to car-ry me home?
2. If you get there be - fore I do, Com - in' for to car-ry me home,

A band of an - gels com - in' af - ter me; Com - in' for to car-ry me home.
Just tell my friends I'm com - in' home too; Com - in' for to car-ry me home.

Swing Low, Sweet Chariot
1872

The chariots of God are twenty thousand, Even thousands of thousands; The Lord is among them . . . Psalm 68:17

I t had been a gray, overcast day in Oberlin, Ohio. Delegates to the National Council of Congregational Churches were weary from the dismal weather and long business sessions. When the meeting recessed, singers from Fisk University filed quietly into the choir loft. Suddenly the clouds parted and sunshine streamed through the windows. Delegates stopped talking, and every face turned toward the music. "Steal away, steal away, steal away to Jesus," came the song in beautiful, brooding harmony. After a moment of stunned silence, the convention burst into wild applause and cries for more.

Among the delegates was Henry Ward Beecher, a noted pastor from Brooklyn who immediately begged the group to cancel its tour and come directly to his church in New York. Unable to do that, director George White offered the group for a December concert.

Knowing the importance of this engagement, White agonized about naming his group; and in Columbus, Ohio, after spending much of the night in prayer, he found the answer. They would be the Jubilee Singers, the biblical year of Jubilee in Leviticus 25 being a time of liberation for slaves.

On December 27, 1871, the Jubilee Singers sang at Plymouth Church in Brooklyn. Rev. Beecher, deeply moved, stood and said, "Ladies and gentlemen, I'm going to do what I want every person in this house to do." He turned his pockets inside out, giving all the money to the Jubilee Singers. That night the offering was $1,300! Newspapers picked up the story, and soon the Jubilee Singers had engagements around the world.

In their concerts, the section that most stirred their audiences was their "spirituals"—those soulful plantation songs born of slavery and full of yearning.

In 1872, gospel music publisher Biglow & Main hired a musician to meet the Jubilee Singers and record these timeless, authorless songs on paper. Later that year, a little volume was published under the title: *Jubilee Songs: Complete. As Sung by the Jubilee Singers of Fisk University.* It was a milestone for both gospel and popular music; it introduced the "Negro Spiritual" to America and to the world. Among the favorites were "Nobody Knows the Trouble I've Seen" and "Swing Low, Sweet Chariot."

Thanks to the Jubilee Singers, Fisk University is still training young people today—and still sending out its Jubilee Singers to churches and concert halls across America and around the world.

Whiter Than Snow

James Nicholson   William G. Fischer

1. Lord Je - sus, I long to be per - fect - ly whole; I
2. Lord Je - sus, look down from Thy throne in the skies And
3. Lord Je - sus, be - fore You I pa - tient - ly wait; Come

want Thee for - ev - er to live in my soul. Break down ev - ery
help me to make a com - plete sac - ri - fice. I give up my -
now and with - in me a new heart cre - ate. To those who have

i - dol, cast out ev - ery foe. Now wash me and I shall be
self and what - ev - er I know, Now wash me and I shall be
sought Thee, Thou nev - er saidst, "No." Now wash me and I shall be

whit - er than snow. Whit - er than snow, Yes, whit - er than

snow, Now wash me and I shall be Whit - er than snow.

Whiter Than Snow

1872

Wash me, and I shall be whiter than snow. Psalm 51:7

James Nicholson, author of "Whiter than Snow," was a dedicated Christian who lived in Washington, D.C., where he worked for the post office. Born in Ireland in the 1820s, James had immigrated to America in the 1850s, originally settling in Philadelphia where he became active in the Wharton Street Methodist Episcopal Church as a Sunday school and evangelistic worker. In 1871, he moved to Washington to assume his new duties with the post office, and the next year he published this hymn.

"Whiter Than Snow" is based on Psalm 51:7, the prayer of repentance offered by King David after his sin with Bathsheba: "Wash me, and I shall be whiter than snow." It originally had six stanzas, all of them beginning, "Dear Jesus . . ." An unknown editor later altered the words to "Lord Jesus." "Whiter Than Snow" was first published in 1872 by the Methodist Episcopal Book Room in Philadelphia, in a sixteen-page pamphlet entitled, *Joyful Songs No. 4.*

Philadelphia musician William Gustavus Fischer composed the music to this hymn. He learned to read music while attending singing classes at a German-speaking church in Philadelphia. When he started his life's occupation as a bookbinder, he still spent his evenings pursuing music. He was eventually hired to teach music at a Philadelphia college, and late in life he entered the piano business.

Fischer was best known as a popular song leader for revival meetings. In 1875, he led the 1,000-voice choir at the D. L. Moody/Ira Sankey Campaign in the great tabernacle at Thirteenth and Market Streets in Philadelphia. He composed over two hundred hymn tunes, including this one. He also composed the melody for "I Love to Tell the Story."

The splendor of snowfall is only one of the pictures used in Scripture to illustrate God's forgiveness of sin. Micah 7:19 says God casts our sins into the ocean. Psalm 103 says He removes them as far from us as East from West. According to Isaiah 38:17, God casts them behind His back. Colossians 2:14 says they are wiped out like erased handwriting. If you're suffering pangs of guilt and regret, needing a fresh experience of God's forgiveness, try singing this old hymn with new sincerity:

Break down every idol, cast out every foe,
Now wash me, and I shall be whiter than snow.

There's a Song in the Air

Josiah G. Holland

Karl P. Harrington

1. There's a song in the air! There's a star in the sky!
2. There's a tu - mult of joy O'er the won - der - ful birth,
3. In the light of that star Lie the a - ges im - pearled;
4. We re - joice in the light, And we ech - o the song

There's a moth - er's deep prayer, And a ba - by's low cry!
For a Vir - gin's sweet Boy, Is the Lord of the earth.
And that song from a - far Has swept o - ver the world.
That comes down thro' the night From the heav - en - ly throng.

And the star rains its fire while the beau - ti - ful sing,
Lo, the star rains its fire while the beau - ti - ful sing,
Ev - ery hearth is a - flame, and the beau - ti - ful sing
Ay! we shout to the love - ly E - van - gel they bring,

For the man - ger of Beth - le - hem, cra - dles a King!
For the man - ger of Beth - le - hem cra - dles a King!
In the homes of the na - tions that Je - sus is King!
As we greet in His cra - dle our Sav - ior and King!

There's a Song in the Air
1872

Praise the LORD! Sing to the LORD a new song, And His praise in the assembly of saints. Psalm 149:1

For a long time, Josiah Gilbert Holland was known to his friends as a failure at just about everything he tried. Dropping out of high school, he tried his hand at photography, then calligraphy. When those professions didn't pan out, Josiah, twenty-one, enrolled in Berkshire Medical College. After graduation, he practiced medicine in Springfield, Massachusetts for a while before quitting to start a newspaper. The paper folded after six months. At length, he joined the editorial staff of another newspaper, *The Springfield Republican*, and there he finally found his niche in writing.

In 1865, the world was stunned by the tragic assassination of Abraham Lincoln. The next year, it was Josiah Holland who published the first major biography of Lincoln. In it, he presented Lincoln as a "true-hearted Christian" and provided a number of stories to reinforce the point. When Lincoln's free-thinking law partner, William Herndon, read the book, he refuted it. Lincoln was an "infidel," declared Herndon, and he died as an "unbeliever." To this day, historians argue about Lincoln's religious faith, or lack of it. But the notoriety put Josiah Holland on the literary map of his day.

In 1870, he became a founder and the senior editor of *Scribner's Magazine*. He continued publishing books and was quite prolific. In 1872, he published *The Marble Prophecy and Other Poems*. In it were the four stanzas of "There's a Song in the Air." It was an unusual poem, in that the first four lines of each stanza contained six syllables each, but the fifth and sixth lines were twice as long. Two years later, it was set to music in a collection of Sunday school songs, but didn't achieve widespread popularity.

Several years after Josiah's death in 1881, a Latin professor named Karl Pomeroy Harrington read "There's a Song in the Air." Harrington was an amateur musician who had begun writing melodies as a youngster on the small organ in his childhood home. Harrington later inherited that old Estey organ and moved it to his vacation cottage in North Woodstock, New Hampshire. While spending the summer there in 1904, he sat down at the old instrument, pumping the bellows with the foot pedals, and hammered out the lovely melodic tune to which "There's a Song in the Air" is now widely sung.

Blessed Assurance

Fanny J. Crosby

Phoebe P. Knapp

1. Bless - ed as - sur - ance, Je - sus is mine! Oh, what a fore - taste of
2. Per - fect sub - mis - sion, per - fect de - light! Vi - sions of rap - ture now
3. Per - fect sub - mis - sion, all is at rest. I in my Sav - ior am

glo - ry di - vine! Heir of sal - va - tion, pur - chase of God,
burst at my sight! An - gels de - scend - ing bring from a - bove
hap - py and blest; Watch - ing and wait - ing, look - ing a - bove,

Born of His Spir - it, washed in His blood!
Ech - oes of mer - cy, whis - pers of love. This is my sto - ry,
Filled with His good - ness, lost in His love.

this is my song, Prais - ing my Sav - ior all the day long. This is my

sto - ry, this is my song, Prais - ing my Sav - ior all the day long.

Blessed Assurance

1873

. . . nevertheless I am not ashamed, for I know whom I have believed and am persuaded that He is able to keep what I have committed to Him until that Day.
2 Timothy 1:12

rances Ridley Havergal and Frances (Fanny) Crosby never met, but they became dear pen pals—the two most famous women hymnists of their age, the former in England and the latter in America. Havergal once wrote a poem about her American counterpart:

Sweet, blind singer over the sea, | Tuneful and jubilant! How can it be, | That the songs of gladness, which float so far, | As if they fell from the evening star | Are the notes of one who may never see | 'Visible music' of flower and tree . . . . | Oh, her heart can see, her heart can see! | And its sight is strong and swift and free . . . .

Another of Fanny's dearest friends was Phoebe Knapp. While Fanny lived in the Manhattan slums and worked in rescue missions, Phoebe lived in the Knapp Mansion, a palatial residence in Brooklyn, where she entertained lavishly. She was an extravagant dresser with a wardrobe full of elaborate gowns and diamond tiaras. Her music room contained one of the finest collections of instruments in the country, and Fanny was a frequent houseguest.

One day in 1873, while Fanny was staying at the Knapp Mansion, Phoebe said she had a tune she wanted to play. Going to the music room, she sat at the piano and played a new composition of her own while the blind hymnist listened. Fanny immediately clapped her hands and exclaimed, "Why, that says, 'Blessed Assurance!'" She quickly composed the words, and a great hymn was born.

Many years later, D. L. Moody was preaching in New York at the 23rd Street Dutch Reformed Church. The Moody/Sankey meetings had popularized Fanny Crosby's hymns around the world and had made the blind poetess a household name. But whenever she attended a Moody/Sankey meeting, she refused to be recognized, disavowing acclaim.

This day the church was so crowded she could find nowhere to sit. Moody's son, Will, seeing her, offered to find her a seat. To her bewilderment, he led her onto the platform just as the crowd was singing "Blessed Assurance." Moody, Sr., jumped to his feet, raised his hand, and interrupted the singing. "Praise the Lord!" he shouted. "Here comes the authoress!"

Fanny took her seat amid thunderous ovation, humbly thanking God for making her a blessing to so many.

It Is Well with My Soul

Horatio G. Spafford

Philip P. Bliss

1. When peace like a riv-er, At-tend-eth my way, When sor-rows, Like
2. My sin, O the bliss Of this glo-ri-ous tho't, My sin not in
3. O, Lord haste the day When my faith shall be sight, The clouds be rolled

sea bil-lows roll; What-ev-er my lot, Thou hast taught me to say,
part But the whole Is nailed to the cross And I bear it no more.
back As a scroll; The trump shall re-sound And the Lord shall de-scend,

"It is well, It is well, with my soul." It is well,
Praise the Lord, Praise the Lord, O my soul! It is well
"E-ven so" it is well With my soul.

with my soul, It is well, It is well, with my soul.
with my soul,

It Is Well with My Soul
1873

Many are the afflictions of the righteous, but the LORD delivers him out of them all. Psalm 34:19

When the great Chicago fire consumed the Windy City in 1871, Horatio G. Spafford, an attorney heavily invested in real estate, lost a fortune. About that time, his only son, age 4, succumbed to scarlet fever. Horatio drowned his grief in work, pouring himself into rebuilding the city and assisting the 100,000 who had been left homeless.

In November of 1873, he decided to take his wife and daughters to Europe. Horatio was close to D. L. Moody and Ira Sankey, and he wanted to visit their evangelistic meetings in England, then enjoy a vacation.

When an urgent matter detained Horatio in New York, he decided to send his wife, Anna, and their four daughters, Maggie, Tanetta, Annie, and Bessie, on ahead. As he saw them settled into a cabin aboard the luxurious French liner *Ville du Havre,* an unease filled his mind, and he moved them to a room closer to the bow of the ship. Then he said good-bye, promising to join them soon.

During the small hours of November 22, 1873, as the *Ville du Havre* glided over smooth seas, the passengers were jolted from their bunks. The ship had collided with an iron sailing vessel, and water poured in like Niagara. The *Ville du Havre* tilted dangerously. Screams, prayers, and oaths merged into a nightmare of unmeasured terror. Passengers clung to posts, tumbled through darkness, and were swept away by powerful currents of icy ocean. Loved ones fell from each other's grasp and disappeared into foaming blackness. Within two hours, the mighty ship vanished beneath the waters. The 226 fatalities included Maggie, Tanetta, Annie, and Bessie. Mrs. Spafford was found nearly unconscious, clinging to a piece of the wreckage. When the 47 survivors landed in Cardiff, Wales, she cabled her husband: "Saved Alone."

Horatio immediately booked passage to join his wife. En route, on a cold December night, the captain called him aside and said, "I believe we are now passing over the place where the *Ville du Havre* went down." Spafford went to his cabin but found it hard to sleep. He said to himself, "It is well; the will of God be done."

He later wrote his famous hymn based on those words.

⌒⌒

The melody for "It Is Well," titled VILLE DU HAVRE, was written by Philip Bliss who was himself soon to perish, along with his wife, in a terrible train wreck in Ohio.*

---

*See the story of "I Will Sing of My Redeemer."

Another Year Is Dawning

Frances R. Havergal

Samuel S. Wesley

1. An - oth-er year is dawn-ing: Dear Fa-ther, let it be,
2. An - oth-er year of mer-cies, Of faith-ful-ness and grace;
3. An - oth-er year of ser-vice, Of wit-ness for Thy love;

In work-ing or in wait-ing, An - oth-er year with Thee;
An - oth-er year of glad-ness In the shin-ing of Thy face;
An - oth-er year of train-ing For ho-lier work a - bove.

An - oth-er year of pro-gress, An - oth-er year of praise,
An - oth-er year of lean-ing Up - on Thy lov-ing breast;
An - oth-er year is dawn-ing: Dear Fa-ther, let it be,

An - oth-er year of prov-ing Thy pres-ence all the days.
An - oth-er year of trust-ing, Of qui-et, hap-py rest.
On earth or else in heav-en, An - oth-er year for Thee.

Another Year Is Dawning

1874

Create in me a clean heart, O God, and renew a steadfast spirit within me. Psalm 51:10

In many churches, the first Sunday of the year wouldn't be complete without singing Frances Ridley Havergal's great "Another Year is Dawning." Its words reflect the deep consecration that marked her poems. Frances considered every New Year's Day a never-to-be-missed opportunity of rededication to Christ, and several New Year's hymns came from her pen.

This particular poem, "Another Year is Dawning," was written as a prayer for the beginning of 1874. Frances composed it near the end of the old year and had it printed on a specially designed greeting card to be sent to friends. The caption said, "A Happy New Year! Ever Such May It Be!"

As it turned out, Frances herself needed that prayer, because just a few days later she suffered a stunning disappointment. She was hoping to be launched as an author in America, and her agent in New York had made reassuring promises. Then came a letter she thought would bear the first of many royalty checks. Instead it reported that her publisher had gone bankrupt in the Stock Market crash of 1873.

But as Frances had only recently turned all her affairs over to the Lord, she bore the crisis with peace, writing to a friend:

> I have just had such a blessing in the shape of what would have been only two months ago a really bitter blow to me. . . . I was expecting a letter from America, enclosing thirty-five pounds now due me, and possibly news that [my book] was going on like steam. The letter has come, and, instead of all this, my publisher has failed in the universal crash. He holds my written promise to publish only with him as the condition of his launching me, so this is not simply a little loss, but an end of all my American prospects . . . .
>
> I really had not expected that He would do for me so much above all I asked, as not merely to help me to acquiesce in this, but positively not to feel it at all, and only to rejoice in it as a clear test of the reality of victorious faith which I do find brightening almost daily. Two months ago this would have been a real trial to me, for I had built a good deal on my American prospects; now "Thy will be done" is not a sigh but only a song.

Bringing in the Sheaves

Knowles Shaw

George A. Minor

1. Sow - ing in the morn - ing, sow - ing seeds of kind - ness,
2. Sow - ing in the sun - shine, sow - ing in the shad - ows,
3. Go - ing forth with weep - ing, sow - ing for the Mas - ter,

Sow - ing in the noon - tide and the dew - y eve, Wait - ing for the har - vest
Fear - ing nei - ther clouds nor win - ter's chill - ing breeze; By and by the har - vest
Though the loss sus - tained our spir - it oft - en grieves; When our weep - ing's o - ver

and the time of reap - ing- We shall come re - joic - ing, bring - ing in the sheaves.
and the la - bor end - ed- We shall come re - joic - ing, bring - ing in the sheaves.
He will bid us wel - come- We shall come re - joic - ing, bring - ing in the sheaves.

Bring - ing in the sheaves, bring - ing in the sheaves, We shall come re - joic - ing,

1.

2.

bring - ing in the sheaves. We shall come re - joic - ing, bring - ing in the sheaves.

Bringing in the Sheaves

<u>1874</u>

. . . The harvest truly is plentiful, but the laborers are few. Matthew 9:37

Knowles Shaw, the "Singing Evangelist," wrote this gospel song in 1874. Four years later, on June 7, 1878, he and Elder Kirk Baxter boarded a train in Dallas, en route to McKinney, Texas, where Shaw was beginning an evangelistic campaign. As the train chugged across Texas, the two men fell into conversation with a Methodist minister named Malloy. Baxter later wrote:

Malloy asked him to tell the secret of his success in protracted meetings, which Brother Shaw proceeded to do in an earnest manner, saying he depended much on the power of song; preached Christ; always kept Jesus before the people; made them feel that they were sinners and needed just such a Savior as he preached; that he never became discouraged; had confidence in the gospel truth as the power of God; that he loved his work, and became wholly absorbed in it; and added: "Oh, it is a grand thing to rally people to the Cross of Christ."

At that moment, I felt the car was off the track, bouncing over the ties. I saw Brother Shaw rise from his seat and realized at once the car was going over. All became dark as night. When I came to myself, the coach was at the bottom of the embankment. I looked round, but all were gone. When I got out, I saw the passengers on the railroad track above me, and made my way up to them. The first one I met was Mr. Malloy. I said, "Have you seen Brother Shaw?" "No," said he, "I fear he is under the wreck; but he saved my life by pushing me from the position in which he himself fell."

I waited to hear no more, but ran down to the wreck, looked in, and saw a man's hand pointing upward out of the water. It was Brother Shaw's. I called for help, and in about fifteen minutes he was taken lifeless from the water.

I sent a telegram to Dallas, telling the sad news. In a short time, a deep gloom pervaded the whole city, as from house to house passed the sad words, "Brother Shaw is dead."

But his life proved his song. According to records found in his diary, Shaw recorded more than 11,400 conversions to Christ under his nineteen years of preaching. He entered heaven rejoicing, bringing in the sheaves.

Take My Life and Let It Be

Take My Life and Let It Be

1874

Yet indeed I also count all things loss for the excellence of the knowledge of Christ Jesus my Lord, for whom I have suffered the loss of all things, and count them as rubbish, that I may gain Christ. Philippians 3:8

Although hymnist Frances Havergal, 36, had served the Lord for years, she felt something was missing in her Christian experience. Then one day in 1873, she received a little book called, "All for Jesus," which stressed the importance of making Christ the King of every corner and cubicle of one's life. Soon thereafter, she made a fresh and complete consecration of herself to Christ.

Years later when asked about it, she replied, "Yes, it was on Advent Sunday, December 2, 1873, I first saw clearly the blessedness of true consecration. I saw it as a flash of electric light, and what you see you can never un-see. There must be full surrender before there can be full blessedness."

Not long afterward, she found herself spending several days with ten people in a house, some of them unconverted. Others were Christians, but not fully surrendered to Christ. "Lord, give me all in this house," she prayed. She went to work witnessing, and before she left, all ten were yielded Christians. On the last night of her visit, Frances—too excited to sleep—wrote this great consecration hymn, "Take My Life . . . ."

In the years that followed, Frances frequently used this hymn in her own devotions, especially every December 2, on the anniversary of her consecration.

On one occasion, as she pondered the words, "Take my voice and let me sing / Always only for my King," she felt she should give up her secular concerts. Her beautiful voice was in demand, and she frequently sang with the Philharmonic. But from that moment, her lips were exclusively devoted to the songs of the Lord.

On another occasion she was praying over the stanza that says, "Take my silver and my gold / Not a mite would I withhold." She had accumulated a great deal of jewelry, but she now felt she should donate it to the Church Missionary Society. Writing to a friend, she said, "I retain only a brooch for daily wear, which is a memorial to my dear parents; also a locket with the holy portrait I have of my niece in heaven. Evelyn, I had no idea I had such a jeweler's shop; nearly fifty articles are being packed off. I don't think I need to tell you I never packed a box with such pleasure."

Have you given your whole life—everything—over to Jesus? Why not make this the date of your own complete consecration?

I Will Sing of My Redeemer

Philip P. Bliss

James McGranahan

1. I will sing of my Re - deem-er, And His won - drous love to me.
2. I will tell the won - drous sto - ry, How my lost es - tate to save,
3. I will praise my dear Re - deem-er; His tri - um - phant power I'll tell.

On the cru - el cross He suffered, From the curse to set me free.
In His boundless love and mer - cy He the ran - som free - ly gave.
How the vic - to - ry He giv-eth O - ver sin and death and hell.

Sing, oh sing, of my Re - deem-er. With His blood He pur - chased

me. On the cross He sealed my par-don, Paid the debt and made me free.

I Will Sing of My Redeemer

1874

For you were bought at a price; therefore glorify God in your body and in your spirit, which are God's. 1 Corinthians 6:20

As a ten-year-old boy, when Philip Paul Bliss heard the sounds of a piano for the first time, his imagination was deeply stirred.* Later, riding his horse, Old Fanny, he had become a traveling musician. In 1870, he joined the staff of a Chicago church as music director and Sunday school superintendent. In March, 1874, he became the song leader and children's director for the evangelistic campaigns of Major Daniel W. Whittle. All the while, Philip was penning some of America's favorite gospel songs.

By the end of 1876, Philip needed a break. He had just written the music to "It is Well With My Soul," and finished a whirlwind tour of meetings with Major Whittle. While he and his wife Lucy were spending the Christmas holidays with his family in Pennsylvania, a telegram arrived requesting they come to Chicago to sing at Moody's Tabernacle on the last Sunday of the year.

On December 29, 1876, leaving their two small children with Philip's mother, they boarded the *Pacific Express.* The snow was blinding, and the eleven-coach train was running about three hours late. About eight o'clock that night as the train creaked over a chasm near Ashtabula, Ohio, the trestle bridge collapsed. The engine reached solid ground on the other side of the bridge, but the other cars plunged 75 feet into the ravine.

Philip survived the crash and crawled out through a window. But within moments, fire broke out, and Lucy was still inside, pinned under the twisted metal of the iron seats. The other survivors urged Philip not to crawl back into the flaming wreckage. "If I cannot save her, I will perish with her," he shouted, plunging into the fiery car. Both Philip and Lucy died. He was thirty-eight.

Philip's trunk finally arrived in Chicago safely. In it were found the words to the last hymns he had written, one of which was:

I will sing of my Redeemer,
And His wondrous love to me;
On the cruel cross He suffered,
From the curse to set me free.

Sing, oh sing, of my Redeemer,
With His blood, He purchased me.
On the cross, He sealed my pardon,
Paid the debt, and made me free.

---

*See the story behind "Jesus Loves Even Me."

Christ Arose!

Robert Lowry

Robert Lowry

1. Low in the grave He lay, Je - sus, my Sav - ior! Wait - ing the
2. Vain - ly they watched His bed, Je - sus, my Sav - ior! Vain - ly they
3. Death can - not keep his prey, Je - sus, my Sav - ior! He tore the

com - ing day, Je - sus, my Lord!
seal the dead, Je - sus, my Lord! Up from the grave He a - rose,
bars a - way, Je - sus, my Lord! He a - rose,

With a might - y tri - umph o'er His foes; He a - rose a vic - tor from the
He a - rose;

dark do - main, And He lives for - ev - er with His saints to reign; He a-

rose! He a - rose! Hal - le - lu - jah! Christ a - rose!
He a - rose! He a - rose!

Christ Arose!

1874

He is not here, but is risen! Luke 24:6

What can exhausted pastors do to relax on Sunday nights after a hard day's work? Baptist preacher Robert Lowry went home to his wife and three sons—and wrote hymns. "Dr. Lowry will continue to preach the gospel in his hymns long after his sermons have been forgotten," Ira Sankey once wrote. "Many of his hymns were written after the Sunday evening service, when his body was weary but his mind refused to rest."

Robert Lowry was born in Pennsylvania in 1826. At his conversion at age seventeen, he joined a Baptist church. Shortly afterward, he enrolled at the University of Lewisburg (now Bucknell University in Lewisburg, Pennsylvania). After graduating, he pastored churches in New York, New Jersey, and Pennsylvania. He also taught at Bucknell and at one time served as its chancellor. Lowry gained a reputation for keen biblical scholarship and powerful, picturesque preaching.

When gospel song editor William Bradbury died in 1868, Lowry was chosen to replace him as a publisher of Sunday school music. He's best known, however, for his own gospel songs, including:

"Nothing But the Blood" (words and music)
"Shall We Gather at the River?" (words and music)
"Where Is My Wandering Boy Tonight?" (words and music)
"All the Way My Savior Leads Me" (music)
"I Need Thee Every Hour" (music)
"Marching to Zion" (music)

"Music, with me has been a side issue," he once said. "I would rather preach a gospel sermon to an appreciative audience than write a hymn. I have always looked upon myself as a preacher and felt a sort of depreciation when I began to be known more as a composer."

This hymn, "Christ Arose!" was written one evening during the Easter season of 1874 while Lowry was engaged in his devotions. He became deeply impressed with Luke 24:6–8, especially the words of the angel at the tomb of Christ: "Why do you seek the living among the dead? He is not here, but is risen!"

The words and music began forming together in his mind. Going to the little pump organ in his home, Lowry soon completed what was to become one of our greatest resurrection hymns.

All the Way My Savior Leads Me

Fanny J. Crosby

Robert Lowry

1. All the way my Sav-ior leads me; What have I to ask be-side?
2. All the way my Sav-ior leads me, Cheers each wind-ing path I tread,
3. All the way my Sav-ior leads me O, the full-ness of His love!

Can I doubt His ten-der mer-cy, Who thro' life has been my guide?
Gives me grace for ev-'ry tri-al, Feeds me with the liv-ing bread.
Per-fect rest to me is prom-ised In my Fa-ther's house a-bove.

Heav'n-ly peace, di-vin-est com-fort, Here by faith in Him to dwell!
Tho' my wea-ry steps may fal-ter, And my soul a-thirst may be,
When my spir-it, clothed im-mor-tal, Wings its flight to realms of day,

For I know, what-e'er be-fall me, Je-sus do-eth all things well;
Gush-ing from the Rock be-fore me, Lo! A spring of joy I see;
This my song thro' end-less a-ges: Je-sus led me all the way;

All the Way My Savior Leads Me

1875

. . . that you may be filled with the knowledge of His will in all wisdom and spiritual understanding. Colossians 1:9

When Fanny Crosby wrote, "All the way my Savior leads me, / What have I to ask beside?" she was expressing her own testimony of God's guidance. Even her blindness, she realized, was part of His plan.

When Fanny was about six weeks old, her parents had realized with alarm that something was wrong with her eyes. The local doctor was away, but the Crosbys found a man—no one afterward recalled his name—who claimed to be a physician. He put hot poultice on the baby's inflamed eyes, insisting it would draw out the infection. The infection did clear up, but white scars appeared, and in the months that followed the baby registered no response to objects held before her. As it turned out, Fanny was not totally blind. Even in old age she could discern day from night. But her vision was gone.

Yet this stimulated other gifts, such as her phenomenal memory. As a child, Fanny memorized whole sections of the Bible, including most of the Pentateuch, the four Gospels, all of Proverbs, and vast portions of other books. Whenever she wanted to "read" a passage, she just turned there in her mental "Bible" and read it verbatim. "This Holy Book," she said when eighty-five, "has nurtured my entire life."

Years later, Fanny viewed her blindness as a special gift from God, believing He had given her a particular "soul-vision" which equipped her for a special work. "It was the best thing that could have happened to me," she declared. "How in the world could I have lived such a helpful life had I not been blind?"

"Don't blame the doctor," Fanny said on another occasion. "He is probably dead by this time. But if I could meet him, I would tell him that he unwittingly did me the greatest favor in the world."

Though this hymn expressed Fanny Crosby's lifelong testimony, it was prompted by a specific incident in 1874. One day she didn't have enough money to pay her rent. Just as she committed the matter to God in prayer, a stranger appeared at her door and pressed a ten-dollar bill in her hand before disappearing. It was the very amount needed. That night, she wrote the words to "All the Way My Savior Leads Me."

O the Deep, Deep Love of Jesus

Samuel Trevor Francis

Thomas J. Williams

1. O the deep, deep love of Je - sus, Vast, un - mea - sured, bound - less, free!
2. O the deep, deep love of Je - sus, Spread His praise from shore to shore!
3. O the deep, deep love of Je - sus, Love of ev - 'ry love the best!

Roll - ing as a might - y o - cean In its full - ness o - ver me!
How He lov - eth, ev - er lov - eth, Chang - eth nev - er, nev - er - more!
'Tis an o - cean full of bless - ing, 'Tis a ha - ven giv - ing rest!

Un - der - neath me, all a - round me, Is the cur - rent of Thy love,
How He watch - es o'er His loved ones, Died to call them all His own;
O the deep, deep love of Je - sus, 'Tis a heav'n of heav'ns to me;

Lead - ing on - ward, lead - ing home - ward, To my glo - rious rest a - bove!
How for them He in - ter - ced - eth, Watch - eth o'er them from the throne!
And it lifts me up to glo - ry, For it lifts me up to Thee!

O the Deep, Deep Love of Jesus

1875

For I am persuaded that neither death nor life, nor angels nor principalities nor powers, nor things present nor things to come, nor height nor depth, nor any other created thing, shall be able to separate us from the love of God which is in Christ Jesus our Lord. Romans 8:38–39

Few hymns paint such a vivid picture of God's love as this one by Samuel Trevor Francis: *. . . vast, unmeasured, boundless free; / rolling as a mighty ocean in its fullness over me. / Underneath me, all around me, is the current of Thy love . . . .* It helps us visualize the immensity of Christ's liquid-love, overwhelming and submerging us in the depths of His tender, triumphant heart.

Samuel was born on November 19, 1834, in a village north of London, but his parents soon moved to the city of Hull midway up the English coast. His father was an artist. As a child, Samuel enjoyed poetry and even compiled a little hand-written volume of his own poetry. He also developed a passion for music, joining the church choir at age nine. But as a teenager, he struggled spiritually, and when he moved to London to work, he knew things weren't right in his heart.

One day, as he later wrote, "I was on my way home from work and had to cross Hungerford Bridge to the south of the Thames. During the winter's night of wind and rain and in the loneliness of that walk, I cried to God to have mercy on me. I stayed for a moment to look at the dark waters flowing under the bridge, and the temptation was whispered to me: 'Make an end of all this misery.' I drew back from the evil thought, and suddenly a message was borne into my very soul: 'You do believe in the Lord Jesus Christ?' I at once answered, 'I do believe,' and I put my whole trust in Him as my Savior."

Francis went on to become a London merchant, but his real passion was Kingdom work—especially hymn writing and open-air preaching—which occupied his remaining seventy-three years. He traveled widely and preached around the world for the Plymouth Brethren. He died on December 28, 1925, at age ninety-two.

EBENEZER, the ponderous, rolling melody for this hymn is traditionally called "Ton-Y-Botel" ("Tune in a Bottle") because of a legend that it was found in a bottle along the Welsh Coast. It was actually composed by Thomas J. Williams and first appeared as a hymn tune in 1890 in a Welsh hymnal entitled *Llawlyfn Moliant*.

To God Be the Glory

Fanny J. Crosby

William H. Doane

1. To God be the glo-ry, great things He hath done. So loved He the world that He gave us His Son, Who yield-ed His life, an a-tone-ment for sin, And o-pened the life-gate, that all may go in.

Praise the Lord, praise the Lord, Let the earth hear His voice! Praise the Lord, praise the Lord, Let the peo-ple re-joice! O come to the Fa-ther thru Je-sus the Son, And give Him the glo-ry, great things He hath done.

To God Be the Glory

<u>1875</u>

Be exalted, O God, above the heavens, And Your glory above all the earth. Psalm 108:5

O ccasionally a hymn drops into the furrows of history to be buried and forgotten awhile, only to later spring to life for future generations. That's what happened with Fanny Crosby's "To God Be the Glory." It first appeared in *Brightest and Best*, a little volume of hymns published in 1875 by William Doane and Robert Lowry. This small hymnal proved to be a treasure trove, introducing such classics as "Christ Arose," "All the Way My Savior Leads Me," "Savior, More Than Life to Me," "I Am Thine, O Lord," "Rescue the Perishing," "Jesus, Keep Me Near the Cross," and this one—"Praise for Redemption" (as it was originally called).

As it turned out, "Praise for Redemption" wasn't much of a hit. It wasn't widely sung nor included in many hymnals; it just lay hidden for eighty years.

In 1954, Billy Graham was planning an evangelistic crusade at London's Harringay Arena. As Cliff Barrows, music director for the Graham team, was compiling hymns for the *Greater London Crusade Song Book*, Rev. Frank Colquhoun, a prolific British preacher at Norwich Cathedral and a great lover of hymns, approached him. Colquhoun gave Barrows a copy of "Praise for Redemption," with its exuberant chorus: "Praise the Lord! Praise the Lord! Let the earth hear His voice!" Though unfamiliar with the hymn, Barrows decided to use it anyway.

Meanwhile problems were mounting for Graham. The British Press was critical of the young evangelist and an Anglican bishop predicted he would return to America with "his tail between his legs." Funds were short, forcing the Graham team to take pay cuts. A Member of Parliament threatened a challenge in the House of Commons, accusing Graham of interfering in British politics under the guise of religion. Friends in high places were advising Graham to cancel or postpone the meetings. Graham, shaken, dropped to his knees repeatedly, beseeching help from heaven.

As it turned out, Harringay Arena was packed for three months, and the crusade sparked a sense of revival across Great Britain. "To God Be the Glory" seemed a fitting theme. Fanny Crosby's old hymn was sung almost every night in Harringay, launching it into worldwide popularity as one of Christianity's favorite hymns.

I Am Thine, O Lord

Fanny J. Crosby

William H. Doane

1. I am Thine O Lord; I have heard Thy voice, And it told Thy
2. Con - se - crate me now to Thy ser - vice Lord, By the power of
3. O the pure de - light of a sin - gle hour That be - fore Thy
4. There are depths of love that I can - not know 'Til I cross the

love to me. But I long to rise in the arms of faith,
grace di - vine; Let my soul look up with a stead - fast hope,
throne I spend, When I kneel in prayer, and with Thee my God,
nar - row sea; There are heights of joy that I may not reach

And be clos - er drawn to Thee.
And my will be lost in Thine.
I com - mune as friend with friend!
'Til I rest in peace with Thee.

Draw me near - er, near - er bless - ed Lord,

To the cross where Thou hast died. Draw me near - er, near - er,

near - er bless - ed Lord, To Thy pre - cious bleed - ing side.

I Am Thine, O Lord

1875

Let us draw near with a true heart in full assurance of faith. Hebrews 10:22

She's called the "Queen of American Hymn Writers," and the "Mother of Congregational Singing in America." During her ninety-five years, Fanny Crosby wrote over eight thousand hymns. In addition, she was one of the three most prominent evangelical leaders in America during the last part of the 1800s, the others being D. L. Moody and Ira Sankey. She was one of America's most popular preachers and lecturers; in many cases lines of people would circle the block where she was scheduled to speak, hoping to get a seat.

When she traveled, it was usually by train; and she was fiercely independent, insisting on traveling alone, despite her blindness, until she was up in her eighties. Fanny lived in the rundown tenements of lower Manhattan so she'd be nearer her beloved Rescue Missions where she worked with the homeless and addicted.

But to me, the most remarkable thing about Fanny Crosby was her phenomenal memory. After her eyes were blinded in infancy, her grandmother Eunice took a special interest in teaching her Bible verses. Later a woman named Mrs. Hawley, the Crosbys' landlady, took over the job, committed to helping Fanny memorize the entire Bible! Every week, the child was given a certain number of chapters to learn, and Mrs. Hawley drilled them into her during their review sessions together. Fanny learned by heart all of Genesis, Exodus, Leviticus, Numbers, and Deuteronomy, plus the four Gospels, most of the Psalms, all of Proverbs, and many portions of the rest of the Bible.

From the fountainhead of these Scriptures flowed her hymns.

Ira Sankey, in his autobiography, gives us the story behind this particular hymn: "Fanny Crosby was visiting Mr. W. H. Doane, in his home in Cincinnati, Ohio. They were talking together about the nearness of God, as the sun was setting and evening shadows were gathering around them. The subject so impressed the well-known hymn-writer, that before retiring she had written the words to this hymn, which has become one of the most useful she has ever written. The music by Mr. Doane so well fitted the words that the hymn has become a special favorite wherever the gospel hymns are known."

It was first published in 1875 in the little hidden treasure of hymns called *Brightest and Best*. Underneath the hymn was this Scripture quotation: "Let us draw near with a true heart" (Heb. 10:22).

Peace, Perfect Peace

Edward H. Bickersteth

Orlando Gibbons

1. Peace, per-fect peace, in this dark world of sin?
2. Peace, per-fect peace, by throng - ing du - ties pressed?
3. Peace, per-fect peace, with sor - rows surg - ing round?
4. Peace, per-fect peace, with loved ones far a - way?
5. Peace, per-fect peace, our fu - ture all un - known?

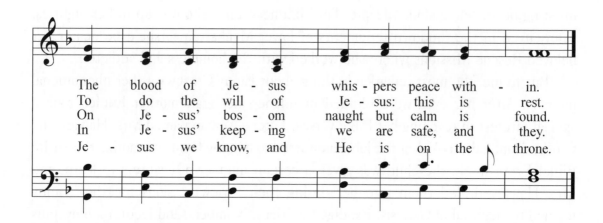

The blood of Je - sus whis - pers peace with - in.
To do the will of Je - sus: this is rest.
On Je - sus' bos - om naught but calm is found.
In Je - sus' keep - ing we are safe, and they.
Je - sus we know, and He is on the throne.

Peace, Perfect Peace

1875

You will keep him in perfect peace, Whose mind is stayed on You, because he trusts in You. Isaiah 26:3

dward Bickersteth, author of this hymn, was born in London, into a clergyman's family, in 1825. After attending Cambridge, he entered the Anglican ministry. He wrote a number of hymns, but "Peace, Perfect Peace" is his most popular. His son explained how it came to be written:

It was written in Harrogate, in a house facing the Stray, in August 1875. On a Sunday morning, the Vicar of Harrogate, Canon Gibbon, preached from the text, "Thou wilt keep him in perfect peace, whose mind is stayed on Thee" and alluded to the fact that in the Hebrew the words are "Peace, peace," twice repeated, and happily translated in our version by the phrase, "Perfect peace." This sermon set my father's mind working on the subject. He always found it easier to express in verse what was on his mind, so that when on that afternoon he visited an aged and dying relative, Archdeacon Hill of Liverpool, and found him somewhat troubled in mind, it was natural to him to express in verse the spiritual comfort which he desired to convey. Taking up a sheet of paper, he there and then wrote down the hymn exactly as it stands, and read it to this dying Christian.

I was with my father at the time, being home from school for the summer holiday: I well recollect his coming in to tea, a meal we always had with him on Sunday afternoon, and saying, "Children, I have written you a hymn," and reading us "Peace, Perfect Peace." I may add that it was his custom to expect each one of us on Sunday at tea to repeat a hymn, and he did the same, unless, as frequently happened, he wrote us a special hymn himself. . . .

It is not always noticed that the first line of each verse of "Peace, Perfect Peace" is in the form of a question, referring to some one or other of the disturbing experiences of life, and the second line of each verse endeavors to give the answer. The hymn has been translated into many languages, and for many years I doubt if my father went many days without receiving from different people assurances of the comfort and help which the hymn had been to them.

Hallelujah, What a Savior!

Philip P. Bliss

Philip P. Bliss

1. "Man of sor - rows!" what a name
2. Bear - ing shame and scoff - ing rude,
3. Guilt - y, vile, and help - less we,
4. Lift - ed up was He to die,
5. When He comes, our glo - rious King,

For the Son of God who came; Ru - ined sin - ners
In my place con - demned He stood, Sealed my par - don
Spot - less Lamb of God was He; Full a - tone - ment!
"It is fin - ished!" was His cry; Now in heaven ex -
All His ran - somed home to bring, Then a - new this

to re - claim! Hal - le - lu - jah! What a Sav - ior!
with His blood; Hal - le - lu - jah! What a Sav - ior!
Can it be? Hal - le - lu - jah! What a Sav - ior!
alt - ed high, Hal - le - lu - jah! What a Sav - ior!
song we'll sing, Hal - le - lu - jah! What a Sav - ior!

Hallelujah, What a Savior!

1875

And my spirit has rejoiced in God my Savior. Luke 1:47

hilip Bliss and Lucy Young, deeply in love, were married on June 1, 1859. Philip was twenty years old at the time, with a strong physique and a remarkable talent for music. The young couple was devoted to Christ and they often thrilled fellow church members with beautiful duets.

Believing God had given her husband a special talent, Lucy schemed for ways to afford him proper musical training. With her encouragement, he began traveling on an old horse from town to town, carrying a twenty-dollar melodeon and holding singing schools.

When Lucy's grandmother gave them thirty dollars, Philip attended a six-week course at the Normal Academy of Music in New York. Upon completion, he became a full-time music teacher and was soon recognized as a local music authority.

Philip and Lucy moved to Chicago so he could pursue a ministry of music there. Between 1865 and 1873, he held music conventions, singing schools, and church meetings. In 1869, he attracted the attention of evangelist D. L. Moody, who continually urged him to enter the full-time ministry of music.

Moody would later write: "In my estimate, he was the most highly honored of God of any man of his time as a writer and singer of gospel songs, and with all his gifts he was the most humble man I ever knew. I loved him as a brother."

With Lucy's encouragement, Philip joined Moody's associate, Major Daniel W. Whittle, as song leader in a series of evangelistic campaigns; and "Whittle and Bliss" became almost as famous as "Moody and Sankey." Successful crusades were held in Illinois, Wisconsin, Pennsylvania, Kentucky, Minnesota, Mississippi, Alabama, and Georgia.

Philip wrote such favorites as "Wonderful Words of Life," "Almost Persuaded," "Dare to Be a Daniel," "Hold the Fort," "Jesus Loves Even Me," "Let the Lower Lights Be Burning," "The Light of the World Is Jesus," "I Will Sing of My Redeemer," and the music to "It Is Well with My Soul." By 1876, Philip, only thirty-six, was known as one of the greatest hymnists of his generation.

Late that year, Philip conducted a service for inmates at the Michigan State Prison and sang one of his last hymns, "Hallelujah, What a Savior!" Many of the prisoners wept openly and confessed Christ as Savior.

No one dreamed that the young songwriter and his wife had but a month remaining to live.

The Light of the World Is Jesus

Philip P. Bliss

Philip P. Bliss

1. The whole world was lost in the dark-ness of sin; The Light of the
2. No dark - ness have we who in Je - sus a - bide; The Light of the
3. Ye dwell - ers in dark-ness with sin - blind - ed eyes, The Light of the
4. No need of the sun-light in Heav - en, we're told, The Light of the

world is Je - sus; Like sun - shine at noon - day His glo - ry shone in,
world is Je - sus; We walk in the Light when we fol - low our Guide;
world is Je - sus; Go, wash at His bid - ding, and light will a - rise,
world is Je - sus; The Lamb is the light in the Cit - y of Gold;

The Light of the world is Je - sus. Come to the Light, 'tis

shin - ing for thee! Sweet - ly the Light has dawned up-on me; Once I was

blind, but now I can see; The Light of the world is Je - sus!

The Light of the World Is Jesus

1875

You are the light of the world. A city that is set on a hill cannot be hidden. Matthew 5:14

On the last Thursday of 1876, Philip Bliss prayed with his boys, Paul, two, and George, four, and explained that he and Lucy were leaving by train for Chicago to sing at D. L. Moody's Tabernacle at year's end. "I would far rather stay than go if it were God's will," he told them, "but I must be about the Master's work." The boys were left in the care of relatives.

Another passenger on the Chicago-bound train, Mr. J. E. Burchell, later told the story: "There were eleven cars on the train that left Buffalo at two o'clock Friday afternoon . . . in a blinding snowstorm. We neared the bridge (over the Ashtabula River in Ohio) at about 7:45. . . . We ran on the structure at a rate of about ten miles an hour, and the whole train was on the bridge when it gave way. The bridge is about 200 feet long, and only the first engine had passed over when the crash came. . . . The first thing I heard was a cracking in the front part of the car, and then the same cracking in the rear. Then . . . a sickening oscillation and a sudden sinking, and I was thrown stunned from my seat. . . . The iron work bent and twisted like snakes, and everything took horrid shapes. I heard a lady scream in anguish . . . then I heard the cry of fire. . . . The crackling of the flames, the whistling wind, the screaming of the hurt, made a pandemonium of that little valley, and the water of the freezing creek was red with blood or black with the flying cinders. . . . The fire stole swiftly along the wreck, and in a few moments the cars were all in flames. The sight was sickening. The whole wreck was then on fire, and from out the frozen valley came great bursts of flame. . . ."

According to Mr. Burchell, Philip initially survived the wreck but crawled back through a window to save his wife. Both perished together.

Among Philip's last hymns was "The Light of the World Is Jesus" with its fitting final lines:

> *No need of the sunlight in Heaven we're told,*
> *The Light of the world is Jesus!*
> *The Lamb is the Light in the city of gold,*
> *The Light of the world is Jesus!**

---

*The Bliss family home in Rome, Pennsylvania, is now the P. P. Bliss Gospel Songwriters Museum.

Jesus, I Am Resting, Resting

Jean S. Pigott

James Mountain

1. Je - sus, I am rest-ing, rest-ing, In the joy of what Thou art;
2. O, how great Thy lov-ing kind-ness, Vast-er, broad-er than the sea!
3. Sim-ply trust-ing Thee, Lord Je-sus, I be-hold Thee as Thou art,
4. Ev - er lift Thy face up-on me As I work and wait for Thee;

I am find-ing out the great-ness Of Thy lov-ing heart.
O, how mar-ve-lous Thy good-ness, Lav-ished all on me!
And Thy love, so pure, so change-less, Sa-tis-fies my heart;
Rest-ing 'neath Thy smile, Lord Je-sus, Earth's dark sha-dows flee.

Thou hast bid me gaze up-on Thee, And Thy beau-ty fills my soul,
Yes, I rest in Thee, Be-lov-èd, Know what wealth of grace is Thine,
Sa - tis - fies its deep-est long-ings, Meets, sup-plies its ev-ery need,
Bright-ness of my Fa-ther's glo-ry, Sun-shine of my Fa-ther's face,

For by Thy trans-form-ing pow-er, Thou hast made me whole.
Know Thy cer-tain-ty of prom-ise, And have made it mine.
Com-pass-eth me round with bless-ings: Thine is love in-deed!
Keep me ev-er trust-ing, rest-ing, Fill me with Thy grace.

Jesus, I Am Resting, Resting

1876

Abide in Me, and I in you. As the branch cannot bear fruit of itself, unless it abides in the vine, neither can you, unless you abide in Me. John 15:4

This poem, written by an Irish woman named Jean Sophia Pigott, became the favorite hymn of J. Hudson Taylor, the great missionary to China. Often, taking a break from his crushing load of work, Hudson would sit at his little reed organ and sing this hymn. It perfectly expressed his greatest life-lesson.

Hudson had envisioned a missionary task greater than any since the days of Paul—the evangelization of China. He had established the China Inland Mission in 1865, but it almost proved his undoing. Overwhelmed by worry, work, and responsibility, he was near a breakdown when he received a letter from a fellow missionary, John McCarthy. In it, McCarthy spoke from John 15 about abiding in Christ.

"Abiding, not striving or struggling," wrote McCarthy, "looking off unto Him; trusting Him for present power. . . . This is not new, and yet 'tis new to me. . . . Christ literally all seems to me now the power, the only power for service; the only ground for unchanging joy."

As Hudson read this letter at his mission station in Chin-kiang on Saturday, September 4, 1869, his eyes were opened. "As I read," he recalled, "I saw it all. I looked to Jesus, and when I saw, oh how the joy flowed!"

Writing to his sister in England, he said: "As to work, mine was never so plentiful, so responsible, or so difficult; but the weight and strain are all gone. The last month or more has been perhaps the happiest of my life, and I long to tell you a little of what the Lord has done for my soul. . . . When the agony of soul was at its height, a sentence in a letter from dear McCarthy was used to remove the scales from my eyes, and the Spirit of God revealed the truth of our oneness with Jesus as I had never known it before. McCarthy, who had been much exercised by the same sense of failure, but saw the light before I did, wrote: 'But how to get faith strengthened? Not by striving after faith but by resting on the Faithful One.'

"As I read, I saw it all! . . . As I thought of the Vine and the branches, what light the blessed Spirit poured into my soul!"

Like a River Glorious

Frances R. Havergal

James Mountain

1. Like a riv-er glo-rious   Is God's per-fect peace,   O - ver all vic - to-rious
2. Hid-den in the hol-low   Of His bless-ed hand,   Nev - er foe can fol-low,
3. Ev - ery joy or tri - al   Fall-eth from a - bove,   Traced up-on our di - al

In   its bright in - crease;   Per-fect,   yet   it   flow - eth   Full-er ev - ery   day,
Nev-er trai - tor stand;   Not a   surge of   wor - ry,   Not a shade of   care,
By   the Sun of   Love.   We may trust Him   ful - ly   All for us to   do;

Per - fect,   yet   it   grow-eth Deep - er   all   the   way.
Not   a   blast of   hur - ry Touch the Spir - it   there. Stayed up-on Je - ho - vah,
They who trust Him   whol - ly   Find Him whol - ly   true.

Hearts are ful - ly   blest;   Find-ing,   as He   prom-ised,   Per-fect peace and   rest.

Like a River Glorious
1876

. . . I will extend peace to her like a river . . . Isaiah 66:12

In 1876, while vacationing in the south of Wales, Frances Havergal caught a severe cold and suffered inflammation of the lungs. Told she might die, her response was: "If I am really going, it is too good to be true." Her friends were amazed at how peacefully she faced the prospect of dying. That same year, she wrote the hymn:

> *Like a river glorious, is God's perfect peace,*
> *Over all victorious, in its bright increase;*
> *Perfect, yet it floweth, fuller every day,*
> *Perfect, yet it groweth, deeper all the way.*
> *Stayed upon Jehovah, hearts are fully blest*
> *Finding, as He promised, perfect peace and rest.*

Three years later, while meeting some boys to talk with them about the Lord, she ran into cold, wet weather and became chilled. As her fever grew worse, her family became alarmed. It gradually became apparent that Frances, 42, was dying. On Whitsunday, as one of her doctors left the room, he said, "Goodbye, I shall not see you again."

"Then you really think I am going?" asked Frances.

"Yes."

"Today?"

"Probably."

"Beautiful," said Frances. "Too good to be true."

Soon afterward she looked up smiling and said, "Splendid to be so near the gates of heaven!" She asked her brother to sing some hymns to her, then he said to her, "You have talked and written a great deal about the King, and you will soon see Him in His beauty."

"It's splendid!" she replied. "I thought He would have left me here a long while; but He is *so* good to take me now."

A little later she whispered, "Come, Lord Jesus, come and fetch me."

A terrible rush of convulsions seized her, and when they ceased, the nurse gently laid her back on her pillows. Frances' sister later wrote: "Then she looked up steadfastly, as if she saw the Lord. Surely nothing less heavenly could have reflected such a glorious radiance upon her face. For ten minutes we watched that almost visible meeting with her King, and her countenance was so glad, as if she were already talking to Him! Then she tried to sing, but after one sweet, high note, "HE—," her voice failed and her brother commended her soul into the Redeemer's hand."

Beulah Land

Edgar P. Stites

John R. Sweney

1. I've reached the land of joy di - vine, And all its beau - ty now is mine,
2. The Sav - iour comes and walks with me, And sweet com - mu - nion here have we;
3. A sweet per - fume up - on the breeze, Is borne from ev - er ver - nal trees,
4. The zeph - yrs seem to float to me, Sweet sounds of heav - en's mel - o - dy,

Here shines un - dimmed one bliss - ful day, For all my night has passed a - way.
He gent - ly leads me with His hand, For this is heav - en's bor - der-land.
And flow'rs that nev - er fad - ing grow Where streams of life for - ev - er flow.
As an - gels, with the white-robed throng, Join in the sweet re - demp-tion song.

O Beu - lah Land, sweet Beu - lah Land, As on thy high - est mount I stand,

I look a - way a - cross the sea, Where man-sions are pre - pared for me,

And view the shin - ing glo - ry shore, My heav'n, my home for - ev - er more!

Beulah Land

1876

*You shall be called Hephzibah, and your land Beulah; for the L*ORD *delights in you . . .* Isaiah 62:4

The author of this hymn, Edgar Stites, was a descendant of John Howland, who came to America on the *Mayflower*. He was born in Cape May, New Jersey, in March of 1836, and was born again in Philadelphia during the Revival of 1857. He served Union Forces during the Civil War by feeding the troops that passed through Philadelphia.

After the war Edgar became a riverboat pilot on the Delaware River and a Methodist preacher. He also served a stint as home missionary to South Dakota. For more than sixty years, he was a member of the First Methodist Episcopal Church of Cape May, New Jersey. In 1870 he joined a number of other ministers and laymen in founding the Ocean Grove Camp Meeting Association. Today Ocean Grove is a full-fledged town as well as Christian community and conference center.

It was in Ocean Grove that "Beulah Land" was first sung.

The word "Beulah" is an Old Testament term that occurs only in Isaiah 62:4: "You shall no longer be termed Forsaken, nor shall your land be Desolate; but you shall be called Hephzibah, and your land Beulah; for the Lord delights in you, and your land shall be married." "Beulah" comes from a Hebrew word meaning "to marry." The idea is a land that is loved, that is as delightful to the Lord as a beautiful bride. As such, it has come to represent heaven.

"It was in 1876 that I wrote 'Beulah Land,'" Edgar Stites said. "I could write only two verses and the chorus, when I was overcome and fell on my face. That was one Sunday. On the following Sunday I wrote the third and fourth verses, and again I was so influenced by emotion that I could only pray and weep. The first time it was sung was at the regular Monday morning meeting of Methodists in Philadelphia. Bishop McCabe sang it to the assembled ministers. Since then it is known wherever religious people congregate. I have never received a cent for my songs. Perhaps that is why they have had such a wide popularity. I could not do work for the Master and receive pay for it."

Trusting Jesus

Edgar P. Stites

Ira D. Sankey

1. Sim - ply trust - ing ev - ery day, Trust-ing through a storm - y way;
2. Bright - ly doth His Spir - it shine In - to this poor heart of mine.
3. Sing - ing if my way is clear, Pray - ing if the path be drear;
4. Trust - ing Him while life shall last, Trust - ing Him till earth be past;

E - ven when my faith is small, Trust - ing Je - sus, that is all.
While He leads I can - not fall, Trust - ing Je - sus, that is all.
If in dan - ger, for Him call, Trust - ing Je - sus, that is all.
'Til I hear His fi - nal call, Trust - ing Je - sus, that is all.

Trust - ing as the mo - ments fly, Trust - ing as the days go by;

Trust - ing Him what - e'er be - fall, Trust - ing Je - sus, that is all.

Trusting Jesus
1876

The word of the LORD is proven; He is a shield to all who trust in Him. 2 Samuel 22:31

Riverboat pilot turned Methodist preacher, Edgar Stites, the author of "Beulah Land," also wrote another well-known hymn, "Trusting Jesus." It was published in a newspaper, and a clipping of the poem was handed to D. L. Moody in Chicago. Moody, reading the poem, passed it to his song leader, Ira Sankey, asking Sankey to write a tune. Sankey agreed on condition that Moody vouch for the doctrine taught in the verses, which he did.

Who was this Ira Sankey who wrote the popular tune to "Trusting Jesus"? Sometimes called the "Father of Gospel Music," Sankey was born in 1840 in Pennsylvania and came to Christ as a teenager in a revival meeting. When the War Between the States broke out, he joined Union forces and often led the soldiers in singing during chapel services.

He took time in the middle of the Civil War to marry Fanny Edwards, daughter of a Pennsylvania state senator, and after the war the couple settled down in Newcastle, Pennsylvania. Ira found a job with the Internal Revenue Service. The couple had two sons, and joined the Methodist Episcopal Church where Ira led the singing.

It was in Indianapolis, Indiana, in June of 1870, while attending a YMCA convention, that Ira Sankey met D. L. Moody. Moody, hearing Sankey lead the singing, began peppering him with questions: "Where are you from? Are you married? What is your business?"

Moody, with his usual directness, told Sankey he'd have to give up his job with the IRS to become the song leader for his campaigns. "I have been looking for you for the last eight years," said Moody.

For the next thirty years, the names of Moody and Sankey would be linked in the world's greatest evangelistic undertakings. As the nineteenth century wore to a close, Sankey's beautiful voice became raspy due to overuse in the great halls and arenas where Moody preached, and his eyesight failed due to glaucoma. His years of notes and research on gospel music as well as the only manuscript of his autobiography were lost in a fire. But his work lives on. He composed the music to about twelve hundred songs during his lifetime, including "Faith Is the Victory," "The Ninety and Nine," "A Shelter in the Time of Storm," "Under His Wings," and this one—"Trusting Jesus."

I Am His, and He Is Mine

George Robinson

James Mountain

1. Loved with ev - er - last - ing love, Led by grace that love to know,
2. Heav'n a - bove is soft - er blue, Earth a - round is sweet - er green;
3. Things that once were wild a - larms Can - not now dis - turb my rest;
4. His for - ev - er, on - ly His, Who the Lord and me shall part?

Spir - it breath - ing from a - bove, Thou hast taught me it is so!
Some - thing lives in ev - ery hue Christ - less eyes have nev - er seen!
Closed in ev - er - last - ing arms, Pil - lowed on the lov - ing breast!
Ah, with what a rest of bliss Christ can fill the lov - ing heart!

O this full and per - fect peace From His pres - ence all di - vine-
Birds with glad - der songs o'er - flow, Flow'rs with deep - er beau - ties shine,
O to lie for - ev - er here, Doubt and care and self re - sign,
Heav'n and earth may fade and flee, First - born light in gloom de - cline,

In a love which can - not cease, I am His and He is mine; mine.
Since I know, as I now know, I am His and He is mine; mine.
While He whis - pers in my ear, I am His and He is mine; mine.
But while God and I shall be, I am His and He is mine; mine.

I Am His, and He Is Mine

1876

... The birds of the heavens have their home; They sing among the branches. Psalm 104:12

Some hymnals list this as "Loved with Everlasting Love." It's a wonderful hymn of assurance, written by an Irish pastor named George Wade Robinson. Born in Cork, Ireland, in 1838, Robinson attended college in Dublin, then in London; and he later pastored in both Dublin and London, then in the seacoast community of Brighton. He enjoyed writing poetry, and three volumes were published: *Iona and Other Sonnets, Loveland,* and *Songs in God's World.* This poem is the only one that has endured the generations.

I especially like the second verse, for it reminds us of the freshness that fills our hearts when we trust Christ as our Savior. The words say:

> *Heav'n above is softer blue, Earth around is sweeter green!*
> *Something lives in every hue Christless eyes have never seen;*
> *Birds with gladder songs o'erflow, flowers with deeper beauties shine,*
> *Since I know, as I now know, I am His, and He is mine.*

I have no way of proving this, but I believe Robinson's words were inspired by Moody's testimony. D. L. Moody and Ira Sankey were setting Great Britain on fire. Their first evangelistic campaign to England and Ireland occurred in 1873, and Moody must have given his testimony many times and in many places. Robinson must have listened in rapt attention. Compare his verse to what Moody later wrote about the time he came to Jesus Christ as a teenager in Boston:

> *I remember the morning on which I came out of my room after I had first trusted*
> *Christ. I thought the old sun shone a good deal brighter than it ever had before—I*
> *thought it was just smiling upon me; and as I walked out upon Boston Common and*
> *heard the birds singing in the trees I thought they were all singing a song to me. Do*
> *you know, I fell in love with the birds? I had never cared for them before. It seemed*
> *to me that I was in love with all creation. I had not a bitter feeling against any man.*

The presence of Christ in our hearts makes the sun brighter, the sky bluer, the grass greener, the birds sweeter, and the flowers lovelier—since we know, as now we know, that "I am His, and He is mine."

Nothing but the Blood

Robert Lowry

Robert Lowry

1. What can wash a - way my sin? Noth-ing but the blood of Je - sus;
2. For my par-don, this I see, Noth-ing but the blood of Je - sus;
3. Noth-ing can for sin a-tone, Noth-ing but the blood of Je - sus;
4. This is all my hope and peace, Noth-ing but the blood of Je - sus;

What can make me whole a-gain? Noth-ing but the blood of Je - sus.
For my cleans-ing, this my plea, Noth-ing but the blood of Je - sus.
Naught of good that I have done, Noth-ing but the blood of Je - sus.
This is all my righ-teous-ness, Noth-ing but the blood of Je - sus.

O! pre-cious is the flow That makes me white as snow;

No oth-er fount I know; Noth-ing but the blood of Je - sus.

Nothing but the Blood
1876

... almost all things are purified with blood, and without shedding of blood there is no remission. Hebrews 9:22

s we thumb through our Bibles, we run across beloved and deeply under-lined verses like these:

And when I see the blood, I will pass over you ... It is the blood that makes atonement for the soul ... For this is My blood of the new covenant, which is shed for many for the remission of sins ... The church of God which He purchased with His own blood ... Christ Jesus whom God set forth as propitiation by His blood ... In Him we have redemption through His blood, the forgiveness of sins, according to the riches of His grace ... With His own blood He entered the Most Holy Place once for all, having obtained eternal redemption ... The precious blood of Christ, as of a lamb ... The blood of Jesus Christ His Son cleanses us from all sin.*

We shouldn't be surprised, then, as we study the great hymnists of history, to find their souls thrilled and their songs filled with this theme.

In 1739, Count Zinzendorf wrote his great "Jesus, Thy Blood and Righteous-ness." That same year, Charles Wesley penned, "His blood can make the foulest clean, / His blood availed for me."

The melancholy William Cowper wrote, "There is a fountain filled with blood / drawn from Emmanuel's veins / And sinners plunged beneath that flood / Lose all their guilty stains."

Perhaps the most popular hymn about the blood is this one, written by two men who came to Christ as teenagers. Robert Lowry, author of the words, came to Christ at age seventeen. William Doane confessed Christ as His Savior while in high school. Together they wrote hymns and published gospel songbooks.

When "Nothing but the Blood" was published in 1876, the attached Scripture was from Hebrews 9:22: "Without shedding of blood there is no remission." Most of our hymnals omit Lowry's original final two stanzas:

> *Now by this I'll overcome—Nothing but the blood of Jesus,*
> *Now by this I'll reach my home—Nothing but the blood of Jesus.*
>
> *Glory! Glory! This I sing—Nothing but the blood of Jesus,*
> *All my praise for this I bring—Nothing but the blood of Jesus.*

---

*Exodus 12:13, Leviticus 17:11; Matthew 26:28; Acts 20:28; Romans 3:24–25; Ephesians 1:7; Hebrews 9:12; 1 Peter 1:18; 1 John 1:7

God of Our Fathers

Daniel C. Roberts

George W. Warren

Trumpets before each stanza

1. God of our fa - thers, whose Al - might - y hand
2. Thy love di - vine hath led us in the past,
3. From war's a - larms, from dead - ly pes - ti - lence,
4. Re - fresh Thy peo - ple on their toil - some way,

Leads forth in beau - ty all the star - ry band
In this free land by Thee our lot is cast;
Be Thy strong arm our ev - er sure de - fense;
Lead us from night to nev - er end - ing day;

Of shin - ing worlds in splen - dor through the skies,
Be Thou our Rul - er, Guard - ian, Guide, and Stay,
Thy true re - li - gion in our hearts in - crease,
Fill all our lives with love and grace di - vine,

Our grate - ful songs be - fore Thy throne a - rise.
Thy word our law, Thy paths our cho - sen way.
Thy boun - teous good - ness nour - ish us in peace.
And glo - ry, laud, and praise be ev - er Thine!

God of Our Fathers

1876

The God of our fathers has chosen you that you should know His will, and see the Just One, and hear the voice of His mouth. Acts 22:14

This patriotic hymn represents a double celebration of America's one hundredth birthday. The words were written in 1876 by a New England pastor in honor of the one hundredth anniversary of the signing of the Declaration of Independence. The music was written twelve years later in celebration of the one hundredth anniversary of the adoption of the United States Constitution.

Daniel Crain Roberts, a thirty-four-year-old veteran of the Civil War, authored the words. Born on Long Island in New York in 1841, Daniel attended college in Ohio and served as a private with the 84th Ohio Volunteers during the War Between the States. As the war ended, he was ordained as a deacon in the Presbyterian Episcopalian church, and shortly afterward as a priest. He served for the next thirty years pastoring Episcopalian churches in New England, including a decades-long pastorate of St. Paul's Church in Concord, New Hampshire.*

It was while serving as rector of St. Thomas Episcopal Church in Brandon, Vermont, as the nation celebrated its one hundredth birthday, that Daniel wrote this hymn. He later submitted it anonymously to the committee for the Episcopal hymnal, and it was accepted. It is the only hymn for which he is remembered.

The majestic melody is not the one to which it was originally sung. When Daniel wrote "God of Our Fathers," he set the words to the tune of the Russian national anthem! It was twelve years later that George William Warren, a self-taught organist, composed the stately tune with its trumpet fanfares. It was called NATIONAL HYMN, written to commemorate the one hundredth anniversary of the U.S. Constitution.

George Warren, lacking formal training, had originally pursued a business career. But his natural talent soon shoved him into music, and he eventually became one of America's premier organists. During his career, he served various congregations in New York City, and he also composed anthems and edited *Warren's Hymns and Tunes as Sung at St. Thomas' Church*, in 1888. He also wrote GUIDE ME for the words of the great Welsh hymn, "Guide Me, O Thou Great Jehovah."

When George Warren died in 1902, there was a feeling that no organist could play as well as he could, so not a single note of music was played at his funeral, which was attended by thousands.

---

*Interestingly, this is the same church in which, in 2003, the controversial Rev. Gene Robinson was ordained as Episcopalians' first openly homosexual bishop.

Immortal, Invisible, God Only Wise

Walter Chalmers Smith

Welsh Hymn Melody

1. Im - mor - tal, in - vis - i - ble, God on - ly wise,
2. Un - rest - ing, un - hast - ing, and si - lent as light;
3. To all, life Thou giv - est, to both great and small;
4. Great Fa - ther of glo - ry, pure Fa - ther of light;

In light in - ac - ces - si - ble hid from our eyes;
Nor want - ing, nor wast - ing, Thou rul - est in might.
In all life Thou liv - est, the true life of all;
Thine an - gels a - dore Thee, all veil - ing their sight;

Most bless - ed, most glo - rious, the An - cient of Days;
Thy jus - tice, like moun - tains, high soar - ing a - bove
We blos - som and flour - ish as leaves on the tree,
All praise we would ren - der: O help us to see

Al - might - y, vic - to - rious, Thy great name we praise.
Thy clouds, which are foun - tains of good - ness and love.
And with - er and per - ish, but naught chang - eth Thee.
'Tis on - ly the splen - dor of light hid - eth Thee.

Immortal, Invisible, God Only Wise

1876

Now to the King eternal, immortal, invisible, to God who alone is wise, be honor and glory forever and ever. Amen. 1 Timothy 1:17

The city of Edinburgh, Scotland, with its Royal Mile and rugged hilltop castle, has produced some of Christianity's greatest hymnists: George Matheson ("O Love That Wilt Not Let Me Go"), Horatius Bonar ("I Heard the Voice of Jesus Say"), Elizabeth Celphane ("Beneath the Cross of Jesus"), and William MacKay ("Revive Us Again"), to name a few. And who but the sturdy Scotch Presbyterians could produce such a powerful hymn on the sovereign, eternal power of God as "Immortal, Invisible, God Only Wise"?

The author, Walter Chalmers Smith, was born in Aberdeen on December 5, 1824. After attending grammar school at the University of Aberdeen, he enrolled in New College, Edinburgh, and was ordained as a minister in the Free Church of Scotland in 1850. He pastored churches in several places, including the lovely Scottish village of Milnathort from 1853 to 1858.

In 1874, he became pastor of the Free High Church (Presbyterian) of Edinburgh, a charge he kept until his retirement in 1894.* Two years into his pastorate, he published a collection of hymns titled *Hymns of Christ and the Christian Life*. It was here that "Immortal, Invisible, God Only Wise" was introduced to the world.

Walter Smith was blessed with two other honors. In 1893, he was elected Moderator of the Free Church of Scotland. And in 1902, a collection of his poetry was published. His poems reflect his Scottish nature and remind us of Robert Burns. A number of them had appeared in various publications over the years, published under the pseudonyms "Orwell" and "Herman Knott." One of his best-known poems, "Glenaradale," begins:

> *There is no fire of the crackling boughs / On the hearth of our fathers,*
> *There is no lowing of brown-eyed cows / On the green meadows,*
> *Nor do the maidens whisper vows / In the still gloaming,*
> *Glenaradale.*

"Immortal, Invisible, God Only Wise" was based on 1 Timothy 1:17. It was originally published in six stanzas. When the hymn was republished in 1884, Smith made a few alterations. Today's version uses Smith's first three stanzas, and the fourth stanza is pieced together from lines in the now-discarded verses.

The powerful melody is called ST. DENIO based on a Welsh folk song.

---

*The beautiful building of Edinburgh's Free High Church was vacated by its members in 1934, and now serves as the Library for the University of Edinburgh. It is obvious to anyone who enters the library that it was originally a church.

A Child of the King

Harriet E. Buell

John B. Sumner

1. My Fa - ther is rich in hous - es and lands, He hold - eth the
2. I once was an out - cast stran - ger on earth, A sin - ner by
3. A tent or a cot - tage, why should I care? They're build - ing a

wealth of the world in His hands! Of ru - bies and dia - monds, of
choice, and an al - ien by birth; But I've been a - dopt - ed, my
pal - ace for me o - ver there; Though ex - iled from home, yet

sil - ver and gold, His cof - fers are full, He has rich - es un - told.
name's writ - ten down, An heir to a man - sion, a robe, and a crown.
still I may sing: All glo - ry to God, I'm a child of the King.

I'm a child of the King, A child of the King,

With Je - sus my Sav - ior I'm a child of the King.

A Child of the King

1877

But God demonstrates His own love toward us, in that while we were still sinners, Christ died for us. Romans 5:8

As I left my hometown of Cazenovia, New York," wrote the author of this hymn, Harriet (Hattie) Buell, "bound for the 1876 camp meeting held at the Thousand Island Park in upper New York State, my heart was hungering for the spiritual food I knew would be awaiting me there. It was an occasion I looked forward to each year, for God seemed to speak to people's hearts and especially to mine in an unusual way at that hallowed spot.

"I will never forget the opening Sunday morning service. Beginning with the doxology and through each hymn and Scripture, it all served to remind me of the greatness of a God who had made the earth, the skies, and the great universe, yet loved and cared for us, His children.

"The speaker that morning chose as his topic our relationship to God through His Son, Jesus Christ. How man, as a sinner, was alienated and far from God; but how he became an heir of God and a joint heir with Jesus Christ through faith in His finished work on the Cross. In the course of the message, the speaker could control himself no longer and shouted, 'Christian friends, we are the children of a King! Our Heavenly Father's a King! Poor ones, take heart, you'll have a palace someday built for you by Jesus Himself!'

"I don't have to tell you that I felt as if I were walking on air as I left that service and as I walked toward my cottage. The complete set of words had come to me, and I entitled them, 'The Child of a King.'"*

Meanwhile the Lord was preparing John Sumner to compose the music for Hattie's poem. Sumner, a young pastor in Pennsylvania, had traveled with his family throughout the Susquehanna Valley, teaching singing schools. One of his greatest joys had been meeting hymnist Philip Bliss. When the stunning news came of the terrible train wreck that took Bliss's life, Sumner knelt and prayed that in some way he might continue and complete Bliss's work.

The following February, while reading a Methodist revival magazine, *The Northern Christian Advocate,* he found Hattie's poem and set it to music. Gaining quick popularity, it soon found its place beside Bliss's songs in the gospel hymnbooks of the day.

---

*I'm indebted to the "Dean of Gospel Music," Alfred B. Smith, for this account which he preserved in his *Treasury of Hymn Histories.*

Break Thou the Bread of Life

Mary A. Lathbury, stanzas 1 & 2
Alexander Groves, stanzas 3 & 4

William F. Sherwin

1. Break Thou the bread of life, Dear Lord, to me,
2. Bless Thou the truth, dear Lord, To me, to me,
3. Thou art the Bread of Life, O Lord, to me,
4. O send Thy Spir - it, Lord, Now un - to me,

As Thou didst break the loaves be - side the sea;
As Thou didst bless the bread By Gal - i - lee;
Thy ho - ly Word the truth That sav - eth me;
That He may touch my eyes And make me see;

Be - yond the sa - cred page I seek Thee, Lord,
Then shall all bon - dage cease, All fet - ters fall;
Give me to eat and live With Thee a - bove;
Show me the truth con - cealed with - in Thy Word,

My spir - it pants for Thee, O liv - ing Word.
And I shall find my peace, My All in all.
Teach me to love Thy truth, For Thou art love.
For in Thy book re - vealed I see Thee, Lord.

Break Thou the Bread of Life

1877

And Jesus said to them, "I am the bread of life. He who comes to Me shall never hunger, and he who believes in Me shall never thirst." John 6:35

n August 4, 1874, Methodist ministers John Vincent and Lewis Miller organized a Sunday school training camp beside Lake Chautauqua in New York. It was a hit. Families arrived in large numbers, paid the entrance fees, and moved into tents or cottages near an outdoor amphitheater.

Wanting national exposure, Vincent and Miller plotted to get President U. S. Grant to visit. "It would be a positive gain for the Bible, the Sunday school, and the Christian church if the President of the United States should come," wrote Vincent.

Somehow they pulled it off. On August 14, 1875, Grant's special train pulled into the station as cannons boomed and local bands played "Hail to the Chief." After an elaborate twelve-course lunch in a local home, Grant's party boarded a procession of steamboats and proceeded to the Chautauqua Camp Grounds where twenty thousand cheering people greeted the president.

Among them was Mary A. Lathbury, a local Christian who had been informally designated the "Poet Laureate of Chautauqua." She had written a "Song of Welcome" with which to greet the Commander-in-Chief on his arrival. The chorus:

> *Greet him! Let the air around him benedictions bear!*
> *Let the hearts of all the people circle him with prayer!*

This was one of the high points in the simple life of Mary Artemesia Lathbury. The daughter of a Methodist preacher, Mary was a native New Yorker who served as general editor of publications for the children/youth division of the Methodist Sunday School Union. She was also involved in the temperance movement and in the Chautauqua training programs.

Her hymns, however, have been her most enduring legacy, including the popular "Day Is Dying in the West," written on the shore of Lake Chautauqua.

In 1877, John Vincent asked Mary to write a hymn for the Chautauqua Bible Study Hour. Its focus was on studying Jesus Christ, the "Bread of Life" (John 6:35). In response, Mary wrote a two-stanza hymn entitled, "Break Thou the Bread of Life." (The final two stanzas were added later by Alexander Groves.)

Regarding her gift for art and verse, Mary Lathbury said that God had once told her: "Remember, my child, that you have a gift of weaving fancies into verse and a gift with the pencil of producing visions that come to your heart; consecrate these to Me as thoroughly as you do your inmost spirit."

Who Is on the Lord's Side?

Frances R. Havergal

C. Luise Reichardt

1. Who is on the Lord's side? Who will serve the King? Who will be His help-ers, Oth-er lives to bring? Who will leave the world's side? Who will face the foe? Who is on the Lord's side? Who for Him will go? By Thy call of mer-cy, By Thy grace di-vine, We are on the Lord's side— Sav-ior, we are Thine.

2. Not for weight of glo-ry, Not for crown and palm, En-ter we the ar-my, Raise the war-rior psalm; But for love that claim-eth Lives for whom He died; He whom Je-sus nam-eth Must be on His side. By Thy love con-strain-ing,

3. Fierce may be the con-flict, Strong may be the foe, But the King's own ar-my None can o-ver-throw. 'Round His stan-dard rang-ing, Vic-tory to se-cure, For His truth un-chang-ing Makes the tri-umph sure. Joy-ful-ly en-list-ing

Who Is on the Lord's Side?

1877

Then Moses stood in the entrance of the camp, and said, "Whoever is on the LORD's side—come to me!" Exodus 32:26

hen people ask me my favorite hymn, I thrash about for an answer, but when I'm asked for my favorite hymn writer, I respond quickly: Frances Ridley Havergal, author of such hymns as "Take My Life and Let It Be" and "Like a River Glorious."

Frances was born just before Christmas in 1846 in Astley, Worcestershire, England. Her father, Rev. William Henry Havergal, was a humble but influential pastor who passionately worked to improve the hymnody of the Anglican Church. He is the composer of the tune ZOAN ("I Sing the Mighty Power of God"), and the author of one hundred hymns.

As a child, Frances worried that she was not among the "Elect." As her mother was dying, she called Frances, eleven, to her bedside and said, "You are my youngest little girl, and I feel more anxious about you than the rest. I do pray for the Holy Spirit to lead and guide you. And remember, nothing but the precious blood of Christ can make you clean and lovely in God's sight."

It wasn't until Frances was fifteen that she found assurance of salvation in Christ. Soon she was writing poems and hymns to the Lord. Frances had a quick mind, a clarion voice, and a radiant personality that drew people like a magnet. During her thirties she began writing devotional books, and the combination of her hymns, poetry, and books made her one of the most popular Christian authors in England.

The year 1877 was very busy for Frances. To a friend, she wrote "What shall I do? Your letter would take two hours to answer, and I have not ten minutes; fifteen to twenty letters to write every morning, proofs to correct, editors waiting for articles, poems and music I cannot touch, American publishers clamoring for poems or any manuscripts, Bible readings or classes weekly, many anxious ones waiting for help, a mission week coming and other work after that. And my doctor says my physique is too weak to balance the nerves and brain, and that I ought not to touch a pen."

But she did touch a pen that year. After studying Exodus 32:26, she wrote this great hymn, "Who Is on the Lord's Side?" with its resounding answer:

By Thy call of mercy, by Thy grace divine,
We are on the Lord's side—Savior, we are Thine!

Truehearted, Wholehearted

Frances R. Havergal

George C. Stebbins

1. True - heart - ed, whole - heart - ed, faith - ful and loy - al,
2. True - heart - ed, whole - heart - ed, Full - est al - le - giance
3. True - heart - ed, whole - heart - ed, Sav - ior all - glo - rious!

King of our lives, by Thy grace we will be;
Yield - ing hence - forth to our glo - ri - ous King;
Take Thy great pow - er and reign there a - lone,

Un - der the stan - dard ex - alt - ed and roy - al,
Val - iant en - deav - or and lov - ing o - be - dience,
O - ver our wills and af - fec - tions vic - to - rious,

Strong in Thy strength we will bat - tle for Thee.
Free - ly and joy - ous - ly now we would bring.
Free - ly sur - ren - dered and whol - ly Thine own.

Truehearted, Wholehearted

1878

And he commanded them, saying, "Thus you shall act in the fear of the LORD, faithfully and with a loyal heart." 2 Chronicles 19:9

I treasure my small collection of Frances Havergal's old devotional books. Many of them are based on her favorite theme—the joy of trusting and serving Jesus the King. "How glad we are that He Himself is our King," she wrote. "We are so sure He is able to subdue all things unto Himself in this inner kingdom which we cannot govern at all. We are so glad to take Him at His word and give up the government into His hands, asking Him to be our King in very deed, and to set up His throne of peace in the long-disturbed and divided citadel (of our minds), praying that He would bring every thought into captivity of His gentle obedience."

It was along these lines in 1878 that she wrote "Truehearted, Wholehearted, Faithful, and Loyal, / King of our Lives, by Thy grace, we will be."

Unknown to Frances, her time of earthly service to the King was ending. The next year, her health failed alarmingly. She was only forty-two, and very busy. Not only was her writing ministry in full bloom, but she was traveling widely promoting Christian and missionary causes.

She was aware of her decline, however; and one Sunday in April 1878, while walking to church, Frances turned to her sister, saying, "Marie, I've come to the conclusion it would be very nice to go to heaven."

A month later, her strength collapsed. When the doctor called on her, she startled him by asking, "Do you think I've a chance of going?" As her loved ones gathered at her bedside, they were astonished by her attitude. "If I am going, it is too good to be true," she told them. A little later, she looked up smiling and said, "Splendid to be so near the gates of heaven! I am lost in amazement! There has not failed one word of all His good promises!"

Shortly afterward, Frances looked up steadfastly as if seeing the Lord. "For ten minutes we watched that almost visible meeting with her King," wrote Maria, "and her countenance was so glad, as if she were already talking to Him! Then she tried to sing, but after one sweet, high note—'He . . .'—her voice failed and her brother commended her soul into the Redeemer's hand, and she passed away."

Follow On

William O. Cushing

Robert Lowry

Follow On

1878

Then Jesus spoke to them again, saying, "I am the light of the world. He who follows Me shall not walk in darkness, but have the light of life." John 8:12

Someone said that when God closes a door He always opens a window. What we don't realize is that the window is often much bigger than the door.

William Cushing (the man who converted George Root's Civil War song into the gospel hymn "Ring the Bells of Heaven") was born on the last day of 1823 into a Unitarian home in Massachusetts. He was converted as a child. Entering the ministry with the Disciples of Christ, he served twenty years as a faithful pastor in several New York cities and towns.

In 1870, William's wife died and his own health broke. Though only forty-seven, he suffered a paralysis that affected his voice and made it nearly impossible for him to preach. He fell into depression, but finally offered this prayer of resignation: "Lord, give me something to do for Thee."

Shortly thereafter he began writing hymns, especially for children. His little song, "Jewels," for example, became one of the most popular children's hymns of the late nineteenth century. The words said:

> *When He cometh, when He cometh | To make up His jewels,*
> *All His jewels, precious jewels, | His loved and His own.*
> *Like the stars of the morning, | His brightness adorning,*
> *They shall shine in their beauty, | Bright gems for His crown.*

In subsequent years, William produced more than three hundred hymns, including the favorite "Under His Wings."

About "Follow On," William later told Ira Sankey:

> *I wrote this hymn in 1878. Longing to give up all for Christ who had given his life for me, I wanted to be willing to lay everything at his feet, with no wish but to do his will, to live henceforth only for his glory. Out of this feeling came the hymn, "Follow On." It was written with the prayer and the hope that some heart might by it be led to give up all for Christ. Much of the power and usefulness of the hymn, however, are due to Mr. Lowry, who put it into song.*

Sankey added that William's work as a hymnist has "blessed tens of thousands throughout the world, whom his voice as a preacher could never have reached."

Are You Washed in the Blood?

Elisha A. Hoffman

Elisha A. Hoffman

1. Have you been to Je - sus for the cleans - ing power? Are you
2. Are you walk - ing dai - ly by the Sav - ior's side? Are you
3. Lay a - side the gar - ments that are stained with sin And be

washed in the blood of the Lamb? Are you ful - ly trust - ing in His
washed in the blood of the Lamb? Do you rest each mo - ment in the
washed in the blood of the Lamb. There's a foun - tain flow - ing for the

grace this hour? Are you washed in the blood of the Lamb?
Cru - ci - fied? Are you washed in the blood of the Lamb? Are you
soul un - clean, O be washed in the blood of the Lamb!

washed in the blood, in the soul-cleans-ing blood of the Lamb? Are your

gar - ments spot-less? Are they white as snow? Are you washed in the blood of the Lamb?

Are You Washed in the Blood?

1878

To Him who loved us and washed us from our sins in His own blood . . . to Him be glory and dominion forever and ever. Amen. Revelation 1:5, 6

 s a preacher, Elisha Hoffman was of average ability, but as a minister who cared for the poor and downtrodden, he excelled. He also stands among the giants of the gospel song era, the author of such favorites as: "I Must Tell Jesus," "Down at the Cross," and "Leaning on the Everlasting Arms."

Elisha was born on May 7, 1839, in Orwigsburg, Pennsylvania, and died ninety years later, in 1929, in Chicago. His parents, Rev. Francis A. and Rebecca Ann Hoffman, were devoted to Christ and devoted to a denomination called the Evangelical Association. They gave their son the middle name of Albright in honor of Jacob Albright, the denomination's founder.

Elisha attended public school in Philadelphia, then enrolled in Union Bible Seminary at New Berlin, Pennsylvania, planning to follow his father's footsteps into the ministry. When the Civil War erupted, Elisha served with the 47th Pennsylvania Infantry Division. Near the war's end, he married Susan Orwig, the daughter of one of the bishops of the Evangelical Association. The couple moved to Cleveland, Ohio, where Elisha was hired as the publishing agent for the Board of Publications of the Evangelical Association. He later pastored churches in Ohio, Illinois, and Michigan.

In 1894, Elisha became the first music editor for the Hope Publishing Company of Chicago. He remained in that post until 1912. Through his years at Hope, he published fifty songbooks and hymnals and wrote the words or music to at least one thousand gospel and Sunday school songs. Some sources put the number at two thousand.

"Are You Washed in the Blood?" first appeared in *Spiritual Songs for Gospel Meetings and Sunday School,* published in 1878. Three years later, it was included in Ira Sankey's *Sacred Songs and Solos,* published in England.

Elisha Hoffman is credited for popularizing the element of "altar" into hymnology of his day. Consider this well-known hymn that came from his pen:

You have longed for sweet peace, | And for faith to increase,
And have earnestly, fervently prayed; | But you cannot have rest, or be perfectly blest,
Until all on the altar is laid.

Is your all on the altar of sacrifice laid? | Your heart does the Spirit control?
You can only be blest, and have peace and sweet rest,
As you yield Him your body and soul.

Breathe on Me

Edwin Hatch

B.B. McKinney

1. Ho - ly Spir-it, breathe on me, Un - til my heart is clean;
2. Ho - ly Spir-it, breathe on me, My stub-born will sub - due.
3. Ho - ly Spir-it, breathe on me, Fill me with pow'r di - vine;
4. Ho - ly Spir-it, breathe on me, Till I am all Thine own,

Let sun - shine fill its in-most part, With not a cloud be-tween.
Teach me in words of liv - ing flame What Christ would have me do.
Kin - dle a flame of love and zeal With - in this heart of mine.
Un - til my will is lost in Thine, To live for Thee a - lone.

Breathe on me, breathe on me, Ho - ly Spir-it, breathe on me;

Take Thou my heart, cleanse ev-'ry part, Ho - ly Spir - it, breathe on me.

Breathe on Me

1878

And when He had said this, He breathed on them, and said to them, "Receive the Holy Spirit." John 20:22

John 20:22 has inspired several great hymns of aspiration. This one, "Breathe on Me," was written in 1878 by an Anglican priest named Edwin Hatch, who, deeply impressed with the words of John 20:22, wanted to be included in our Lord's blessing to His disciples. Hatch published his hymn in a privately printed leaflet entitled *Between Doubt and Prayer.*

During his lifetime, Hatch was one of England's greatest theologians. He became a scholar of Pembroke College, Oxford, and won the Ellerton prize in 1858. He was professor of classics in Trinity College, Toronto, from 1859 to 1862, when he became rector of the high school at Quebec. Returning to England in 1867, he was appointed vice-principal of St. Mary Hall at Oxford. He gave the famous Bampton Lectures in 1880 and the Hibbert Lectures in 1888. One commentator remarked that Hatch's religious poems were "a beautiful supplement to his theology and reveal the depth and tenderness of his religious life."

In 1937, inspired by Hatch's hymn, the Southern Baptist hymnist, B. B. McKinney, wrote an "updated version" which he titled, "Holy Spirit, Breathe on Me." It is essentially a "paraphrase" of Hatch's hymn. McKinney was a Southern Baptist pastor, educator, and songwriter who published over 500 hymns. He would have undoubtedly written many others but for his sudden death in a car accident in 1952.

Jesus' words in John 20:22 have inspired a number of similar verses. Wesley's great hymn, "Love Divine, All Loves Excelling" echoes this thought in the stanza that says: "Breathe, O breathe Thy Loving Spirit into every troubled breast! / Let us all in Thee inherit; let us find that second rest."

Alfred Vine wrote a hymn (often sung to the tune "O Master Let Me Walk with Thee") that says:

> *O breath of God, breathe on us now, / And move within us while we pray:*
> *The Spring of our new life art Thou, / The very light of our new day.*

My favorite treatment of this theme is Bessie Head's 1914 hymn, "O Breath of Life," which says:

> *O Breath of life, come sweeping through us, / Revive Thy church with life and power;*
> *O Breath of life, come, cleanse, renew us, / And fit Thy church to meet this hour.*

May our Lord answer all these prayers. Come now, Lord, and breathe on us.

O Master, Let Me Walk with Thee

Washington Gladden

H. Percy Smith

1. O Mas - ter, let me walk with Thee
2. Help me the slow of heart to move
3. Teach me Thy pa - tience still with Thee
4. In hope that sends a shin - ing ray

In low - ly paths of ser - vice free;
By some clear, win - ning word of love;
In clos - er, dear - er com - pa - ny,
Far down the fu - ture's broad - 'ning way,

Tell me Thy se - cret; Help me bear
Teach me the way - ward feet to stay,
In work that keeps faith sweet and strong,
In peace that on - ly Thou canst give,

the strain of toil, The fret of care.
And guide them in the home - ward way.
In trust that tri - umphs o - ver wrong.
With Thee, O Mas - ter, let me live.

O Master, Let Me Walk with Thee

1879

Therefore you shall keep the commandments of the LORD your God, to walk in His ways and to fear Him. Deuteronomy 8:6

Washington Gladden (so named because his great-grandfather served as George Washington's bodyguard during the Revolutionary War) was a Congregational pastor. He served in New York, Massachusetts, and Ohio during the post-Civil War industrial era when racial and economic injustice was rampant. People everywhere were searching for a new American ethic.

Washington wanted to give them one, and he is remembered today as the father of the Social Gospel in America, an activist who crusaded tirelessly for political and moral reform in industry, commerce, and politics. He was a champion of the "working man," a strong supporter of union rights, and he was unafraid to attack corruption in politics.

Unfortunately, Washington advanced the liberal-leaning biblical criticism that undercut conservative theology at the turn of the century. He was more concerned with applied Christianity than with biblical Christianity. He wrote thirty-eight books on such themes. In one of them he said: "The Bible is not an infallible Book, in the sense in which it is popularly supposed to be infallible. . . . The Book is not infallible historically. . . . It is not infallible scientifically. . . . It is not infallible morally. . . ."

He embraced evolution and opposed the outreach efforts of evangelists like Billy Sunday. He infuriated his own denomination by railing against a large gift to foreign missions because it was donated by the Standard Oil Company. Not surprisingly, conservative Christians opposed Washington's liberal theology. During a period of heavy criticism, he sat alone in his church and wrote this hymn.

Dr. Charles H. Richards later saw it in a magazine, and, while loving the poem, was troubled by the second verse:

> *O Master, let me walk with Thee / Before the taunting Pharisee; /*
> *Help me to bear the sting of spite, / The hate of men who hide Thy light, /*
> *The sore distrust of souls sincere / Who cannot read Thy judgments clear, /*
> *The dullness of the multitude, / Who dimly guess that Thou art good.*

After discarding that verse, Richards selected music for the remaining stanzas and included them in his book *Christian Praise.*

Ironically, Christians of all stripes have embraced this as a prayer of their own while laboring for the Master in a world desperately needing the transformation of Christ.

God Be with You

Jeremiah E. Rankin

William G. Tomer

1. God be with you 'til we meet a-gain;   By His coun-sels guide, up - hold you,
2. God be with you 'til we meet a-gain;   'Neath His wings pro - tect - ing hide you,
3. God be with you 'til we meet a-gain;   Keep love's ban - ner float - ing o'er you,
4. God be with you 'til we meet a-gain;   When life's per - ils thick con - found you,

With His sheep se - cure-ly fold you;   God be with you 'til we meet a - gain.
Dai - ly man - na still pro - vide you;   God be with you 'til we meet a - gain.
Smite death's threat'ning wave be - fore you;   God be with you 'til we meet a - gain.
Put His arms un - fail-ing round you;   God be with you 'til we meet a - gain.

'Til we meet,   'til we meet,   'Til we meet at Je - sus' feet;

'Til we meet,   'til we meet,   God be with you 'til we meet a - gain.

God Be with You

1880

Grace, mercy, and peace will be with you from God the Father and from the Lord Jesus Christ, the Son of the Father, in truth and love. 2 John 3

n September 19, 1945, missionary Darlene Deibler was liberated from the Japanese Prison Camp at Kampili, seventeen days after Japan had signed the Instrument of Surrender aboard the USS *Missouri*. She was in bad shape, having been subjected to years of physical suffering and mental torture.

Eight years before, Darlene and her husband, Russell, had landed as missionaries in New Guinea. Plunging into the work, they were making solid progress in building a growing church, aided by Darlene's dear friend and mentor, Dr. Robert Jaffray. Now both Russell and Dr. Jaffray were dead, and Darlene was leaving behind two lonely white crosses on the hillside. As a 28-year-old widow, she was returning home without a single possession. All her mementos and private keepsakes were gone, her loved ones were dead, and her body was debilitated by exhaustion, starvation, malaria, beriberi, and dysentery.

For over four years, she had witnessed atrocities that can scarcely be described. Prisoners all around her had suffered horrible deaths, and she herself had seen the inside of death cells. During that time, not one letter or package had reached her.

As the boat carried her from her island prison, she prayed a bitter prayer: "Lord, I'll never come to these islands again. They've robbed me of everything that was most dear to me."

Suddenly she heard voices, Indonesian voices ringing from the distance. There on the shore were those who had come to know the Lord through her mission, raising their voices, singing: "God be with you till me meet again. / By His counsels guide, uphold you, / With His sheep securely fold you; / God be with you till we meet again."

Darlene later wrote in her autobiography, *Evidence Not Seen*: "This song released the waters of bitterness that had flooded my soul, and the hurt began to drain from me as my tears flowed in a steady stream. The healing had begun. I knew then that some day, God only knew when, I would come back to these my people and my island home."

"God Be With You Till We Meet Again," was written by Jeremiah Rankin, pastor of Washington's First Congregational Church and president of Howard University, the great African-American college in the nation's capital. He wrote it, he said, after discovering that the term "good-bye" meant "God be with you."

Softly and Tenderly

Will L. Thompson

Will L. Thompson

1. Soft - ly and ten - der - ly Je - sus is call - ing, Call - ing for
2. Why should we tar - ry when Je - sus is plead - ing, Plead - ing for
3. O for the won - der - ful love He has prom - ised, Prom - ised for

you and for me. See, on the por - tals He's wait - ing and watch - ing,
you and for me? Why should we lin - ger and heed not His mer - cies,
you and for me! Though we have sinned, He has mer - cy and par - don,

Watch - ing for you and for me. Come home, come home,
Mer - cies for you and for me? Come home, come home,
Par - don for you and for me.

Ye who are wea - ry, come home; Ear - nest - ly,

ten - der - ly Je - sus is call - ing, Call - ing, "O sin - ner, come home!"

Softly and Tenderly

1880

When Jesus heard it, He said to them, ". . . I did not come to call the righteous, but sinners, to repentance." Mark 2:17

T he author of this hymn, Will Lamartine Thompson, was born on November 7, 1847, in East Liverpool, Ohio, a small town on the Ohio River across from Kentucky. His father was a local merchant and a member of the Ohio State Legislature. Will attended Mt. Union College in nearby Alliance, Ohio. His musical abilities took him on to the Boston Conservatory of Music and to Leipzig, Germany, to study with the greats.

Will was interested in writing secular and patriotic songs; but when he traveled to Cleveland to sell his music manuscripts, he was offered only twenty-five dollars. Feeling slighted, Will rolled up his music, returned to East Liverpool, and prayed about what to do next.

When his father sent him to New York on business, Will took his songs to a printer, intent on publishing and selling them himself. "My Home on the Old Ohio," and "Gathering Shells from the Sea" were hits, and Will soon became known as the "Bard of Ohio." He became a millionaire.

The young man credited the Lord with his success, and, wanting to return thanks, he dedicated himself to writing Christian songs—and Christian songs only. He established Will L. Thompson & Co. with offices in East Liverpool and Chicago, and his quartet numbers sold two million copies.

In 1880, this hymn, "Softly and Tenderly," appeared in a book entitled *Sparkling Gems, Nos. 1 and 2 Combined*, published by Thompson & Co.

Despite his success and wealth, Will was known as a simple and sincere man. He felt concerned that while famous musicians traveled to the great cities to perform before large crowds, people in the rural areas and small towns seldom had anyone to come and minister to them in like fashion. So he loaded an upright piano on his two-horse wagon and drove into the country to sing and play his own songs in small churches throughout the Midwest.

In the late 1890s, he paid a visit to evangelist D. L. Moody, who was very ill and near death. Most visitors had been turned away, but when Moody heard that Thompson was downstairs, he called for him. "Will," he said, "I would rather have written 'Softly and Tenderly Jesus Is Calling,' than anything I have been able to do in my whole life."

A Shelter in the Time of Storm

Vernon J. Charlesworth

Ira D. Sankey

1. The Lord's our Rock, in Him we hide, A shel-ter in the time of storm;
2. A shade by day, de-fense by night, A shel-ter in the time of storm;
3. The rag-ing storms may round us beat, A shel-ter in the time of storm;
4. O Rock di-vine, O Ref-uge dear, A shel-ter in the time of storm;

Se - cure what-ev-er ill be-tide, A shel-ter in the time of storm.
No fears a-larm, no foes af-fright, A shel-ter in the time of storm.
We'll nev-er leave our safe re-treat, A shel-ter in the time of storm.
Be Thou our help-er ev-er near, A shel-ter in the time of storm.

O Je - sus is a Rock in a wea-ry land, A

wea - ry land, a wea-ry land; O Je - sus is a

Rock in a wea-ry land; A Shel-ter in the time of storm.

A Shelter in the Time of Storm

1880

You are my hiding place; You shall preserve me from trouble; You shall surround me with songs of deliverance. Selah. Psalm 32:7

fter a prolonged period of personal sorrow, I came to church one Sunday night broken in spirit. I'd asked my friend, missionary Tim Kenner, to bring the evening message. As he spoke from Colossians 3:3, a peace swept over me that has never left: "For you died, and your life is hidden with Christ in God."

Somehow I realized we must just die to our struggles, our sorrows, and our insolvable problems. We must flee to the Rock that is higher than we are (Psalm 61:2). We have to say, "Lord, if all around me collapses, my security is still in You. I'm hiding in You till the storm passes by."

The author of this hymn, Vernon John Charlesworth, was a British pastor, remembered in history for three things. First, he wrote an enduring biography of Rowland Hill, the British nonconformist preacher who used his personal wealth to build London's famous Surrey Chapel, where Vernon would later serve as co-pastor (along with Rev. Newman Hall).

Second, he left Surrey Chapel to become administrator of Charles Spurgeon's orphanage. Spurgeon's early biographer, W. Y. Fullerton, wrote, "The coming as headmaster of the orphanage of the Rev. Vernon J. Charlesworth, who up to then had been assistant to Newman Hall at Surrey Chapel, was an event of first importance. His influence on the boys, his advocacy of the orphanage, and his guidance of affairs were a great asset for many years, until in 1914 he finished his course."

Third, he wrote "A Shelter in the Time of Storm," based, it is said, on his study of Psalm 32:7: "You are my hiding place; You shall preserve me from trouble; You shall surround me with songs of deliverance."

Someone apparently set it to music, and it became popular along the coast of England. Ira Sankey, in his autobiography, wrote, "I found this hymn in a small paper published in London called *The Postman*. It was said to be a favorite song of the fishermen on the north coast of England, and they were often heard singing it as they approached their harbors in the time of storm. As the hymn was set to a weird minor tune, I decided to compose one that would be more practical, one that could be more easily sung by the people."

The Lily of the Valley

Charles W. Fry

William S. Mays

1. I have found a friend in Jesus, He's ev-'ry-thing to me, He's the fair-est of ten thou-sand to my soul; The Lil-y of the Val-ley, in Him a-lone I see All I need to cleanse and make me ful-ly whole. In sor-row He's my com-fort, in trou-ble He's my stay, He tells me ev-'ry care on Him to roll; He's the

2. He all my grief has tak-en and all my sor-rows borne, In temp-ta-tion He's my strong and might-y tow'r; I have all for Him for-sak-en and all my i-dols torn From my heart, and now He keeps me by His pow'r. Though all the world for-sake me and Sa-tan tempt me sore, Through Je-sus I shall safe-ly reach the goal; He's the

3. He will nev-er, nev-er leave me nor yet for-sake me here, While I live by faith and do His bless-ed will; A wall of fire a-bout me, I've noth-ing now to fear, From His man-na He my hun-gry soul shall fill. Then sweep-ing up to glo-ry I'll see His bless-ed face, Where riv-ers of de-light shall ev-er roll; He's the

Lil-y of the Val-ley, the

Fine

Bright and Morn-ing Star, He's the fair-est of ten thou-sand to my soul.

D.S. al Fine

Hal - le - lu - jah!

The Lily of the Valley
1881

I am the rose of Sharon, And the lily of the valleys. Song of Solomon 2:1

 s Christianity flourished during England's Victorian Era, great concern emerged for the orphans, the poor, the homeless, and the great masses battered by the rising Industrial Revolution. One man determined to make a difference.

William Booth, born in Nottingham in 1829, became a Christian as a teenager and instantly began winning others to Christ. He moved to London to open a pawn-broker's shop, but soon left his business to travel around as a Methodist evangelist. By 1865, his ministry was primarily focused among the poor of London's East End. Some evenings, he stumbled home, haggard with fatigue, his clothes torn, and bloody bandages swathing his head where a stone had struck him.

In 1878 Booth began calling his ministry "The Salvation Army," and something about that name captured people's imagination. Men, women, and children saw their conversion as leaving their old lives behind to enlist in a new army—the Lord's army. The movement spread throughout England and around the world.

That very year, 1878, a group of Salvation Army workers sought to establish a ministry in Salisbury, about ninety miles west of London. They were treated badly, bricks and eggs flying in their direction whenever they tried to preach on the streets.

There lived in Salisbury a local builder and amateur musician named Charles Fry, an active layman in the Methodist Church. Seeing the abuse hurled at the Salvation Army workers, Charles offered, along with his three strapping sons—musicians all— to serve as bodyguards.

The next day the four Frys showed up bearing their weapons—two cornets, a trombone, and a small tuba. Between fighting off hooligans, the four drew crowds for the preachers with their music. Thus was born the first of the now-famous Salvation Army Brass Bands.

In 1881, Charles Fry wrote "The Lily of the Valley." It was published that year in the December 29th issue of the Salvation Army magazine, *The War Cry*.

The next August, Charles passed away. Another verse he had written was inscribed on his grave:

The former things are past, and ended is the strife,
I'm safe home at last! I live an endless life!

O Love That Wilt Not Let Me Go

George Matheson

Albert L. Peace

1. O love that wilt not let me go, I rest my weary soul in Thee. I give Thee back the life I owe, That in Thine o-cean depths its flow, May rich - er, full - er be.

2. O light that fol-low'st all my way, I yield my flick-'ring torch to Thee. My heart re - stores its bor - rowed ray, That in Thy sun - shine's blaze its day, May bright - er, fair - er be.

3. O joy that seek - est me through pain, I can - not close my heart to Thee. I trace the rain - bow through the rain, And feel the prom - ise is not vain, That morn shall tear - less be.

4. O cross that lift - est up my head, I dare not ask to fly from Thee. I lay in dust life's glo - ry dead, And from the ground there blos - soms red, Life that shall end - less be.

O Love That Wilt
Not Let Me Go
1882

. . . Let me fall into the hand of the Lord, for His mercies are very great . . .
1 Chronicles 21:13

George Matheson was only a teenager when he learned that his poor eyesight was deteriorating further. Not to be denied, he continued straightaway with his plans to enroll in Glasgow University, and his determination led to his graduating at age nineteen. But as he pursued graduate studies for Christian ministry he became totally blind. His sisters joined ranks beside him, learning Greek and Hebrew to assist him in his studies, and he pressed faithfully on. But his spirit collapsed when his fiancée, unwilling to be married to a blind man, broke their engagement and returned his ring.

George never married, and the pain of that rejection never totally left him. Years later, his sister came to him, announcing her engagement. He rejoiced with her, but his mind went back to his own heartache. He consoled himself in thinking of God's love which is never limited, never conditional, never withdrawn, and never uncertain. Out of this experience it is said he wrote the hymn, *O Love That Wilt Not Let Me Go*, on June 6, 1882.

George Matheson became a powerful and popular preacher pastoring in the Scottish village of Innellan. Despite his flourishing ministry, there was one winter's evening when the Sunday night crowd was miserably small. George had worked hard on his sermon, but the empty chairs nearly defeated him. Nevertheless he did his best, not knowing that in the congregation was a visitor for the large St. Bernard's Church in Edinburgh, which was seeking a pastor. As a result, in 1886, he was called to St. Bernard's where he became one of Scotland's favorite preachers.

"Make every occasion a great occasion," Matheson later said. "You can never tell when somebody may be taking your measure for a larger place."

Recently while in Edinburgh, I tracked down George Matheson's old church, St. Bernard's, in a lovely residential neighborhood not far from Princess Street. The doors were locked shut, and this curious notice was posted to the front door:

Public Entertainment License
The premises will be used as a concert and dance hall,
and for no other purpose without written permission from the council.

Take Time to Be Holy

William D. Longstaff

George C. Stebbins

1. Take time to be ho - ly. Speak oft with thy Lord;
2. Take time to be ho - ly. The world rush - es on;
3. Take time to be ho - ly. Let Him be thy Guide;
4. Take time to be ho - ly, Be calm in thy soul;

A - bide in Him al - ways, And feed on His Word.
Spend much time in se - cret With Je - sus a - lone.
And run not be - fore Him, What - ev - er be - tide.
Each tho't and each mo - tive Be - neath His con - trol;

Make friends with God's chil - dren; Help those who are weak,
By look - ing to Je - sus, Like Him thou shalt be;
In joy or in sor - row, Still fol - low thy Lord,
Thus led by His Spir - it To foun - tains of love,

For - get - ting in noth - ing His bless - ing to seek.
Thy friends in thy con - duct His like - ness shall see.
And, look - ing to Je - sus, Still trust in His Word.
Thou soon shalt be fit - ted For ser - vice a - bove.

Take Time to Be Holy

1882

Because it is written, "Be holy, for I am holy." 1 Peter 1:16

The words to "Take Time to Be Holy" were written about 1882 by William Longstaff, a wealthy Englishman who served as treasurer of the Bethesda Free Chapel in Sunderland, a port city in Northeast England. His church hosted the first meetings held by D. L. Moody and Ira Sankey in that area, and Longstaff became a great supporter of the two.

In his book of hymn stories, Ira Sankey said that "Take Time to Be Holy" was prompted by a sermon William heard in New Brighton on the text "Be holy, for I am holy" (1 Peter 1:16). George C. Stebbins, who composed the music, said Longstaff was inspired to write this poem after hearing a missionary to China quoted as saying, "Take time to be holy." There's no reason why both stories can't be true.

The tune, HOLINESS, was composed by George C. Stebbins, who cast a long shadow over gospel music. In his book, *Reminiscences and Gospel Hymn Stories*, Mr. Stebbins told of his travels and ministries with people like D. L. Moody, Major Daniel Whittle, Philip P. Bliss, Ira Sankey, William Doane, and Fanny Crosby.

In 1890, Stebbins spent time in India working with evangelist George Pentecost. Someone mentioned the need for a hymn on holiness. Stebbins had a habit of making notebooks of poems and hymns by cutting and pasting.* Searching through his pages, he found a poem previously clipped and saved—Longstaff's "Take Time to Be Holy." He composed music for the stanzas and sent the words and music to Ira Sankey in New York where it was published. This hymn has not only aged well; it has become more and more relevant. If people in the 1880s needed to slow down and be holy, how much more now!

George Stebbins aged well, too. He lived to be nearly 100 years old, dying in 1945. When he was 95, living in a house in the Catskills, he received a visit from George Beverly Shea, who was just beginning the ministry of sacred song. Shea later described him as hard-of-hearing, but alert, "a tall man with whiskers" who "exuded great dignity and warmth."

Shea was persuaded to sing for the old man, but he had to sing loudly—and right into his ear.

---

*Over one hundred of these notebooks are now in the The George C. Stebbins Memorial Collection, housed in the rare book library of Washington's National Cathedral.

'Tis So Sweet to Trust in Jesus

Louisa M. R. Stead

William J. Kirkpatrick

1. 'Tis so sweet to trust in Je - sus, Just to take Him at His word;
2. O how sweet to trust in Je - sus, Just to trust His cleans - ing blood;
3. Yes, 'tis sweet to trust in Je - sus, Just from sin and self to cease;
4. I'm so glad I learned to trust Thee, Pre - cious Je - sus, Sav - ior friend;

Just to rest up - on His prom - ise; Just to know "Thus saith the Lord."
Just in sim - ple faith to plunge me, Neath the heal - ing, cleans - ing flood!
Just from Je - sus sim - ply tak - ing Life and rest and joy and peace.
And I know that Thou art with me, Wilt be with me to the end.

Je - sus, Je - sus how I trust Him! How I've proved Him o'er and o'er!

Je - sus, Je - sus, pre - cious Je - sus! O for grace to trust Him more!

'Tis So Sweet to Trust in Jesus

1882

In God I have put my trust; I will not be afraid. Psalm 56:11

How fitting that a missionary should write this hymn about faith and trust. Louisa M. R. Stead was born about 1850 in Dover, England, and became a Christian at age nine. She felt a burden to become a missionary in her teenage years. When she was 21 or so, she emigrated to the United States and attended a revival meeting in Urbana, Ohio. There the Lord deeply impressed her with a ringing missionary call.

She made plans to go to China, but her hopes were dashed when her health proved too frail for the climate there. Shortly afterward, she married a man named Stead. But sometime around 1879 or 1880, Mr. Stead drowned off the coast of Long Island. Some accounts say that he saved a boy who was drowning, and other accounts say both Mr. Stead and the boy perished. Other records suggest it was his own four-year-old daughter, Lily, that he saved. In any event, the family's beach-side picnic ended in tragedy for Louisa.

Shortly afterward, taking little Lily, Louisa went to South Africa as a missionary, and it was there during those days she wrote, "'Tis So Sweet to Trust in Jesus."

Louisa served in South Africa for fifteen years, and while there she married Robert Wodehouse. When her health forced a return to America, Robert pastored a local Methodist Church. In 1900, her health restored, Robert and Louisa attended a large missionary conference in New York, and were so enthused by the experience they again offered themselves as missionary candidates.

They arrived as Methodist missionaries in Rhodesia on April 4, 1901. "In connection with this whole mission there are glorious possibilities," she wrote. "One cannot in the face of the peculiar difficulties help saying, 'Who is sufficient for these things?' but with simple confidence and trust we may and do say, 'Our sufficiency is of God.'"

Louisa retired in 1911, and passed away in 1917; but her daughter, Lily, married missionary D. A. Carson and continued the work for many years at the Methodist mission station in southern Rhodesia (Zimbabwe).

Jesus Saves

Priscilla J. Owens

William J. Kirkpatrick

1. We have heard the joy-ful sound: Je-sus saves! Je-sus saves!
2. Waft it on the roll-ing tide: Je-sus saves! Je-sus saves!
3. Sing a-bove the bat-tle strife: Je-sus saves! Je-sus saves!
4. Give the winds a might-y voice: Je-sus saves! Je-sus saves!

Spread the tid-ings all a-round: Je-sus saves! Je-sus saves!
Tell to sin-ners far and wide: Je-sus saves! Je-sus saves!
By His death and end-less life: Je-sus saves! Je-sus saves!
Let the na-tions now re-joice: Je-sus saves! Je-sus saves!

Bear the news to ev-'ry land, Climb the steeps and cross the waves;
Sing ye is-lands of the sea; Ech-o back, ye o-cean caves;
Sing it bright-ly through the gloom, When the heart for mer-cy craves;
Shout sal-va-tion full and free, High-est hills and deep-est caves;

On-ward! 'tis our Lord's com-mand; Je-sus saves! Je-sus saves!
Earth shall keep her ju-bi-lee: Je-sus saves! Je-sus saves!
Sing in tri-umph o'er the tomb: Je-sus saves! Je-sus saves!
This our song of vic-to-ry: Je-sus saves! Je-sus saves!

Jesus Saves

1882

Believe in the Lord Jesus, and you will be saved—you and your household. Acts 16:31 (NIV)

This hymn came from the pen of a public school teacher named Priscilla Owens, a lifelong native of Baltimore, Maryland. For forty-nine years she taught school in Baltimore, devoting her spare time to her local Methodist Episcopal Church. In addition, Priscilla wrote prose and poetry, much of it being published in the *Methodist Protestant* and the *Christian Standard*. Priscilla wrote this hymn in 1882 for the anniversary of the Union Square Methodist Sunday School in Baltimore. Her original version said, "We have heard a joyful sound," but in later editions it was changed to "*the* joyful sound."

You might be familiar with another of Priscilla's poems, "Will Your Anchor Hold?"—a rousing hymn based on Hebrews 6:19: "This hope we have as an anchor of the soul, both sure and steadfast . . ." Most hymnals omit several of these verses, but they're too picturesque and perfect to be missed:

Will your anchor hold in the storms of life, / When the clouds unfold their wings of strife?
When the strong tides lift and the cables strain, / Will your anchor drift, or firm remain?

It is safely moored, 'twill the storm withstand, / For 'tis well secured by the Savior's hand;
And the cables, passed from His heart to mine, / Can defy that blast, thro' strength divine.

It will surely hold in the Straits of Fear— / When the breakers have told that the reef is near;
Though the tempest rave and the wild winds blow, / Not an angry wave shall our bark (boat) o'erflow.

It will firmly hold in the Floods of Death— / When the waters cold chill our latest breath,
On the rising tide it can never fail, / While our hopes abide within the Veil.

When our eyes behold through the gath'ring night / The city of gold, our harbor bright,
We shall anchor fast by the heav'nly shore, / With the storms all past forevermore.

CHORUS:
We have an anchor that keeps the soul / Steadfast and sure while the billows roll,
Fastened to the Rock which cannot move, / Grounded firm and deep in the Savior's love.

I Know Whom I Have Believed

Daniel W. Whittle

James McGranahan

1. I know not why God's won-drous grace To me He hath made known;
2. I know not how this sav-ing faith To me He did im - part,
3. I know not how the Spir - it moves, Con-vinc-ing men of sin,
4. I know not what of good or ill May be re-served for me.
5. I know not when my Lord may come, At night or noon - day fair,

Nor why, un-wor - thy, Christ in love Re - deemed me for His own.
Nor how be - liev - ing in His Word Wrought peace with - in my heart.
Re - veal-ing Je - sus through the Word, Cre - at - ing faith in Him.
Of wea - ry ways or gold - en days, Be - fore His face I see.
Nor if I'll walk the vale with Him, Or meet Him in the air.

But "I know whom I have be - liev - ed, And am per - suad - ed that He is

a - ble To keep that which I've com - mit-ted, Un-to Him a - gainst that day."

I Know Whom I Have Believed

1883

I know whom I have believed and am persuaded that He is able to keep what I have committed to Him until that Day. 2 Timothy 1:12

he golden era of English hymnody gave us names like Watts, Wesley, Newton, and Cowper. The lighter, more emotional age of American gospel music gave us a new set of names: Sankey, Crosby, Bliss, and the author of this hymn—Major Daniel Webster Whittle.

Whittle entered the world in Chicopee Falls, Massachusetts, about ninety miles west of Boston, on November 22, 1840. He left home as a teenager and moved to Chicago, where he secured a job as cashier at the Wells Fargo Bank.

When the Civil War broke out, Whittle enlisted in the 72nd Illinois Infantry. He had fallen deeply in love at the time, and on the day prior to his departure, he married his sweetheart, Abbie Hanson. With trembling heart, Abbie watched her new groom leave with Company B, heading into the bloodiest conflict in American history. Imagine her alarm when news came that he had been badly wounded in the Battle of Vicksburg and taken prisoner by the Confederates. His injuries were serious. He had lost his right arm.

But the Lord was in it, for while in the hospital recovering from his wounds, the young POW grew bored. Looking around for something to read, Whittle grabbed a spare New Testament. As he read its words, his heart was moved and he felt a need to accept Christ as his Savior. He wasn't ready to do that, however, and he drifted into sleep.

Shortly, a hospital orderly awakened him, saying that another POW was dying and wanted someone to pray with him. Whittle replied that he was unable, that someone else should be called. The orderly said, "But I thought you were a Christian; I have seen you reading your Bible."

Whittle later wrote, "I dropped on my knees and held the boy's hand in mine. In a few broken words, I confessed my sins and asked Christ to forgive me. I believed right there that He did forgive me. I then prayed and pleaded God's promises. When I arose from my knees, he was dead. A look of peace had come over his troubled face, and I cannot but believe that God who used him to bring me to the Savior used me to lead him to trust Christ's precious blood and find pardon."

Daniel Whittle later wrote this hymn—"I Know Whom I Have Believed"—as an expression of his testimony of faith in Jesus Christ.

There Shall Be Showers of Blessing

Daniel W. Whittle   James McGranahan

1. There shall be show-ers of bless-ing: This is the prom-ise of love;
2. There shall be show-ers of bless-ing: Pre-cious re-viv-ing a - gain;
3. There shall be show-ers of bless-ing: Send them up-on us, O Lord;
4. There shall be show-ers of bless-ing: O, that to-day they might fall,

There shall be sea-sons re - fresh-ing,   Sent from the Sav-ior a - bove.
O - ver the hills and the val-leys,   Sound of a - bun-dance of rain.
Grant to us now a re - fresh-ing,   Come, and now hon-or Thy Word.
Now as to God we're con - fess-ing,   Now, as on Je - sus we call!

Show - ers of bless-ing,   Show-ers of bless-ing we need:
Show - ers, show-ers of bless-ing,

Mer-cy drops 'round us are fall - ing,   But for the show-ers we plead.

There Shall Be Showers of Blessing

1883

I will cause showers to come down in their season; there shall be showers of blessing. Ezekiel 34:26

There Shall Be Showers of Blessing" by Major Daniel Whittle is one of those songs which, if learned in childhood, is never forgotten. Based on Ezekiel 34:26, it uplifts us with the happy assurance of God's unceasing blessing on our lives, even during our worst days.

When Howard Rutledge's plane was shot down over Vietnam, he parachuted into a little village and was immediately attacked and imprisoned. For the next seven years he endured brutal treatment. His food was little more than a bowl of pig fat. He was frequently cold, alone, and often tortured. How did he keep his sanity?

In his book, *In the Presence of Mine Enemies*, Rutledge wrote, "I wanted to talk about God and Christ and the church. But in Heartbreak (his concentration camp), there was no pastor, no Sunday school teacher, no Bible, no hymnbook. . . . I had completely neglected the spiritual dimension of my life. It took prison to show me how empty life is without God, and so I had to go back in my memory to those Sunday school days in Tulsa, Oklahoma. If I couldn't have a Bible and hymnbook, I would try to rebuild them in my mind.

"I tried desperately to recall . . . gospel choruses from childhood, and hymns we sang in church. The first three dozen songs were relatively easy. Every day I'd try to recall another verse or a new song. One night there was a huge thunderstorm—it was the season of the monsoon rains—and a bolt of lightning knocked out the lights and plunged the entire prison into darkness. I had been going over hymn tunes in my mind and stopped to lie down and sleep when the rains began to fall. The darkened prison echoed with wave after wave of water. Suddenly, I was humming my thirty-seventh song, one I had entirely forgotten since childhood.

Showers of blessing, showers of blessing we need!
Mercy drops round us are falling, but for the showers we plead.

"The enemy knew that the best way to break a man's resistance was to crush his spirit in a lonely cell," Howard wrote. "In other words, some of our POWs after solitary confinement lay down in a fetal position and died. All this talk of Scripture and hymns may seem boring to some, but it was the way we conquered our enemy and overcame the power of death around us."*

---

*Howard and Phyllis Rutledge with Mel and Lyla White, *In the Presence of Mine Enemies* (Old Tappan, NJ: Fleming H. Revell Co., 1973), excerpts taken from chapter 5.

Dear Lord and Father of Mankind

John C. Whittier

Frederick Charles Maker

Dear Lord and Father of Mankind

1884

For we ourselves were also once foolish, disobedient, deceived, serving various lusts and pleasures, living in malice and envy, hateful and hating one another. Titus 3:3

John Greenleaf Whittier was born into a poor Quaker family in Haverhill, Massachusetts, during the Christmas season of 1807. He worked hard on the family farm, receiving only scant education at the village school, but he fell in love with books and reading. At age 14, he borrowed his schoolteacher's copy of the poems of Robert Burns, and soon Whittier was writing compositions of his own.

The editor of a New England journal became so impressed with the teenage poet that he made a long journey just to meet the lad and to encourage him to pursue a career in journalism. That proved the inspiration Whittier needed, and later, at age twenty, he left home to devote his life to poetry, journalism, and literature, eventually becoming one of America's best-known poets.

That's not all he did. Few people realize that John Greenleaf Whittier was an ardent abolitionist who sat in the Massachusetts legislature, ran for Congress, and became one of the founders of the Republican Party.

His first love, however, was poetry; and several of Whittier's poems became popular hymns, though he once admitted, "I am really not a hymn writer, for the good reason that I know nothing of music." In fact, being a Quaker, Whittier himself never sang in church. Others, however, set his poems to music and nearly a hundred of them wound up on the pages of popular hymnals.

His best-known hymn, "Dear Lord and Father of Mankind," came from an unexpected source. In April, 1872, having read about the Hindu religion, Whittier published a poem in the *Atlantic Monthly* entitled "The Brewing of Soma." It told of the brewing of an intoxicating drink as part of a religious ritual in India in a foolish attempt to have a transcendent religious experience. Sometimes as Christians, Whittier suggested, we do something similar with our various services and ceremonies. "We brew in many a Christian clime, the heathen Soma still."

Whittier ended his poem with a series of verses that began, "Dear Lord and Father of mankind, forgive our foolish ways," in which he described the true worship that should characterize the church. In 1884, a hymnal editor named W. Garrett Horder extracted this portion of "The Brewing of Soma" and adapted it as a Christian hymn that still ranks as one of the finest ever written by an American author:

Dear Lord and Father of mankind, | Forgive our foolish ways;
Reclothe us in our rightful mind, | In purer lives Thy service find,
In deeper reverence, praise.

How Great Thou Art

Carl Boberg

Swedish Folk Melody

1. O Lord, my God, When I in awe-some won-der, Con-sid-er
2. When thru the woods and for-est glades I wan-der, And hear the
3. And when I think that God, His Son not spar-ing, Sent Him to
4. When Christ shall come With shout of ac-cla-ma-tion And take me

all the worlds Thy hands have made; I see the stars, I hear the roll-ing
birds sing sweet-ly in the trees; When I look down from loft-y moun-tain
die, I scarce can take it in; That on the cross my bur-den glad-ly
home, What joy shall fill my heart! Then I shall bow In hum-ble ad-o-

thun-der, Thy pow'r through-out The u-ni-verse dis-played.
gran-deur And hear the brook and feel the gent-le breeze.
bear-ing, He bled and died To take a-way my sin.
ra-tion, And there pro-claim, "My God, how great Thou art!"

Then sings my soul, My Sav-ior God, to Thee, How great Thou art! How great Thou art!

Then sings my soul, My Sav-ior God, to Thee, How great Thou art! How great Thou art!

How Great Thou Art

1885

For thus says the LORD, Who created the heavens, Who is God, Who formed the earth and made it, Who has established it, Who did not create it in vain, Who formed it to be inhabited: "I am the LORD, and there is no other." Isaiah 45:18

arl Boberg, a 26-year-old Swedish minister, wrote a poem in 1885 which he called "O Store Gud"—"O Mighty God." The words, literally translated to English, said:

When I the world consider | Which Thou has made by Thine almighty Word
And how the webb of life Thou wisdom guideth | And all creaion feedeth at Thy board.
Then doth my soul burst forth in song of praise | Oh, great God, Oh, great God!

His poem was published and "forgotten"—or so he thought. Several years later, Carl was surprised to hear it being sung to the tune of an old Swedish melody; but the poem and hymn did not achieve widespread fame.

Hearing this hymn in Russia, English missionary, Stuart Hine, was so moved he modified and expanded the words and made his own arrangement of the Swedish melody. He later said his first three verses were inspired, line upon line, by Russia's rugged Carpathian Mountains. The first verse was composed when he was caught in a thunderstorm in a Carpathian village, the second as he heard the birds sing near the Romanian border, and the third as he witnessed many of the Carpathian mountain-dwellers coming to Christ. The final verse was written after Dr. Hine returned to Great Britain.

Some time later, Dr. J. Edwin Orr* heard "How Great Thou Art" being sung by Naga Tribespeople in Assam, in India, and decided to bring it back to America for use in his own meetings. When he introduced it at a conference in California, it came to the attention of music publisher, Tim Spencer, who contacted Mr. Hine and had the song copyrighted. It was published and recorded.

During the 1954 Billy Graham Crusade in Harringay Arena, George Beverly Shea was given a leaflet containing this hymn. He sang it to himself and shared it with other members of the Graham team. Though not used in London, it was introduced the following year to audiences in Toronto.

In the New York Crusade of 1957, it was sung by Bev Shea ninety-nine times, with the choir joining the majestic refrain:

Then sings my soul, my Savior God to Thee,
How great Thou art! How great Thou art!

---

*See the story behind the hymn "Search Me, O God."

The Banner of the Cross

Daniel W. Whittle

James McGranahan

1. There's a roy-al ban-ner giv-en for dis-play To the sol-diers
2. Though the foe may rage and gath-er as the flood, Let the stan-dard
3. O - ver land and sea, wher-ev-er man may dwell, Make the glo-rious
4. When the glo-ry dawns, 'tis draw-ing ver-y near, It is has-tening

of the King; As an en-sign fair we lift it up to-day,
be dis - played; And be-neath its folds, as sol-diers of the Lord,
tid-ings known; Of the crim-son ban-ner now the sto-ry tell,
day by day; Then be-fore our King the foe shall dis-ap-pear,

While as ran-somed ones we sing.
For the truth be not dis - mayed! March-ing on, march-ing
While the Lord shall claim His own! on, on
And the cross the world shall sway!

on, For Christ count ev-ery-thing but loss! And to
on, on, ev-ery-thing, ev-ery-thing but loss!

crown Him King, toil and sing 'Neath the ban-ner of the cross!
we'll Be- neath

The Banner of the Cross

You have given a banner to those who fear You, that it may be displayed because of the truth. Selah. Psalm 60:4

hile recovering from wounds sustained in the Civil War, Daniel Whittle became a Christian; and after the War, he returned to his new bride in Chicago. He had lost his right arm, but had found eternal life. He also had a new title. He had reached the rank of Major in the Union Army, and henceforth he was known as "Major Whittle."

Back in Chicago, he became treasurer of the Elgin Watch Company. But his newfound faith in Christ burned in his heart, and he was drawn into the ministry of the Chicago-based evangelist, D. L. Moody.* Whittle served as superintendent of one of the largest mission Sunday schools in Chicago, and often preached to the children, using blackboard illustrations and chemical experiments to keep their attention.

In 1873, at Moody's urging, Whittle resigned his work to enter fulltime evangelism. He proved to be a powerful preacher, eventually becoming one of the greatest evangelists of his time.

In about 1877, Whittle also began writing gospel songs, usually publishing them under the penname "El Nathan." He's the author of such favorites as "Moment by Moment," "I Know Whom I Have Believed," and "Showers of Blessing."

The lowest point in the Major's life came in 1894. While preaching in Pennsylvania, Major Whittle received news that his son had been killed in an accident. Hurrying home, he comforted his family as best he could before, at length, returning to his Pennsylvania campaign. He assuaged his grief by writing a poem that begins: *Be still, my heart! Thy Savior knows full well / The burden on thee laid; / And to thy side He comes, with love to heal / The wound His love hath made.*

One of Whittle's last efforts was with the soldiers in the Spanish-American War. Remembering how he had come to Christ while in the army, he joined the men at their camp, eating with them, sleeping with them, traveling with them, and preaching to them. The effort overtaxed him, and afterward Whittle returned home to live with his daughter in Northfield, Massachusetts. He passed away on March 4, 1901, after years of faithful service under the banner of the Cross.

Marching on, marching on, for Christ count everything but loss!
And to crown Him King, we'll toil and sing, 'neath the banner of the cross!

---

*Whittle's daughter, May, later married Moody's son, Will.

Standing on the Promises

R. Kelso Carter

R. Kelso Carter

1. Stand-ing on the prom-is-es Of Christ my King, Thro' e - ter - nal a - ges Let His
2. Stand-ing on the prom-is-es That can - not fail, When the howl-ing storms Of doubt and
3. Stand-ing on the prom-is-es Of Christ the Lord, Bound to Him e - ter - nal - ly By
4. Stand-ing on the prom-is-es I can - not fall, Lis - t'ning ev - ery mo - ment To the

prais - es ring, Glo - ry in the high - est I will shout and sing, Stand-ing on the
fear as - sail, By the liv - ing Word of God I shall pre - vail, Stand-ing on the
love's strong cord, Ov - er - com - ing dai - ly with The Spir - it's sword, Stand-ing on the
Spir - it's call, Rest - ing in my Sav - ior, As my all in all, Stand-ing on the

prom - is - es of God. Stand - ing, stand - ing,

Stand - ing on the prom - is - es Of God my Sav - ior. Stand - ing,

stand - ing, I'm stand - ing on the prom - is - es of God.

Standing on the Promises

For all the promises of God in Him are Yes, and in Him Amen, to the glory of God through us. 2 Corinthians 1:20

Russell Kelso Carter, author of this hymn, was an athlete, educator, rancher, preacher, and physician. Here is his condensed testimony:

From my birth in 1849, I was surrounded by Christian influences. My father stood for nearly half a century in the rank of Christian workers in Baltimore; by his side I had the example of a patient, loving mother. I cannot remember when I was not subject to deep convictions of sin; yet as a school-boy, I wandered from the truth until age fifteen, when, under the influence of the cadet prayer-meeting in the Pennsylvania Military Academy, I made a profession of faith in Jesus.

But I made a common mistake; I didn't forsake my old companions and habits, and for fourteen years I lived the up-and-down experience so familiar to the average church member. I never enjoyed myself so much as when working in Mr. Moody's meetings in Baltimore; yet even up to that time I was continually slipping and falling. My soul cried for deliverance, and God's *unlimited promises* stood out like stars above me. But I wasn't willing to pay the price.

In the summer of 1879, my heart, which had been chronically diseased for seven years, resisting the remedies of physicians, and, refusing to grow better even after three years of sheep-ranching in California, suddenly broke down so seriously as to bring me to the verge of the grave. I had heard of the "prayer of faith" for healing, but I felt persuaded it would border on blasphemy to ask God for a strength which I didn't propose to use wholly for Him.

Kneeling in my mother's room in Baltimore, I made a consecration that covered everything. All doubtful things were swept aside. I meant every word, and I have never had any doubts about it since. A quietness came over me and I found the Bible wonderfully open and marvelously satisfying, as it had never been before.

Feeling all the more impressed with God's healing promises, I concluded to go to Boston and ask prayer and anointing at the hands of Dr. Cullis. I was terribly weak, but I went. I will only add that I returned in three days, walking by faith, and not by feeling, resumed my college work in September, and at once engaged in all kinds of religious work. I was healed by the power of God alone. Praise the Lord!

I Will Sing the Wondrous Story

Francis H. Rowley

Peter P. Billhorn

1. I will sing the won-drous sto-ry Of the Christ Who died for me,
2. I was lost but Je-sus found me, Found the sheep that went a - stray,
3. I was bruised but Je-sus healed me, Faint was I from man-y a fall.
4. He will keep me till the riv - er Rolls its wat - ers at my feet.

How He left His home in glo - ry For the cross of Cal-va - ry.
Threw His lov - ing arms a - round me, Drew me back in - to His way.
Sight was gone and fears pos - sessed me, But He freed me from them all.
Then He'll bear me safe - ly o - ver, Where the loved ones I shall meet.

Yes, I'll sing the won-drous sto-ry Of the Christ Who died for

me, Sing it with the saints in glo-ry Gath-ered by the crys-tal sea.

I Will Sing the Wondrous Story

1886

Aren't two sparrows sold for only a penny? But your Father knows when any one of them falls to the ground. Matthew 10:29 (CEV)

The Lord of Creation is an animal lover. He made them, saved them during the flood, and often used them in the Bible. Remember Balaam's donkey? Peter's rooster? Jonah's whale? Elijah's ravens? The Lord expressed concern for the cattle of Nineveh (Jonah 4:11), and Jesus said that the heavenly Father notes the flight and fall of the smallest sparrow (Matthew 10:29). There's even a special verse in the Bible for pet owners—Proverbs 12:10: "A wise man cares for the needs of his animal" (NIV).

What does that have to do with singing this hymn?

Dr. Francis Rowley, a dentist's son and star student, was born during the summer of 1854, in Hilton, New York. As a young man, he felt God's call into the ministry, and he was ordained in 1878. He pastored churches in Pennsylvania, Massachusetts, and Illinois.

Dr. Rowley later said, "We were having a revival at the First Baptist Church at North Adams, Massachusetts, in 1886, the third year of my pastorate there, which was one of the richest and most blessed experiences of my entire ministry. I was assisted by a young Swiss musician named Peter Bilhorn who suggested I write a hymn for which he would compose the music. The following night this hymn ["I Will Sing the Wondrous Story"] came to me without any particular effort on my part."

In 1910, Rowley left the pastorate and became president of the Massachusetts Society for the Prevention of Cruelty to Animals. He served in that position until the age of ninety-one, when he was made chairman of the board. Under his tenure, the first motorized horse ambulance was purchased and the Angell Memorial Animal Hospital opened in Boston. Rowley was also instrumental in drafting a resolution that led to the first national "Be Kind to Animals Week." In 1917, he helped establish a permanent animal shelter designed to care for retired police horses, and in 1918, he led in the formation of the Jack London Club to enlist young people in the protection of animals. In 1922, the first Christmas Dinner for Horses was conducted, and in 1929, the Springfield Animal Hospital was opened, later renamed the Rowley Memorial Animal Hospital.

The Rowley School of Humanities at Oglethorpe University in Atlanta is also named for this hymnist whose watchword was: "Sing of your Redeemer—and be kind to His creatures!"

When They Ring the Golden Bells

Daniel (Dion) de Marbelle   Daniel (Dion) de Marbelle

1. There's a land be-yond the riv-er, that we
2. We shall know no sin or sor-row, in that
3. When our days shall know their num-ber, and in

call the sweet for-ev-er, And we on-ly reach that shore by faith's de-cree;
ha-ven of to-mor-row, When our barque shall sail be-yond the sil-ver sea;
death we sweet-ly slum-ber, When the King com-mands the spir-it to be free;

One by one we'll gain the por-tals, there to dwell with the im-mor-tals,
We shall on-ly know the bless-ing of our Fa-ther's sweet ca-ress-ing,
Nev-er-more with an-guish lad-en, we shall reach that love-ly E-den,

When they ring the gold-en bells for you and me.
When they ring the gold-en bells for you and me.
When they ring the gold-en bells for you and me.

you and me.

When They Ring the Golden Bells

1887

. . . Having been justified by His grace we should become heirs according to the hope of eternal life. Titus 3:7

s a child, I remember my mother scurrying around the house, dusting, cleaning, working, and singing a hymn that became quite popular in the early to mid-twentieth century:

> *There's a land beyond the river, that we call the sweet forever,*
> *And we only reach that shore by faith's decree;*
> *One by one we'll gain the portals, there to dwell with the immortals,*
> *When they ring the golden bells for you and me.*

Many hymns were written by pastors and theologians. Some by homemakers and merchants. This one was written by a clown. His name was Daniel (Dion) de Marbelle. He was born in France in 1818, and spent his youth sailing the Arctic on whaling ships. When he was about 30, he joined the American Navy and fought in the Mexican War. Later, during the Civil War, he was a musician with the sixth Michigan infantry regiment.

During Reconstruction, he joined an opera troupe and traveled across America, singing, acting, entertaining in theaters, barns, auditoriums—wherever crowds would gather.

He was 69 when he became one of the first clowns hired by James A. Bailey who took over P. T. Barnum's Circus following the latter's death in 1891. Under Bailey's leadership, the Barnum & Bailey Circus rode the rails on 85 cars and employed more than 1,000 people.

Daniel later organized his own circus. When a fire in Canada destroyed his big top and all his equipment, he came back to the U.S. to assist Buffalo Bill Cody in his famous Wild West Show.

De Marbelle was a multi-talented performer—a magician, actor, ventriloquist, soloist, writer; he was a musician who could play virtually any instrument and a public speaker who said he could make an eloquent speech on any subject at a moment's notice.

But he wasn't a businessman. Despite his many talents, his last years were spent in poverty, and he lived in an abandoned schoolroom. At the local Methodist church in Elgin, Illinois, he sang in the choir and sometimes gave this testimony: "For years I was so busy I didn't have time for God and so rich I didn't need Him. God had to slow me down and take my success away so that He could talk to me about the home beyond the river."

Leaning on the Everlasting Arms

Elisha A. Hoffman

Anthony J. Showalter

1. What a fel-low-ship, what a joy di - vine, Lean-ing on the ev-er - last-ing arms!
2. Oh how sweet to walk in this pil-grim way, Lean-ing on the ev-er - last-ing arms!
3. What have I to dread, what have I to fear, Lean-ing on the ev-er - last-ing arms?

What a bless - ed-ness, what a peace is mine, Lean-ing on the ev-er - last-ing arms!
Oh how bright the path Grows from day to day, Lean-ing on the ev-er - last-ing arms.
I have bless - ed peace with my Lord so near, Lean-ing on the ev-er - last-ing arms.

Lean - ing, lean - ing, Safe and se-cure from all a - larms;
Lean-ing on Je - sus, lean-ing on Je - sus,

Lean - ing, lean - ing, Lean-ing on the ev-er - last-ing arms.
Lean-ing on Je - sus, lean-ing on Je - sus,

Leaning on the Everlasting Arms

1887

The eternal God is your refuge, and underneath are the everlasting arms . . .
Deuteronomy 33:27

The idea for this song came from Anthony Showalter, principal of the Southern Normal Musical Institute in Dalton, Georgia. Showalter, a Presbyterian elder, was a well-known advocate of gospel music. He published over 130 music books with combined sales of two million copies, and he became known through the South for his singing schools in local churches.

Showalter took a personal interest in his students and enjoyed keeping up with them as the years passed. One evening in 1887, he was leading a singing school in a local church in Hartselle, Alabama. After dismissing the class for the evening, he gathered his materials and returned to his boardinghouse.

Two letters had arrived, both from former pupils. Each of the young men was heartbroken, having just lost his wife. Professor Showalter went to the Bible, looking for a verse to comfort them. He selected Deuteronomy 33:27—"The eternal God is your refuge, And underneath are the everlasting arms. . . ." As he pondered that verse, these words came to mind:

> *Leaning, leaning, safe and secure from all alarms;*
> *Leaning, leaning, leaning on the everlasting arms.*

He scribbled replies to his bereaved friends, then, reaching for another piece of paper, he wrote to his friend, hymnist Elisha Hoffman. "Here is the chorus for a good hymn from Deuteronomy 33:27," his letter said, "but I can't come up with any verses." Hoffman wrote three stanzas and sent them back. Showalter set it all to music, and ever since, these words have cheered us in adversity:

> *What have I to dread, what have I to fear, | Leaning on the everlasting arms. |*
> *I have blessed peace with my Lord so near, | Leaning on the everlasting arms.*

God, the eternal God, is our support at all times, especially when we are sinking into deep trouble. There are seasons when we sink quite low. . . . Dear child of God, even when you are at your lowest, underneath are the everlasting arms.—Charles Spurgeon

---

However low the people of God are at any time brought, everlasting arms are underneath them to keep the spirit from fainting and the faith from failing, even when they are pressed above measure . . . everlasting arms with which believers have been wonderfully sustained and kept cheerful in the worst of times. Divine grace is sufficient.—Matthew Henry

417

Trust and Obey

John H. Sammis

Daniel B. Towner

1. When we walk with the Lord In the light of His Word, What a glo - ry He sheds on our way! While we do His good will, He a - bides with us still, And with all who will Trust and o - bey.

2. Not a shad - ow can rise, Not a cloud in the skies, But His smile quick - ly drives it a - way; Not a doubt nor a fear, Not a sigh nor a tear. Can a - bide while we Trust and o - bey.

3. But we nev - er can prove The de - lights of His love Un - til all on the al - tar we lay; For the fa - vor He shows And the joy He be - stows Are for them who will Trust and o - bey.

4. Then in fel - low - ship sweet We will sit at His feet, Or we'll walk by His side in the way; What He says we will do, Where He sends we will go, Nev - er fear, on - ly Trust and o - bey.

Trust and o - bey, For there's no oth - er way To be hap - py in Je - sus, But to trust and o - bey.

Trust and Obey

1887

Trust in the LORD with all your heart, and lean not on your own understanding;
In all your ways acknowledge Him, and He shall direct your paths. Proverbs 3:5–6

Daniel B. Towner, who wrote the melody to this song, inherited his love of music from his father, Professor J. G. Towner, a beloved vocalist and music teacher. While growing up, Daniel studied with some of the finest musicians available and began his career as worship leader in a Methodist church in Binghamton, New York. He later served churches in Ohio and Kentucky before being tapped by evangelist D. L. Moody in the fall of 1885. For several years, Daniel traveled with Moody, singing and doing personal work.

He once explained how this hymn came to be written:

Mr. Moody was conducting a series of meetings in Brockton, Massachusetts, and I had the pleasure of singing for him there. One night a young man rose in a testimony meeting and said, "I am not quite sure—but I am going to trust, and I am going to obey." I just jotted that sentence down, and sent it with the little story to Rev. J. H. Sammis, a Presbyterian minister.

Sammis wrote a poem based on the phrase "trust and obey," and sent it back to Towner, who went to work on the music.

Alfred Smith, in his *Treasury of Hymn Histories*, adds that while working on the music to "Trust and Obey," Dr. Towner grew discouraged. That evening in his home, he crumpled up the paper and threw the manuscript into the wastebasket. The next morning, as his wife was straightening his office, she retrieved the crumpled paper and sang over the words and melody to herself. She left it on the organ and encouraged her husband to work on it some more, telling him, "I feel the melody you have written is just what is needed to carry the message." She was right.

In 1893, Dr. Towner became head of the Music Department of the Moody Bible Institute of Chicago where he trained hundreds of young people to lead worship and minister to the Lord in music. He wrote the melodies of some of our favorite hymns, including: "At Calvary," "My Anchor Holds," and "Grace Greater Than All Our Sins." He also compiled fourteen hymnbooks and wrote several textbooks.

At age 70, while leading singing in revival meetings at Longwood, Missouri, he suffered a seizure and died.

Sunshine in My Soul

Eliza E. Hewitt

John R. Sweney

1. There is sun-shine in my soul to-day, More glo-ri-ous and bright
2. There is mu-sic in my soul to-day, A car-ol to my King;
3. There is spring-time in my soul to-day, For when the Lord is near
4. There is glad-ness in my soul to-day, And hope and praise and love,

Than glows in an-y earth-ly sky, For Je-sus is my light.
And Je-sus, lis-ten-ing can hear The songs I can-not sing.
The dove of peace sings in my heart, The flow'rs of grace ap-pear.
For bless-ings which He gives me now, For joys "laid up" a-bove.

O there's sun-shine, bless-ed sun-shine, When the peace-ful hap-py mo-ments

roll. When Je-sus shows His smil-ing face, There is sun-shine in my soul.

Sunshine in My Soul

1887

But the path of the just is *like the shining sun, That shines ever brighter unto the perfect day.* Proverbs 4:18

dmunds Rhoad, account executive for an information systems company, has spent many hours researching his family tree. In the process, he discovered the diary that his great grandmother, Zeruiah Edmunds, started keeping at age nineteen, and it reveals a passionate love for Christ.

Zeruiah married James S. Hewitt, a young sailor who also kept a journal that tells of harrowing storms, shipwrecks, near escapes—and an earnest faith. One entry, for example, tells of a voyage to China in which he was surrounded by "a rough irreligious body of men who paid no attention or any duty to God on the Sabbath or on any other day. Oaths, card-playing, etc. marked their conduct when at leisure." James, deeply saddened, would slip off to quiet spots to read his Bible and pray.

It was into this Christian home that a daughter was born in 1851, in a house on Christian Street in Philadelphia. Little Eliza grew up in the nurture of the Lord. She was a teenager during the Civil War, but she managed to concentrate on school well enough to graduate valedictorian of her class. She displayed an unusual love for children, and after further study she became a schoolteacher.

In 1887, while teaching at the Northern Home for Friendless Children, Eliza, 35, was struck by an unruly student. He slammed his slate across her, severely injuring her back. The doctor placed her in a heavy cast for six months, and Eliza was virtually immobile, perhaps wondering if she would ever walk again. When the cast was removed in early 1887, the doctor told her to take a short walk in nearby Fairmont Park. It was a warm spring day, and she was overcome with joy. Returning home, she picked up her pen and immediately wrote the hymn:

There's sunshine in my soul today
More glorious and bright,
Than glows in any earthly sky,
For Jesus is my light.

Her injuries were severe enough to preclude school teaching, so she devoted herself Bible study and hymn-writing. Eliza lived many more years and wrote scores of hymns, including "My Faith Has Found a Resting Place," "When We All Get To Heaven," and "Will There Be Any Stars In My Crown?"

Eliza died in 1920, and her grave at Woodlands Cemetery in Philadelphia, reads simply: "Eliza Edmunds Hewitt, Hymnwriter, author of Sunshine in My Soul."*

---

*Edmunds Rhoad is available for presentations on the life of his great aunt, and can be reached at 285 67th Street, Avalon, New Jersey 08202.

Away in a Manger

Anonymous

James R. Murray

1. A - way in a man - ger, no crib for a bed,
2. The cat - tle are low - ing, the ba - by a - wakes,
3. Be near me, Lord Je - sus; I ask Thee to stay

The lit - tle Lord Je - sus laid down His sweet head.
But lit - tle Lord Je - sus, no cry - ing He makes.
Close by me for - ev - er, and love me, I pray.

The stars in the sky look down where He lay,
I love Thee, Lord Je - sus, look down from the sky,
Bless all the dear chil - dren in Thy ten - der care,

The lit - tle Lord Je - sus, a - sleep on the hay.
And stay by my cra - dle till morn - ing is nigh.
And take us to heav - en to live with Thee there.

Away in a Manger

1887

And she brought forth her firstborn Son, and wrapped Him in swaddling cloths, and laid Him in a manger, because there was no room for them in the inn. Luke 2:7

This is commonly known as "Luther's Cradle Hymn." But did the great German Reformer, Martin Luther, really write the words? Did he sing them by the cradle of his little son, Hans? This is a great mystery in hymnology.

In 1887, "Away in a Manger" appeared in a little book of songs entitled *Dainty Songs for Little Lads and Lasses,* published in Cincinnati by the John Church Company. The songbook was compiled by James R. Murray. A notation beneath "Away in a Manger" said: *Luther's Cradle Hymn (Composed by Martin Luther for his children and still sung by German mothers to their little ones.)* Only stanzas one and two were given.

"Away in a Manger" quickly became America's favorite children's carol, the words being sung to forty-one different tunes! Everyone assumed the poem had been written by the great Reformer, Martin Luther.

Then in 1945, Richard Hill published a fascinating article entitled "Not So Far Away in a Manger" in which he announced he had discovered the first two stanzas of "Away in a Manger," in an 1885 songbook entitled *Little Children's Book,* published by German Lutherans in Pennsylvania. No authorship was given. Nor could Hill find any appearance of this carol in German church history or in Luther's works.

After extensive research, Hill concluded: "It seems essential to lay [aside] once for all the legend that Luther wrote a carol for his children, which no one else knew anything about, until it suddenly turned up in English dress 400 years later in Philadelphia. Luther can well afford to spare the honor." But he adds, "Although Luther himself had nothing to do with the carol, the colonies of German Lutherans in Pennsylvania almost certainly did."

So the mystery endures. Who wrote "Away in a Manger"? There were apparently two unknown writers: A German Lutheran in Pennsylvania who wrote the first two stanzas, with another unknown author adding a third verse which first appeared in an 1892 songbook published by Charles H. Gabriel.

Well, who cares? Certainly not the generations of children around the world who have come to love and know the little Jesus through this sweet carol, and who have gone to sleep praying:

I love Thee, Lord Jesus; look down from the sky
And stay by my cradle till morning is nigh.

Jesus, I Come

William T. Sleeper

George C. Stebbins

1. Out of my bond-age, sor-row, and night, Je-sus, I come; Je-sus I come.
2. Out of my shame-ful fail-ure and loss, Je-sus, I come; Je-sus, I come.
3. Out of un-rest and ar-ro-gant pride, Je-sus, I come; Je-sus, I come.
4. Out of the fear and dread of the tomb, Je-sus, I come; Je-sus I come.

In-to Thy free-dom, glad-ness, and light, Je-sus, I come to Thee.
In-to the glo-rious gain of Thy cross, Je-sus, I come to Thee.
In-to Thy bless-ed will to a-bide, Je-sus, I come to Thee.
In-to the joy and light of Thy home, Je-sus, I come to Thee.

Out of my sick-ness, in-to Thy health, Out of my want and in-to Thy wealth.
Out of earth's sor-rows in-to Thy balm, Out of life's storms and in-to Thy calm.
Out of my-self to dwell in Thy love, Out of de-spair to rap-tures a-bove,
Out of the depths of ru-in un-told, In-to the peace-ful, shel-ter-ing fold,

Out of my sin and in-to Thy-self, Je-sus, I come to Thee.
Out of dis-tress to ju-bi-lant psalm, Je-sus, I come to Thee.
Up-ward I rise on wings like a dove, Je-sus, I come to Thee.
Ev-er Thy glo-rious face to be-hold, Je-sus, I come to Thee.

Jesus, I Come

1887

I will exalt you, O LORD, for you lifted me out of the depths . . . Psalm 30:1 (NIV)

One of the best histories of the gospel song era is George Stebbins' autobiography, *Reminiscences and Gospel Hymn Stories*. Stebbins was born in the mid-1800s in New York and showed early musical prowess. At age twenty-three, he moved to Chicago where he worked in churches and became acquainted with some of the "greats" of gospel music, such as Sankey and Bliss. In the late 1870s, D. L. Moody got hold of him, sending him into a lifetime of music evangelism.

Stebbins' first impressions of Moody are fascinating. Major Daniel Whittle had invited him to Northfield, Massachusetts, to meet Moody. That Sunday, Moody preached at the village church, asking Stebbins to lead the singing. Stebbins, a bit nervous, sat at the little organ in front of the pulpit.

As he played the organ and led the congregation, he was discomposed by a terrible wheezing noise. He described it as ". . . a discordant sound I kept hearing during the singing, which I at first thought was caused by something wrong with the organ. I determined to ascertain if my suspicions were well founded, so when there was an interval between verses, I listened to see if there might be one of the notes of the organ sounding when it ought to be silent, and found the discords were not from that source."

"I was not long in doubt, however, for I soon heard the voice of Mr. Moody singing away as heartily as you please, with no more idea of tune or time than a child. I then learned for the first time that he was one of the unfortunates who have no sense of pitch or harmony."

Stebbins went on to work for years alongside Moody, in the process composing several of our favorite hymn tunes. Included among them are the invitation hymns: "Have Thine Own Way, Lord," "Jesus Is Tenderly Calling You Home," "What Will Ye Do with Jesus?" and this one, "Jesus, I Come."

Stebbins' friend, William Sleeper, a New England home missionary and pastor, wrote the words to "Jesus, I Come." The two had previously collaborated on the hymn, "Ye Must Be Born Again." Sleeper developed the words to "Jesus, I Come" and sent them to Stebbins who put them to music. It first appeared in 1887 in *Gospel Hymns, No. 5*. with this Bible verse as a subtitle: "Deliver me, O my God" (Psalm 71:4).

Lead On, O King Eternal

Ernest W. Shurtleff

Henry T. Smart

1. Lead on, O King e-ter - nal, The day of march has come;
2. Lead on, O King e-ter - nal, Till sin's fierce war shall cease,
3. Lead on, O King e-ter - nal, We fol - low not with fears,

Hence - forth in fields of con - quest Thy tents shall be our home.
And ho - li - ness shall whis - per The sweet A - men of peace.
For glad - ness breaks like morn - ing Wher - e'er Thy face ap - pears.

Thro' days of prep - a - ra - tion Thy grace has made us strong, And
For not with swords loud clash - ing, Nor roll of stir - ring drums, With
Thy cross is lift - ed o'er us, We jour - ney in its light; The

now, O King e - ter - nal, We lift our bat - tle song.
deeds of love and mer - cy The heav'n - ly king - dom comes.
crown a - waits the con - quest: Lead on, O God of might.

Lead On, O King Eternal

1887

Now to the King eternal, immortal, invisible, the only God, be honor and glory for ever and ever. Amen. 1 Timothy 1:17 (NIV)

This regal prayer has been sung at graduations around the world every year since 1887, when Ernest W. Shurtleff wrote it for his own graduation. A native of Boston and a graduate at Harvard, Ernest, twenty-six, was a student at Andover Theological Seminary when he envisioned his fellow seminarians marching for their diplomas singing a great prayer for God's guidance on the rest of life. Selecting a tune called LANCASHIRE, Ernest wrote words as regal as the music, and thus a great tradition was born.

Ernest went on to be ordained a Congregational minister and to hold pastorates in Massachusetts, Minnesota, and California. In 1905, he organized a church in Frankfort, Germany. He and his wife also worked tirelessly with European students. When World War I broke out, Ernest labored to exhaustion in relief ministries, feeding the poor and displaced. He died in Paris in 1917, during the war. His life was the embodiment of his hymn; yet nothing he did was as enduring to history as that hymn, written at age twenty-six.

Likewise, nothing that composer Henry Smart did was more enduring than this tune, LANCASHIRE, penned at age twenty-two. Henry had grown up surrounded by music, for his father was a piano and organ builder. As a young man, Henry enrolled in the university to study law; but, unable to get music out of his heart, he switched professions and became a self-taught organist and composer. He wrote LANCASHIRE for a music festival at Blackburn, England, on October 4, 1835, to commemorate the three hundredth anniversary of the English Reformation. Unfortunately, Henry worked so hard at his music that he damaged his eyesight beyond repair.

For nearly fifty years Henry Smart served as organist at various churches in England. He also edited the hymnbook of the United Presbyterian Church of Scotland, and he was often consulted for new organ installations throughout Great Britain. He became one of nineteenth-century England's favorite musicians.

In his final years, Henry was totally blind, yet he continued composing by dictating his pieces to his daughter, and he continued playing the organ by memory until his death at age sixty-three in 1879. Henry Smart wrote over two hundred fifty secular works and several religious compositions, including the beautiful REGENT SQUARE, the melody of "Angels from the Realms of Glory."

Look and Live

William A. Ogden

William A. Ogden

1. I've a mes-sage from the Lord, Hal-le - lu - jah! The mes-sage un - to you I'll give.
2. I've a mes-sage full of love, Hal-le - lu - jah! A mes-sage, O my friend, for you.
3. Life is of-fered un - to you, Hal-le - lu - jah! E - ter - nal life your soul shall have
4. I will tell you how I came, Hal-le - lu - jah! To Je - sus when He made me whole:

'Tis re - cord-ed in His Word, Hal-le - lu - jah! It is on - ly that you "look and live."
'Tis a mes-sage from a - bove, Hal-le - lu - jah! Je - sus said it, and I know 'tis true.
If you'll on - ly look to Him, Hal-le - lu - jah! Look to Je - sus, who a - lone can save.
'Twas be - liev-ing on His name, Hal-le - lu - jah! I trust-ed and He saved my soul.

"Look and live," my broth-er, live. Look to Je - sus now and live.
"Look and live," "look and live,"

'Tis re - cord-ed in His Word, Hal-le - lu - jah! It is on - ly that you "look and live."

Look and Live

1888

Then the LORD said to Moses, "Make a fiery serpent, and set it on a pole; and it shall be that everyone who is bitten, when he looks at it, shall live. Numbers 21:8

This hymn was written by William Ogden, who also wrote the words to "Where He Leads, I'll Follow" and the music to the popular gospel song "Bring Them In."

William was born in Ohio in 1841. He had an inborn love for music, but the Civil War interrupted his studies, and he spent four years serving in the 30th Indiana Volunteer Infantry. After the war, he continued his pursuit of music, studying under Lowell Mason. William went on to become a personable and popular schoolteacher and a featured leader at music conventions. In 1887, he became supervisor for music in the Toledo public schools, a position he retained until his death ten years later.

This hymn was based on the remarkable incident recorded in Numbers 21, when Moses crafted a bronze serpent and raised it among the Israelites. Because of their sin, an infestation of poisonous snakes had left many of them dying, but all who looked at the serpent on the pole lived. Jesus later used the incident as an illustration of His work on the Cross. This strange analogy paved the way for the most famous verse in the Bible—John 3:16:

And as Moses lifted up the serpent in the wilderness, even so must the Son of Man be lifted up, that whoever believes in Him should not perish but have eternal life. For God so loved the world that He gave His only begotten Son, that whoever believes in Him should not perish but have everlasting life" (John 3:14–16).

William Ogden wrote a number of other hymns, many of which have been forgotten with the passing of time. As I surveyed his songs, one stood out in particular, for I remember singing it often as I grew up attending church in the Tennessee mountains. It's unusual in that in the chorus, the melody is in the bass line.

Seeking the lost, yes, kindly entreating / Wanderers on the mountain astray;
"Come unto Me," His message repeating, / Words of the Master speaking today.

CHORUS:
Going afar (going afar) / Upon the mountain (upon the mountain)
Bringing the wanderer back again (back again), / Into the fold (into the fold)
Of my Redeemer (of my Redeemer) / Jesus the Lamb for sinners slain, for sinners slain.

Yesterday, Today, Forever

Albert B. Simpson

James H. Burke

Yes-ter-day, to-day, for-ev - er, Je-sus is the same.

All may change but Je-sus nev - er! Glo-ry to His name!

Glo - ry to His name! Glo - ry to His name!

All may change but Je - sus nev-er! Glo-ry to His name!

Yesterday, Today, Forever

<u>1890</u>

Jesus Christ is the same yesterday, today, and forever. Hebrews 13:8

Many people complain that A. B. Simpson's hymns are hard to sing. Well, maybe. But give them a good try anyway.

Albert Benjamin Simpson was born in 1843, of Scottish parents on Prince Edward Island. Despite his father's misgivings, young Albert announced his call to the ministry as a teenager, and it was arranged for him to preach at the local church. The appointed Sunday came, and the Simpson family was seated nervously in a row. When the moment for the sermon came, Albert rose, announced his text, and spoke so smoothly and powerfully that no one could believe it was his first sermon.

He went on to become a great preacher, a missionary advocate, and the founder of the Christian and Missionary Alliance. His famous four-fold message was Jesus Christ as Savior, Sanctifier, Healer, and Coming King. He wrote more than seventy books, opened a Bible and missionary training school at Nyack on the Hudson, and composed hymns.

A. W. Tozer, in *Wingspread*, his classic little biography of Simpson, wrote: "Simple truth requires us to state that A. B. Simpson does not rate high as a writer of hymns. The effort on the part of some of his admirers to place him along with Watts and Wesley is simply absurd. A hymn, to be great—to be a hymn at all—must meet with certain simple requirements. It must have literary excellence; it must be compact enough to be sung easily; it must express the religious feeling of the Universal Church; the music must have dignity and reserve.

"On none of these counts could Mr. Simpson's compositions qualify. . . . His singing heart sometimes betrayed him into attempting to sing things that simply were not lyrical and could not be sung. . . ."

But Tozer continues: "After saying all this, I would yet confess that hardly a day goes by that I do not kneel and sing, in a shaky baritone comfortably off key, the songs of Simpson. They feed my heart and express my longings, and I can find no other's songs that do this in as full a measure. . . . It is my sober judgment that Simpson has put into a few of his songs more of awful longing, of tender love, of radiant trust, of hope and worship and triumph than can be found in all the popular gospel songs of the last hundred years put together."

The Haven of Rest

Henry L. Gilmour

George D. Moore

1. My soul, in sad ex - ile, was out on life's sea. So bur-dened with
2. I yield-ed my-self to His ten - der em - brace, And, faith tak - ing
3. The song of my soul, since the Lord made me whole, Has been the old

sin and dis - tressed, 'Til I heard a sweet voice say-ing, "Make Me your choice,"
hold of the Word, My fet - ters fell off, and I an-chored my soul,
sto - ry so blest Of Je - sus, who'll save who-so - ev - er will have

And I en-tered the ha - ven of rest. I've an-chored my soul in the
The ha - ven of rest is my Lord.
A home in the ha - ven of rest.

Ha-ven of Rest, I'll sail the wide seas no more; The tem - pest may

sweep o'er the wild, storm - y deep, In Je - sus I'm safe ev - er - more.

The Haven of Rest

1890

He calms the storm, so that its waves are still. Then they are glad because they are quiet; so He guides them to their desired haven. Psalm 107:29–30

Henry Gilmour was always working on people's mouths. Eight months out of the year, he earned his keep as a New Jersey dentist. The remaining months, he filled his audiences' mouths with song. He was a singing evangelist, a camp meeting music director, a Methodist hymnist, and the author of such classics as "The Haven of Rest" and "He Brought Me Out of the Miry Clay" (music and chorus).

Gilmour had emigrated from Ireland as a teen. Arriving in America, he found work as a painter, but was soon caught in the grip of the Civil War where he wore the Union uniform. Captured by Confederate forces, he was marched to Libbey Prison, alongside the cold James River in Richmond, Virginia.

One of Gilmour's fellow prisoners later wrote that they were "taken to Richmond and placed in the old tobacco warehouse commonly known as Libbey Prison. There we received a small loaf of baker's bread and a small piece of meat for 24 hours ration. We had city water for coffee. . . ."

Another POW spoke of suffering paralysis from the bitter cold of the unheated warehouse. Others used words like "dreaded" and "miserable" and "the horrors of Libbey" to describe its discomforts, and some inmates spoke of being stripped naked and deprived of the necessities of life. The young Irishman must have wondered what had possessed him to sail to America.

Many POWs died at Libbey, but Henry survived; and after the war, he became a dentist and moved to Wenonah, New Jersey, where he became active in the Methodist Holiness movement. For over forty years, he worked in Methodist camp meetings, especially in Mountain Lake Park, Maryland, and Ridgeview Park, Pennsylvania. As his popularity grew, he had the opportunity of publishing gospel songbooks and encouraging new hymnists. It was largely through his efforts that Lelia Morris began writing hymns.*

We aren't sure what inspired Gilmour's greatest song, "The Haven of Rest." Was it his POW experiences, or perhaps the memories of his long voyage to America? Whatever it was, he's one dentist who filled the mouths of future generations with one of our greatest gospel songs.

I've anchored my soul in the "Haven of Rest," / I'll sail the wide seas no more;
The tempest may sweep over wild, stormy, deep, / In Jesus I'm safe evermore.

---

*See the stories for "Nearer, Still Nearer" and "Jesus Is Coming to Earth Again."

He Hideth My Soul

Fanny J. Crosby

William J. Kirkpatrick

He Hideth My Soul

1890

So it shall be, while My glory passes by, that I will put you in the cleft of the rock, and will cover you with My hand while I pass by. Exodus 33:22

Bouncing back—that's a quality to be cultivated, because life is full of struggles. How do we become resilient? Unsinkable? Joyful amid the blows and burdens of life? This hymn tells us:

A wonderful Savior is Jesus my Lord, He taketh my burden away;
He holdeth me up, and I shall not be moved, He giveth me strength as my day.

This hymn by Fanny Crosby explains the author's life, for Fanny faced three incredible hardships during her ninety-five years. The first was her blindness, caused by a careless doctor when she was only six weeks of age.

The second was a less-than-ideal marriage. Fanny was teaching at the New York Institution for the Blind when a young musician named Alexander Van Alstyne joined the faculty. Fanny later recalled, "After hearing several of my poems he became deeply interested in my work; and I after listening to his sweet strains of music became interested in him. Thus we soon grew to be very much concerned for each other . . . Love met love, and all the world was changed. We were no longer blind, for the light of love showed us where the lilies bloomed." The two were married on March 5, 1858. No one knows what happened, but years later the two drifted apart and in the end occupied separate addresses.

Fanny's deepest blow was the loss of her child. To this day, no one knows if it was a boy or a girl. Fanny seldom spoke of the infant. The child's death seems to have devastated her, and she privately bore the sadness all her life.

Yet all who knew Fanny Crosby spoke of her energy, her zest for life, her joy. One biographer said, "Even in extreme old age, she would tire out people twenty or thirty years her junior."

She said, "How long am I going to travel and lecture? Always! There is nothing that could induce me to abandon my work. It means nothing to be eighty-four years of age, because I am still young! What is the use of growing old? People grow old because they are not cheerful, and cheerfulness is one of the greatest accomplishments in the world!"

Fanny Crosby lived out her song every day of her life: "He hideth my soul in the depths of His love, and covers me there with His hand."

Make Me a Captive, Lord

George Matheson

George J. Elvey

1. Make me a cap-tive, Lord, And then I shall be free; Force
2. My heart is weak and poor Un - til its Mas - ter find; It
3. My power is faint and low Till I have learned to serve; It
4. My will is not my own Till Thou hast made it Thine; If

me to ren - der up my sword, And I shall con - queror be. I
has no spring of ac - tion sure, It var - ies with the wind. It
wants the need - ed fire to glow, It wants the breeze to nerve; It
it would reach a mon - arch's throne, It must its crown re - sign; It

sink in life's a - larms When by my - self I stand; Im -
can - not free - ly move Till Thou hast wrought its chain; En -
can - not drive the world, Un - til it - self be driv'n; Its
on - ly stands un - bent, A - mid the clash - ing strife, When

pris - on me with - in Thine arms, And strong shall be my hand.
slave it with Thy match-less love, And death-less it shall reign.
flag can on - ly be un - furled When Thou shalt breathe from heav'n.
on Thy bos - om it has leant And found in Thee its life.

Make Me a Captive, Lord

1890

The Spirit of the LORD is upon Me, because He has anointed Me to preach the gospel to the poor; . . . to proclaim liberty to the captives. Luke 4:18

I t was a dark and stormy night—August 16, 1809. Crowds returning from the market crammed onto a ferryboat in Scotland. As the overloaded ferry reached the middle of the Firth, it began tipping in the waves and filling with water. Despite desperate attempts to return to shore, the boat sank, drowning almost all on board—forty-three men and fifty-six women. Among them was George Matheson, who left behind a pregnant wife and two children.

One of the surviving sons was named for his father. It's said that as a young man, this George Matheson considered going into the ministry but was persuaded by a friend to form a business partnership. In time, George became a wealthy merchant and the father of eight children.

One of these children was named George—and he is the author of our hymn. George Matheson III later explained that he inherited a mind for business from his father, and from his mother the gift of song. From both parents, he received a rich and traditional theology and a love for the Lord.

George attended Glasgow University, graduating with a bachelor's degree in 1891, and with a master's in 1892. But he struggled with poor vision. Even in childhood, he used powerful glasses and sat near a window. During his university days, he was declared blind, and only the help of his loyal sister enabled him to finish school and enter the ministry.

Like Fanny Crosby, George was never totally blind; he could vaguely distinguish light and darkness. But also like Fanny Crosby, he was known for his phenomenal memory, optimism, buoyant spirit, and inspiring personality. In fact, many of the people flocking to hear him preach at St. Bernard's in Edinburgh didn't realize he was blind.

Matheson was a prolific student and author. With the help of secretaries and, later, by using a Braille typewriter, he wrote many articles and books. As a preacher, he was among the most popular in Britain. Queen Victoria came to hear him. As a hymnist, he is remembered for "O Love That Wilt Not Let Me Go," and this hymn— "Make Me a Captive, Lord," which speaks of the paradox of Christianity—that surrender to Christ brings victory in life.

Matheson suffered a stroke and died suddenly on August 28, 1906, in Edinburgh, but his songs, sermons, and influence will continue until Christ returns.

Send the Light

Charles H. Gabriel   Charles H. Gabriel

1. There's a   call comes ring - ing o'er the   rest - less wave, "Send the   light!
2. We   have heard the Mac - e - do - nian   call to - day, "Send the   light!
3. Let   us   pray that grace may ev - ery - where a - bound, "Send the   light!
4. Let   us   not grow wea - ry in the   work of love, "Send the   light!

Send the   light!" There are   souls   to   res - cue, There are   souls to save,
Send the   light!" And   a   gold - en   off - 'ring at the   cross we lay,
Send the   light!" And   a   Christ - like   spir - it   ev - 'ry - where be found,
Send the   light!" Let   us   gath - er   jew - els   for a   crown a - bove,

Send the   light! Send the   light! Send the   light,   The bless-ed gos-pel light;

Let   it   shine   from shore to shore! Send the   shine   for-ev-er - more!

Send the Light

1890

Send forth your light and your truth, let them guide me . . . Psalm 43:3 (NIV)

harles Gabriel grew up in Iowa, living on a farm until age seventeen. Even in childhood, he was drawn toward music; and when his Methodist family purchased a small reed organ, he taught himself to play it. With his parents' encouragement, he was leading singing schools by age sixteen.

He married, but because of his frantic schedule of traveling and teaching music, his marriage failed. In 1887, he moved to California to get a new start, and soon he remarried. In 1890, he began working at Grace Methodist Episcopal Church in San Francisco. When the Sunday school superintendent came to him asking for a missionary hymn for Easter Sunday to highlight a Golden Offering, Gabriel wrote "Send the Light." It was sung with enthusiasm that day, March 6, 1890, and a visiting missionary representative who liked the words carried the hymn back to the East.

The immediate popularity of "Send the Light" propelled Gabriel to prominence in the hymn-writing community. Once before he tried supporting himself by writing hymns, but failed. Now, he tried again. Within two years, he was in Chicago, devoting his life full time to writing and publishing hymns.

In all, Gabriel edited thirty-five gospel songbooks, eight Sunday school songbooks, seven books for men's chorus, six for women, ten for children, nineteen collections of anthems, and twenty-three cantatas. He's best known, however, for his amazing output of seven thousand hymns, including these timeless favorites:

"His Eye Is on the Sparrow" (music)
"I Stand Amazed in the Presence" (words and music)
"Brighten the Corner Where You Are" (music)
"What a Savior" (words and music)
"Just When I Need Him" (music)
"He Is So Precious to Me" (words and music)
"That Will Be Glory for Me" (words and music)
"More Like the Master" (words and music)
"Higher Ground" (music)
"In Lovingkindness Jesus Came" (words and music)
"Awakening Chorus" (music)
"Will the Circle Be Unbroken?" (music)
"Since Jesus Came into My Heart" (music)
"The Way of the Cross" (music)

But then, what else would you expect from a man named Gabriel?

My Faith Has Found a Resting Place

Lidie H. Edmunds

Norwegian Folk Melody arr. by William J. Kirkpatrick

1. My faith has found a rest-ing place, Not in de-vice or creed;
2. E - nough for me that Je-sus saves, This ends my fear and doubt;
3. My heart is lean-ing on the Word, The writ-ten Word of God,
4. My great Phy - si - cian heals the sick, The lost He came to save;

I trust the Ev - er - liv - ing One, His wounds for me shall plead.
A sin - ful soul, I come to Him, He'll nev - er cast me out.
Sal - va-tion by my Sav-ior's name, Sal - va - tion through His blood.
For me His pre-cious blood He shed, For me His life He gave.

I need no oth - er ar - gu - ment, I need no oth - er plea,

It is e - nough that Je - sus died, And that He died for me.

My Faith Has Found a Resting Place

1891

Who through Him believe in God, who raised Him from the dead and gave Him glory, so that your faith and hope are in God. 1 Peter 1:21

This hymn was written by the mysterious Lidie H. Edmunds. For years no one seemed to know who she was. As it turns out, this was a pseudonym for a popular hymnwriter named Eliza Edmunds Hewitt.

In those days, hymnists often used pen names because publishers were nervous about having too many hymns from one author in their books. Fanny Crosby, for example, published under the names Carrie Hawthorne, Maud Marion, Louise W. Tilden, Lillian G. Frances, Mrs. Edna Forest, Eleanor Craddock—and 198 others!

The music for "My Faith Has Found a Resting Place" was written by the prolific William J. Kirkpatrick, who was born in Pennsylvania in 1838. His father was his earliest music teacher, and William edited his first hymnbook, *Devotional Melodies*, at age 21. He went on to write the melodies of some of our favorite hymns, including:

- COMING HOME—"I've Wandered Far Away from God" (music and words)
- DUNCANNON—"King of My Life, I Crown Thee Now"
- JESUS SAVES—"We Have Heard the Joyful Sound"
- KIRKPATRICK—"A Wonderful Savior Is Jesus My Lord"
- TRUST IN JESUS—"'Tis So Sweet to Trust in Jesus"
- REDEEMED—"Redeemed, How I Love to Proclaim It"
- And this one, LÅNDES, a traditional Norwegian melody—"My Faith Has Found a Resting Place"

On the evening of September 21, 1921, Professor Kirkpatrick huddled away in his study in Germantown, Pennsylvania, working on a poem he was planning to put to music. His wife, sleeping in a nearby bedroom, awoke and noticed his study light was on. "Professor," she called, "it's very late, don't you think you'd better come to bed?"

"I'm all right, dear," he replied. "I have a little work I want to finish. Go back to sleep, everything is all right."

Mrs. Kirkpatrick went back to sleep, but awakened again later. The study light was still on, and again she called. This time there was no response. She found the Professor slumped over, his last hymn on the desk before him. It said:

Just as Thou wilt, Lord, this is my cry / Just as Thou wilt, to live or die. /
I am Thy servant, Thou knowest best, / Just as Thou wilt, Lord, labor or rest.

Saved by Grace

Fanny J. Crosby

George C. Stebbins

1. Some day the sil - ver cord will break, And I no more as now shall sing;
2. Some day my earth - ly house will fall, I can - not tell how soon 'twill be,
3. Some day when fades the gold - en sun Be-neath the ros - y - tint - ed west,
4. Some day till then I'll watch and wait, My lamp all trimmed and burn-ing bright,

But O the joy when I shall wake With-in the pal - ace of the King!
But this I know: my All in All Has now a place in heav'n for me.
My bless - ed Lord will say, "Well done!" And I shall en - ter in - to rest.
That when my Sav - ior ope's the gate, My soul to Him may take its flight.

And I shall see Him face to face, And tell the sto-ry– Saved by grace;

And I shall see Him face to face, And tell the sto-ry– Saved by grace;

Saved by Grace

1891

We believe it is through the grace of our Lord Jesus that we are saved . . . Acts 15:11 (NIV)

Fanny Crosby continued writing hymns until the day she died, though she did slow down a bit in her eighties, reducing her quota from two hundred hymns a year to about fifty. One of her last popular songs was "Saved by Grace." She later said it was inspired by a sermon preached by Dr. Howard Crosby, a distant relative and dear friend. In his message, Dr. Crosby said that no Christian "should fear death, for if each of us was faithful to the grace given us by Christ, the same grace that teaches us how to live would also teach us how to die."

His remarks deeply moved Fanny, and she wrote "Saved by Grace" as a personal hymn for herself, not to be published.

Some time later at a Bible Conference, D. L. Moody asked Fanny to share a word of testimony. Caught off guard, Fanny used this poem, saying, "There is one hymn I have written which has never been published. I call it my soul's poem. Sometimes when I am troubled, I repeat it to myself, for it brings comfort to my heart."

Soon thereafter it was published, and became one of her "greats."

Several years later, Fanny, who reached the age of ninety-five, realized she was dying—a prospect that brought her great joy. During the last weeks of her life, her face manifested an unusual glow. Numerous people observed it, and it became a curious subject of interest. On February 11, 1915, Fanny said she didn't feel well and would stay in bed that day. "Tomorrow I shall be well," she declared. That evening, she dictated a final hymn: "In the morn of Zion's glory, / When the clouds have rolled away, / And my hope has dropped its anchor / In the vale of perfect day, / When with all the pure and holy / I shall strike my harp anew, / With a power no arm can sever, / Love will hold me fast and true."

At 3:30 in the morning, Fanny's niece, Florence Booth, heard her walking down the hall, presumably going to the bathroom. Rising to see about her, Florence reached her just as she fainted. Florence carried the tiny figure to bed, and Fanny quickly slipped into the presence of the King, fulfilling her own soul's poem:

And I shall see Him face to face
And tell the story—Saved by Grace.

Faith Is the Victory

John H. Yates

Ira D. Sankey

1. En - camped a - long the hills of light, Ye Chris - tian sol - diers, rise, And
2. His ban - ner o - ver us is love, Our sword the Word of God. We
3. To him that o - ver - comes the foe, White rai - ment shall be giv'n; Be -

press the bat - tle ere the night Shall veil the glow - ing skies. A - gainst the foe in
tread the road the saints a - bove With shouts of tri - umph trod. By faith they like a
fore the an - gels he shall know His name con - fessed in heav'n. Then on - ward from the

vales be - low, Let all our strength be hurled; Faith is the vic - to - ry, we know,
whirl-wind's breath, Swept on o'er ev - 'ry field; The faith by which they con-quer'd death
hill of light, Our hearts with love a - flame; We'll van - quish all the hosts of night,

That ov - er - comes the world.
Is still our shin - ing shield. Faith is the vic - to - ry! Faith is the
In Je - sus' con - qu'ring name.

vic - to - ry! O, glo - ri - ous vic - to - ry, That ov - er - comes the world.

Faith Is the Victory

1891

For whatever is born of God overcomes the world. And this is the victory that has overcome the world—our faith. 1 John 5:4

T his hymn was written by a shoe salesman who eventually became a Freewill Baptist pastor in upstate New York.

John Henry Yates was born in Batavia, on November 21, 1837, the son of John and Elizabeth Yates who had emigrated from England. After attending Batavia Union School, John became a shoe seller, and in 1871, he became the local department manager for a hardware firm called E. L. & G. D. Kenyon Store. He worked there fifteen years before becoming editor of the local paper, a job he held for the next ten years.

In 1858, he was licensed to preach in the Methodist church, and he was later ordained. He served for seven years as pastor of the West Bethany Freewill Baptist Church.

Along the way, John Henry wrote poems, and one of them, "The Model Church," came to the attention of Ira Sankey, who, after seeing it in a newspaper wrote music for it and sang it for the first time in Atlanta, Georgia. In his memoirs, Sankey wrote, "Once, in Buffalo, I had the pleasure of meeting Mr. Yates of Batavia, New York; and I urged him to devote more of his time to writing gospel hymns. He has since written several popular songs."

In 1891, Yates sent this "Faith Is the Victory" to Sankey, who wrote the music for it. It first appeared that year in *The Christian Endeavor Handbook* and in *Gospel Hymns No. 6.*

In 1897, John published his one and only book, *Poems and Ballads.* He died three years later, in Batavia, on September 5, 1900.

His other hymns are almost forgotten now, but were quite popular in their day, including one that defended the Bible against critical attacks that were coming in waves from liberal scholars in the late nineteenth century. As with "Faith Is the Victory," it is marked by Yates' gift of imagery:

The old Book stands! O yes, it stands!
Firm as a rock 'mid shifting sands!
Billows may run high, tempests sweep the sky;
Firmly the old Book stands.

Lord, I'm Coming Home

William J. Kirkpatrick

William J. Kirkpatrick

1. I've wan-dered far a-way from God, Now I'm com-ing home;
2. I've wast-ed man-y pre-cious years, Now I'm com-ing home;
3. I'm tired of sin and stray-ing, Lord, Now I'm com-ing home;
4. My soul is sick, my heart is sore, Now I'm com-ing home;

The paths of sin too long I've trod, Lord, I'm com-ing home.
I now re-pent with bit-ter tears, Lord, I'm com-ing home.
I'll trust Thy love, be-lieve Thy Word, Lord, I'm com-ing home.
My strength re-new, my hope re-store, Lord, I'm com-ing home.

Com-ing home, com-ing home, Nev-er-more to roam,

O-pen wide Thine arms of love, Lord, I'm com-ing home.

Lord, I'm Coming Home

1892

I said, "LORD, be merciful to me; Heal my soul, for I have sinned against You."
Psalm 41:4

The Methodist camp meetings of the 1800s changed the shape of Christianity in America, and their influence lingers to this day—especially in our hymnology. Large crowds often numbering in the thousands gathered for days, camping with their families around huge tents, tabernacles, or open-air arenas. The women cooked the meals, the children played together, the teenagers courted, and the men talked politics. Several times a day, they'd gather for fervent singing, emotional testifying, and firebrand preaching.

By the late 1800s, many of these camp meeting sites had become regular conference centers and retreat grounds, providing a place of ministry to the greatest preachers, soloists, and song leaders of the day.

William J. Kirkpatrick, minister of music at Grace Methodist Episcopal Church in Philadelphia, was a popular figure on the summer revival circuit.* On one occasion in the early 1890s, as Kirkpatrick led singing at a camp meeting outside Rawlinsville, Pennsylvania, he began to question the sincerity and salvation of the soloist with whom he was working. The man left the meeting as soon as he had sung, and he withdrew from fellowship times. His name has been lost to us, but we know that Kirkpatrick began earnestly praying for him.

"I became very burdened for him and the Lord led me to use an unusual plan," Kirkpatrick wrote. "[The Lord] told me to write a special song of invitation with just the singer in mind and then I was to have him sing it. This I did, and the very evening he sang it, God so spoke to his heart that he did not go out after singing but stayed to hear the message. Praise God!—he was the first to the altar letting Christ come into his heart. My new song had been the Lord's means of answering my prayer. It was 'Lord, I'm Coming Home.'"

Kirkpatrick's song first appeared in a book of camp meeting hymns in 1892, and has since been a popular hymn of invitation for over one hundred years. Untold numbers have come to Christ through its singing, but the initial convert was the man who first sang this hymn on a summer's night in a camp meeting near Rawlinsville, Pennsylvania.

Coming home, coming home,
Nevermore to roam;
Open now Thine arms of love—
Lord, I'm coming home.

---

*A summary of Kirkpatrick's interesting life is told under the story for "O to Be Like Thee."

America, the Beautiful

Katharine Lee Bates

Samuel A. Ward

1. O beau-ti-ful for spa-cious skies, For am-ber waves of grain,
2. O beau-ti-ful for pil-grim feet, Whose stern, im-pas-sioned stress
3. O beau-ti-ful for he-roes proved In lib-er-at-ing strife,
4. O beau-ti-ful for pa-triot dream That sees be-yond the years

For pur-ple moun-tains maj-es-ties A-bove the fruit-ed plain!
A thor-ough-fare for free-dom beat A-cross the wil-der-ness!
Who more than self their coun-try loved, And mer-cy more than life!
Thine al-a-bas-ter cit-ies gleam, Un-dimmed by hu-man tears!

A-mer-i-ca! A-mer-i-ca! God shed His grace on thee,
A-mer-i-ca! A-mer-i-ca! God mend thine ev-'ry flaw.
A-mer-i-ca! A-mer-i-ca! May God thy gold re-fine
A-mer-i-ca! A-mer-i-ca! God shed His grace on thee,

And crown thy good with broth-er-hood From sea to shin-ing sea!
Con-firm thy soul in self-con-trol, Thy lib-er-ty in law!
Till all suc-cess be no-ble-ness And ev-ery gain di-vine!
And crown thy good with broth-er-hood From sea to shin-ing sea.

America the Beautiful

1893

The heavens are Yours, the earth also is Yours; The world and all its fullness, You have founded them. Psalm 89:11

I n 1892, the United States observed the 400th anniversary of the discovery of America by Christopher Columbus.

As part of the celebration, the city of Chicago sponsored a World's Fair, which carried over to the next year. It was in the early summer of 1893, that a group of professors from Wellesley College visited the Exposition on their way to teach summer school in Colorado. The women later compared the wonders of the man-made Fair with the glory of God's handiwork in the Rockies.

At the close of school, the teachers decided to visit Pike's Peak, elevation 14,000 feet. One of them, Katharine Lee Bates, later wrote, "We hired a prairie wagon. Near the top we had to leave the wagon and go the rest of the way on mules. I was very tired. But when I saw the view, I felt great joy. All the wonder of America seemed displayed there, with the sea-like expanse. . . .

> It was then and there, as I was looking out over the sea-like expanse of fertile country spreading away so far under those ample skies, that the opening lines of the hymn floated into my mind. When we left Colorado Springs the four stanzas were penciled in my notebook. . . . The Wellesley work soon absorbed time and attention again, the notebook was laid aside, and I do not remember paying heed to these verses until the second summer following, when I copied them out and sent them to *The Congregationalist*, where they first appeared in print July 4, 1895. The hymn attracted an unexpected amount of attention. . . . In 1904, I rewrote it, trying to make the phraseology more simple and direct.

The new version first appeared in the *Boston Evening Transcript*, November 19, 1904.

There are two stories about the melody, MATERNA, which was written by Samuel A. Ward, originally for a hymn entitled, "O Mother Dear, Jerusalem." Ward's son-in-law said that the tune was composed in memory of Ward's oldest daughter. One of the employees at Ward's music store in Newark insisted that he composed the tune in 1882 while crossing New York harbor after spending the day at Coney Island. The notes came to him so quickly he jotted them on the cuff of his shirt. Perhaps both stories are true.

When the Roll Is Called Up Yonder

James M. Black

James M. Black

1. When the trum-pet of the Lord shall sound, and
2. On that bright and cloud-less morn-ing when the
3. Let us la - bor for the Mas - ter from the

time shall be no more, And the morn-ing breaks e - ter - nal bright and fair.
dead in Christ shall rise, And the glo - ry of His res - ur - rec - tion share;
dawn 'til set - ting sun, Let us talk of all His won-drous love and care;

When the saints on earth shall gath - er o - ver on the oth - er shore,
When the cho - sen ones shall gath - er to their home be - yond the skies,
And when all of life is o - ver and our work on earth is done,

And the roll is called up yon - der I'll be there.
And the roll is called up yon - der I'll be there.
And the roll is called up yon - der I'll be there.

When the Roll Is Called Up Yonder

<u>1893</u>

I am the resurrection and the life. He who believes in Me, though he may die, he shall live. John 11:25

This old favorite was inspired by disappointment. James Black was calling roll one day for a youth meeting at his Methodist church in Williamsport, Pennsylvania. One name didn't answer—young Bessie, the daughter of an alcoholic. Crestfallen at her absence, James commented, "O God, when my own name is called up yonder, may I be there to respond!" Returning home, a thought struck him while opening the gate. Entering the house, he went to the piano and wrote the words and music effortlessly.

Years later, this song comforted a group of traumatized children in a Japanese concentration camp. In his book, *A Boy's War,* David Mitchell, tells of being in boarding school in Chefoo, China, during the Japanese invasion. On November 5, 1942, the students and faculty were marched from their campus and eventually ended up in Weihsien Concentration Camp.

Among the students was Brian Thompson, a lanky teenager. One evening about a year before the war ended, Brian was restless, waiting for the evening roll call which was long overdue. A bare wire from the searchlight tower was sagging low, and some of the older boys were jumping up and touching it with their fingers. "Whew, I got a shock off that," said one.

Brian decided to try. Being taller than the others, his hand was drawn into the wire, and it came down with him. When his bare feet hit the damp ground, the electricity shot through him like bolts of lightning. His mother, who had been interred with the students, tried to reach him, but the others held her back or she, too, would have been electrocuted. Finally someone found an old wooden stool and managed to detach the electrical wire, but it was too late.

At roll call that night, when the name "Brian Thompson" was called, there was no answer. David Mitchell later wrote: "Our principal and Mr. Houghton led a very solemn yet triumphant funeral service the next day. The shortness of life and the reality of eternity were brought home to us with force as Paul Bruce related that Brian had missed the roll call in camp but had answered one in Heaven. How important it was for us to sing and know, 'When the Roll is called up yonder, I'll be there.'"

Moment by Moment

Daniel W. Whittle

May W. Moody

1. Dy-ing with Je-sus, by death reck-oned mine, Liv-ing with Je-sus a
2. Nev-er a tri-al that He is not there, Nev-er a bur-den that
3. Nev-er a heart-ache, and nev-er a groan, Nev-er a tear-drop and
4. Nev-er a weak-ness that He doth not feel, Nev-er a sick-ness that

new life di-vine, Look-ing to Je-sus 'til glo-ry doth shine, Mo-ment by
He doth not bear, Nev-er a sor-row that He doth not share, Mo-ment by
nev-er a moan; Nev-er a dan-ger but there on the throne, Mo-ment by
He can-not heal; Mo-ment by mo-ment, in woe or in weal, Je-sus, my

mo-ment, O Lord, I am Thine.
mo-ment, I'm un-der His care.
mo-ment, He thinks of His own. Mo-ment by mo-ment I'm kept in His love,
Sav-ior, a-bides with me still.

Mo-ment by mo-ment I've life from a-bove; Look-ing to Je-sus 'til

glo-ry doth shine, Mo-ment by mo-ment, O Lord, I am Thine.

Moment by Moment

1893

Praise be to the Lord, to God our Savior, who daily bears our burdens. Psalm 68:19 (NIV)

uch of our information about the hymns of the gospel song era comes from *My Life and the Story of the Gospel Hymns,* by Ira Sankey, the "singing evangelist," who accompanied D. L. Moody around the world.* Here's what he said about this enduring hymn:

"While I was attending the World's Fair in Chicago, Henry Varley, a lay preacher from London, said to Major Daniel Whittle: 'I do not like the hymn, "I Need Thee Every Hour," very well, because I need Him every moment of the day.' Soon after Major Whittle wrote this sweet hymn, having the chorus:

> *Moment by moment I'm kept in His love;*
> *Moment by moment I've life from above;*
> *Looking to Jesus till glory doth shine;*
> *Moment by moment, O Lord, I am Thine.*

"Mr. Whittle brought the hymn to me in manuscript a little later, saying that he would give me the copyright of both the words and music if I would print for him five hundred copies on fine paper, for distribution among his friends. His daughter, May Whittle, who later became the wife of Will R. Moody, composed the music. I did as Mr. Whittle wished; and I sent the hymn to England, where it was copyrighted on the same day as in Washington.

"In England, the hymn became very popular. Falling into the hands of the well-known Rev. Andrew Murray, of South Africa, then visiting London, he adopted it as his favorite hymn. A year later Mr. Murray visited Northfield, and while holding a meeting for men in the church he remarked, 'If Mr. Sankey only knew a hymn which I found in London, and would sing it; he would find that it embraces my entire creed.'

"I was very anxious to know what hymn it was, and when he had recited it, I said to him, 'Doctor, that hymn was written within five hundred yards of where we are standing.'"

---

*Sankey wrote the original version of his combined autobiography and hymn history in Battle Creek, Michigan, where he was recovering from illness. Unfortunately, a fire broke out and destroyed his one and only manuscript, along with all his collected notes. Greatly depressed, Sankey, who was blind by then, dictated *My Life and the Story of Gospel Hymns* from memory, relying on scraps of information, as best he could. It is still an amazing book.

I Must Tell Jesus

Elisha A. Hoffman

Elisha A. Hoffman

1. I must tell Jesus All of my trials, I cannot bear These
2. I must tell Jesus All of my troubles, He is a kind, Com-
3. O how the world to evil allures me. O how my heart Is

bur - dens a - lone. In my dis - tress He kind - ly will help me.
pas - sion - ate friend. If I but ask Him, He will de - liv - er,
tempt - ed to sin. I must tell Je - sus And He will help me,

He ev - er loves And cares for His own. I must tell Je - sus!
Make of my trou - bles Quick - ly an end. I must tell Je - sus!
O - ver the world The vic - t'ry to win.

I must tell Je - sus! I can - not bear My bur - dens a - lone.

I must tell Je - sus! I must tell Je - sus! Je - sus can help me, Je - sus a - lone.

I Must Tell Jesus

1894

Cast your burden on the LORD, and He shall sustain you; He shall never permit the righteous to be moved. Psalm 55:22

Many New Testament promises have corresponding verses in the Old Testament that reinforce their power. When Peter, for example, said, "Therefore humble yourselves under the mighty hand of God, that He may exalt you in due time, casting all your care upon Him, for He cares for you" (1 Peter 5:6–7), he was but restating David's words in Psalm 55:22: "Cast your burden on the Lord, and He shall sustain you; He shall never permit the righteous to be moved."

Elisha A. Hoffman loved those verses. He was born May 7, 1839, in Orwigsburg, Pennsylvania. His father was a minister, and Elisha followed Christ at a young age. He attended Philadelphia public schools, studied science, then pursued the classics at Union Seminary of the Evangelical Association. He worked for eleven years with the association's publishing house in Cleveland, Ohio. Then, following the death of his young wife, he returned to Pennsylvania and devoted 33 years to pastoring Benton Harbor Presbyterian Church.

Hoffman's pastime was writing hymns, many of which were inspired by pastoral incidents. One day, for example, while calling on the destitute of Lebanon, Pennsylvania, he met a woman whose depression seemed beyond cure. She opened her heart and poured on him her pent-up sorrows. Wringing her hands, she cried, "What shall I do? Oh, what shall I do?" Hoffman knew what she should do, for he had himself learned the deeper lessons of God's comfort. He said to the woman, "You cannot do better than to take all your sorrows to Jesus. You must tell Jesus."

Suddenly the lady's face lighted up. "Yes!" she cried, "That's it! I must tell Jesus." Her words echoed in Hoffman's ears, and he mulled them over as he returned home. He drew out his pen and started writing

I must tell Jesus! I must tell Jesus!
I cannot bear my burdens alone;
I must tell Jesus! I must tell Jesus!
Jesus can help me, Jesus alone.

Hoffman lived to be 90, telling Jesus his burdens and giving the church such hymns as "What A Wonderful Savior," "Down at the Cross," "Are You Washed in the Blood?," "Leaning on the Everlasting Arms," and a thousand more.*

---

*Taken from the author's book, *On This Day* (Nashville: Thomas Nelson Publishers, 1997), installment for May 7th.

The Lord Will Provide

Mrs. A.W. Cook

Phillip Phillips

1. In some way or oth-er the Lord will pro-vide; It
2. At some time or oth-er the Lord will pro-vide; It
3. De-spond then no long-er; the Lord will pro-vide; And
4. March on then right bold-ly; the sea shall di-vide, The

may not be my way, It may not be thy way; And yet, in His
may not be my time, It may not be thy time; And yet, in His
this be the to-ken, No word He hath spo-ken Was ev-er yet
path-way made glor-ious, With shout-ings vic-tor-ious We'll join in the

own way, "The Lord will pro-vide."
own time, "The Lord will pro-vide."
bro-ken: "The Lord will pro-vide."
cho-rus, "The Lord will pro-vide."

Then, we'll trust in the Lord, And

He will pro-vide; Yes, we'll trust in the Lord, And He will pro-vide.

The Lord Will Provide

1894

So Abraham called that place The LORD Will Provide. And to this day it is said, "On the mountain of the LORD it will be provided. Genesis 22:14 (NIV)

This hymn is seldom sung today, and we know little of its author, Mrs. A. W. Cook, but I wanted to include it because it played a part in the conversion of the great evangelist, Rodney "Gypsy" Smith.

Rodney was born in a gypsy tent in England. His father, Cornelius, earned money playing his fiddle at local taverns, where he always got drunk. But one day, he was converted.

"In the agony of his soul," Rodney later wrote, "he fell on the floor unconscious, and lay there wallowing and foaming for half an hour. I was in great distress, and thought my father was dead . . . but presently he came to himself, stood up and, leaping joyfully, exclaimed, 'I am converted!'"

Cornelius, a truly changed man, resolved never to play in taverns again. In his autobiography, Rodney describes the incident that helped lead to his own conversion:

> *All this time my father was very poor, and one winter at Cambridge we were in the hardest straits. . . . I wanted to know what we were going to have for Christmas, and I asked my father. "I do not know, my dear," he said quietly. . . . Then the devil came and tempted him. His fiddle was hanging on the wall, and he looked at it desperately and thought to himself, "If I just . . . go to a public house and play to the people there, my children, too, will have a good Christmas dinner." But the temptation was very soon overcome. My father fell on his knees and began to pray. . . . When he arose from his knees he said, "I don't know quite what we shall have for Christmas, but we will sing." He began to sing with a merry heart: "In some way or other / The Lord will provide: / It may not by my way, / It may not be thy way; / But yet in His own way / The Lord will provide." Just then, while we were singing, there was a knock at the door of the van.*
>
> *"Who is there?" cried my father.*
>
> *It was the old Cambridge town missionary, Mr. Sykes.*
>
> *"It is I, Brother Smith. God is good, is He not? I have come to tell you how the Lord will provide. In a shop in this town there are three legs of mutton and groceries waiting for you and your brothers."*
>
> *A wheelbarrow was needed to bring home the store.*

At Calvary

William R. Newell

Daniel B. Towner

1. Years I spent in van-i-ty and pride, Car-ing not my Lord was cru-ci-fied, Know-ing not it was for me He died On Cal-va-ry.
2. By God's Word at last my sin I learned; Then I trem-bled at the law I'd spurned, Till my guilt-y soul im-plor-ing turned To Cal-va-ry.
3. Now I've giv'n to Je-sus ev-'ry-thing; Now I glad-ly own Him as my King; Now my rap-tured soul can on-ly sing Of Cal-va-ry.
4. O the love that drew sal-va-tion's plan! O the grace that brought it down to man! O the might-y gulf that God did span At Cal-va-ry!

Mer-cy there was great and grace was free; Par-don there was mul-ti-plied to me; There my bur-dened soul found lib-er-ty, At Cal-va-ry.

At Calvary

But God demonstrates His own love toward us, in that while we were still sinners, Christ died for us. Romans 5:8

When Dr. R. A. Torrey was president of the Moody Bible Institute of Chicago, he received a letter from a distressed father. The man, a pastor, had a prodigal son named Bill who was breaking his heart. Would Dr. Torrey let the boy enroll at Moody? Dr. Torrey replied that while he sympathized with the man, it wasn't possible to admit the boy. Moody was a Bible school, not a reformatory. The man wrote back, doubling his entreaties. Finally Dr. Torrey agreed, provided the boy meet with him daily and abide by the rules.

The arrangement didn't go well at first, and Dr. Torrey thought the experiment was hopeless. The boy had serious problems and seemed torn apart by turbulence. But he did keep the rules, and day by day he ventilated his frustrations to Dr. Torrey and—as it turned out—was more attentive to Torrey's answers than it appeared.

To make a long story short, several years later that boy, William R. Newell, himself, was a beloved professor at Moody Bible Institute.

In 1895, William began thinking of putting his testimony into verse form. The idea rolled around in the back of his mind for several weeks, then one day on his way to lecture, the lines came to him. Ducking into an empty classroom, he jotted down the words on the back of an envelope. As he hurried on to class, he happened to meet Dr. Daniel Towner, director of music at the Institute. Handing him the verses, William gently suggested they could use a good melody. By the time Dr. Newell finished his lecture, the completed tune was ready.

"Bill," said Dr. Towner, "I was so taken with the poem you gave me that I went immediately to my studio and composed a tune. I feel that it could be the best song that either of us will ever write in our lifetime."

The two men sang it together, and it was published shortly after.

Bill Newell went on to become a well-known Bible teacher throughout the Midwest and the author of a popular series of Bible commentaries. He once said that had he not gone through his troubled years, he might never have fully understood the importance of Calvary's grace.

> *Mercy there was great, and grace was free;*
> *Pardon there was multiplied to me;*
> *There my burdened soul found liberty at Calvary.*

Jesus Loves the Little Children

C. H. Woolston and Joseph Barlowe

George F. Root

1. Je - sus calls the chil - dren dear, "Come to me and nev - er fear, For I
2. Je - sus is the Shep - herd true, And He'll al - ways stand by you, For He
3. I am com - ing, Lord, to Thee, And Your sol - dier I will be, For You

love the lit - tle chil-dren of the world; I will take you by the hand, Lead you
loves the lit - tle chil-dren of the world; He's a Sav - ior great and strong, And He'll
love the lit - tle chil-dren of the world; And Your cross I'll al - ways bear, And for

to the bet - ter land, For I love the lit - tle chil-dren of the world."
shield you from the wrong, For He loves the lit - tle chil-dren of the world.
You I'll do and dare, For You love the lit - tle chil-dren of the world.

Je-sus loves the lit - tle chil-dren, All the chil-dren of the world. Red and yel-low, black and

white, They are pre-cious in His sight, Je-sus loves the lit - tle chil-dren of the world.

Jesus Loves the Little Children

Before 1895

Let the little children come to Me, and do not forbid them; for of such is the kingdom of God. Luke 18:16

Almost everyone knows "Jesus Loves the Little Children," but few of us have sung the three verses that go along with that chorus. Nor do many people realize this was originally a Civil War ballad.

George Frederick Root was born into a large family in Sheffield, Massachusetts, in 1820, and showed signs of musical genius. By age thirteen, he boasted that he could play thirteen different instruments. As a young adult, he taught music in Boston and New York, and he also composed music and served as church organist.

In 1855, he offered a song called "Rosalie, the Prairie Flower" to his publisher for the hefty sum of $100. Root's publisher, not thinking it worth that much, offered Root a royalty plan instead. In time, Root grossed *thousands* of dollars from "Rosalie," which helped establish him financially.

The outbreak of the Civil War deeply affected George, and he immediately began using his gifts to advance the Union war effort, writing a host of patriotic songs to rally the moral of the North. As a serious, classical composer, he was embarrassed at the simple martial music coming from his pen, so he signed them with the name "Wurzel," the German word for "Root." Among his most popular pieces was a ballad entitled, "Tramp! Tramp! Tramp!"

> *In the prison cell I sit,*
> *Thinking, mother, dear of you,*
> *And our bright and happy home so far away,*
> *And the tears, they fill my eyes,*
> *'Spite of all that I can do,*
> *Tho' I try to cheer my comrades and be gay.*
>
> CHORUS:
> *Tramp! Tramp! Tramp! The boys are marching,*
> *Cheer up, comrades, they will come,*
> *And beneath the starry flag*
> *We shall breathe the air again*
> *Of the free land in our own beloved home.*

After the Civil War, the melody remained popular but the words were dated. A minister named Clare Herbert Woolston, a lyricist whom Root occasionally used, wrote new verses and a chorus. And that's how a Civil War ballad about a soldier in prison became one of the most popular children's choruses in history.

They Were in an Upper Chamber

Charlie D. Tillman

Charlie D. Tillman

1. They were in an up-per cham-ber, They were all with one ac-cord,
2. Yes, this pow'r from heav'n de-scend-ed, With the sound of rush-ing wind;
3. Yes, this "old-time" pow'r was giv-en To our fa-thers who were true;

When the Ho-ly Ghost de-scend-ed, As was prom-ised by our Lord.
Tongues of fire came down up-on them, As the Lord said He would send.
This is prom-ised to be-liev-ers, And we all may have it too.

O Lord, send the pow'r just now, O Lord, send the pow'r just now,

O Lord, send the pow'r just now, And bap-tize ev-'ry one.

They Were in an Upper Chamber
1895

And when they were come in, they went up into the upper chamber, where they were abiding. Acts 1:13 (ASV)

ntil the late 1800s, most American hymnody came from the North and Midwest, from composers in states like Pennsylvania and Illinois. As the South began reconstruction efforts, a few hymnists and music publishers began appearing south of the Mason-Dixon Line. Chief among them was Charles Tillman.

Charles was born in Tallassee, Alabama, in 1861, just as the Civil War was heating up. His father, James Lafayette Tillman, was a traveling evangelist, and young Charles often accompanied him on his campaigns.

Coming of age himself, Charles first worked as a house painter, and then signed up as a traveling salesman for a music company headquartered in Raleigh, North Carolina. He traveled throughout the South during Reconstruction Days, singing comic songs on a traveling wagon that advertised Wizard Oil. He was first tenor in a male quartet.

By 1887, he was ready to launch out on his own as a singing evangelist. In time, Charles established his own publishing company in Atlanta and published about twenty volumes of gospel songs, which became quite popular in the South.

In 1891, as he and his father were ministering together in a tent revival in Lexington, South Carolina, Charles heard a group of Black musicians singing a Negro spiritual called, "Old Time Religion." Writing down the words and music, Tillman published it for the first time. Its popularity paved the way for a number of Tillman's own songs.

Based on the second chapter of Acts, "They Were in an Upper Chamber" was Tillman's prayer for a Pentecost-like revival in the current day. Another highly popular Tillman song, especially in the South, was "Life's Railway to Heaven." The source of the words is unclear, but Tillman was responsible for the music:

> *Life is like a mountain railroad, with an engineer that's brave;*
> *We must make the run successful, from the cradle to the grave;*
> *Watch the curves, the fills, the tunnels; never falter, never quail;*
> *Keep your hand upon the throttle, and your eye upon the rail.*

By the time he died in Atlanta in 1943, Charles Davis Tillman had helped establish Southern gospel music, leaving behind such beloved songs as "My Mother's Bible," and the classic "When I Get to the End of the Way."

No, Not One!

Johnson Oatman, Jr.

George C. Hugg

1. There's not a friend like the low-ly Je-sus, No, not one! No, not one!
2. No friend like Him is so high and ho-ly, No, not one! No, not one!
3. There's not an hour that He is not near us, No, not one! No, not one!
4. Did ev-er saint find this Friend for-sake Him? No, not one! No, not one!
5. Was e'er a gift like the Sav-ior giv-en? No, not one! No, not one!

None else could heal all our soul's dis-eas-es, No, not one! No, not one!
And yet no friend is so meek and low-ly, No, not one! No, not one!
No night so dark but His love can cheer us, No, not one! No, not one!
Or sin-ner find that He would not take Him? No, not one! No, not one!
Will He re-fuse us a home in heav-en? No, not one! No, not one!

Je-sus knows all a-bout our strug-gles, He will guide 'til the day is done;

There's not a friend like the low-ly Je-sus, No, not one! No, not one!

No, Not One!

1895

For He Himself has said, "I will never leave you nor forsake you." Hebrews 13:5

M y keenest memories of this hymn involve a story my father, John Morgan, told about two churches across the road from one another in our native Tennessee mountains. The congregations had originally been one, but a split had occurred and bad feelings lingered. One evening, a passerby paused between the churches to listen to their music. One of the churches was singing, "Will There Be Any Stars in My Crown?" From across the road came the reply: "No, Not One! No, Not One!"

Johnson Oatman, the author of "No, Not One!" was born to Christian parents near Medford, New Jersey, on April 21, 1856. He was a child during the Civil War, and after the war he joined his father in the mercantile business. He also stood beside his father in church, for both men had good voices and enjoyed singing.

Johnson was ordained a Methodist minister as a young man, but spent most of his life working in the business world rather than pastoring. After his father's death, he moved to Mount Holly, New Jersey, where he sold insurance.

In 1892, when he was in his mid-thirties, Johnson began writing gospel songs. The next year, failing health forced him to retire from business, and he began devoting himself to full-time songwriting.

Some sources say that he wrote 3,000 hymns; other sources put the number at 5,000. The usually reliable 1992 edition of *Handbook to the Baptist Hymnal* claims that Oatman wrote more than 7,000 texts. He was usually only paid a dollar or so per song, but he became one of the most important gospel songwriters of the turn of the century.

This song, "No, Not One," emphasizes friendship with Christ. The Gospels call Jesus the "Friend of Sinners" (Matt. 11:19). In John 15, He told His disciples, "Greater love has no one than this, than to lay down one's life for his friends. You are My friends. . . . I have called you friends." Jesus is a friend who "sticks closer than a brother" (Prov. 18:24). If you're feeling lonely today, could you ever find a better, closer, wiser, stronger friend?

No, not one.*

---

*Incidentally, those who complain that today's praise and worship music is too repetitious should notice that in singing Oatman's hymn, we repeat the phrase "No, Not One" thirty times!

Open My Eyes That I May See

Clara H. Scott

Clara H. Scott

1. O-pen my eyes that I may see Glimps-es of truth Thou hast for me;
2. O-pen my ears that I may hear Voic-es of truth Thou send-est clear;
3. O-pen my mouth and let me bear Glad-ly the warm truth ev-ery-where.
4. O-pen my mind that I may read More of Thy love in word and deed.

Place in my hands the won-der-ful key That shall un-clasp and set me free.
And while the wave-notes fall on my ear, Ev-ery-thing false will dis-ap-pear.
O-pen my heart and let me pre-pare Love with Thy chil-dren thus to share.
What shall I fear while yet Thou dost lead? On-ly for light from Thee I plead.

Si-lent-ly now I wait for Thee, Read-y, my God, Thy will to see.

O-pen my eyes, il-lu-mine me, Spir-it di-vine!
O-pen my ears, il-lu-mine me, Spir-it di-vine!
O-pen my heart, il-lu-mine me, Spir-it di-vine!
O-pen my mind, il-lu-mine me, Spir-it di-vine!

Open My Eyes That I May See

The LORD opens the eyes of the blind; The LORD raises those who are bowed down; The LORD loves the righteous. Psalm 146:8

Next time you sit down to read your Bible, try pausing a moment, asking God to bless your time in His Word. Two great biblical prayers teach this. The first is in 1 Samuel 3:9, where the boy Samuel was taught to pray, "Speak, Lord, for Your servant hears." That simple prayer has inspired a number of hymns, such as Frances Havergal's tender "Master, Speak! Thy Servant Heareth!"

> *Thy Master, speak! Thy servant heareth,*
> *Waiting for Thy gracious word,*
> *Longing for Thy voice that cheereth;*
> *Master! let it now be heard.**

The other biblical prayer is Psalm 119:18: "Open my eyes, that I may see wondrous things from Your law." This verse inspired Clara Scott to compose both the words and the music to "Open My Eyes That I May See" in 1895.

Clara was born in 1841, just outside Chicago. She was drawn toward music at an early age, having the privilege of attending the first musical institute of Chicago, conducted by the famous music publisher, C. M Cady.

Three years later, she became the music teacher of an all-girl's school in Iowa. In 1861, she married Henry Clay Scott and began writing songs. Some of her work came to the attention of Horatio Palmer, author of "Yield Not to Temptation." With his encouragement, she started writing in earnest, and Palmer published a number of her songs in his collections.

In 1882, she published *The Royal Anthem Book*, which holds the distinction of being the first volume of anthems ever published by a woman. In 1895, "Open My Eyes That I May See" was published and became her best-known hymn. The next year she published a book called *Truth in Song for Lovers of Truth*.

The next year, 1897, began with the excitement of another book on the way, Clara's *Short Anthems*. But that summer, as she was visiting in the Mississippi River town of Dubuque, Iowa, she climbed into a horse-drawn carriage. Something spooked the horse, sending it careening down the street at breakneck speed. Clara was thrown from the runaway buggy and killed. She was fifty-five.

---

*There's also a glorious old German hymn by Anna Sophia of Hessen-Darmstadt, published in 1658, titled "Speak, O Lord, Thy Servant Heareth." The final stanza says: *"Precious Jesus, I beseech Thee, / May Thy Words take root in me. / May this gift from heav'n enrich me, / That I may bear fruit for Thee."*

I Surrender All

Judson W. Van De Venter

Winfield S. Weeden

1. All to Je-sus I sur-ren-der, All to Him I free-ly give;
2. All to Je-sus I sur-ren-der, Hum-bly at His feet I bow,
3. All to Je-sus I sur-ren-der, Make me Sav-ior whol-ly Thine;
4. All to Je-sus I sur-ren-der, Lord, I give my-self to Thee.

I will ev-er love and trust Him, In His pres-ence dai-ly live.
World-ly pleas-ures all for-sak-en, Take me, Je-sus, take me now.
Let me feel the Ho-ly Spir-it, Tru-ly know that Thou art mine.
Fill me with Thy love and pow-er; Let Thy bless-ings fall on me.

I sur-ren-der all,   I sur-ren-der all.
I sur-ren-der all,   I sur-ren-der all.

All to Thee my bless-ed Sav-ior, I sur-ren-der all.

I Surrender All

1896

But now, O LORD, You are our Father; we are the clay, and You our potter; and all we are the work of Your hand. Isaiah 64:8

Someone once said, "Only in the Christian life does surrender bring victory." Judson Wheeler Van De Venter learned that for himself.

Born on a farm in Monroe Country, Michigan, in 1855, Judson grew up interested in art and music. He was converted to Christ at age 17. After graduating from college in Hillsdale, Michigan, Judson became an art teacher and then supervisor of art for the high school in Sharon, Pennsylvania. In 1885, he toured Europe, visiting art galleries and museums and studying painting. He was also a musician, having studied in numerous singing schools.

All the while, Judson was heavily involved in his local Methodist Episcopal Church where he sang in the choir. He found himself especially fulfilled when participating in evangelistic rallies and revivals in which people received Christ as their personal Savior. Friends encouraged him to resign from the school system to enter fulltime music evangelism, but for five years he struggled with the decision.

Finally falling to his knees, he said, "Lord, if you want me to give my full time to Thy work, I'll do it, I surrender all to Thee." For the next several years he traveled extensively through the United States, England, and Scotland, assisting in evangelistic work, leading the singing for Wilber Chapman and other evangelists, and winning men and women to Christ.

While engaged in meetings in East Palestine, Ohio, Judson stayed in the home of George Sebring (whose family founded Sebring, Ohio, and who himself later founded Sebring, Florida). It was there that he wrote the hymn, "I Surrender All," while recalling his own personal submitting to full-time ministry.

Moving to Tampa in 1923, he began teaching hymnology at Florida Bible Institute. He retired after several years, but still occasionally showed up on campus to lecture or to speak in chapel. In the 1930s, a student at Florida Bible Institute sat wide-eyed, listening to Judson Van De Venter. That student, Billy Graham, later wrote: "One of the evangelists who influenced my early preaching was also a hymnist who wrote 'I Surrender All,' the Rev. J. W. Van De Venter. He was a regular visitor at the Florida Bible Institute (now Trinity Bible College) in the late 1930s. We students loved this kind, deeply spiritual gentleman and often gathered in his winter home at Tampa, Florida, for an evening of fellowship and singing."

Under His Wings

William O. Cushing

Ira D. Sankey

1. Un-der His wings I am safe-ly a-bid-ing, Tho the night
2. Un-der His wings, What a ref-uge in sor-row! How the heart
3. Un-der His wings, O what pre-cious en-joy-ment! There will I

deep-ens And tem-pests are wild; Still I can trust Him I
yearn-ing-ly Turns to His rest! Of-ten when earth has no
hide 'Til life's tri-als are o'er! Shel-tered, pro-tect-ed, No

know He will keep me, He has re-deemed me And I am His child.
balm for my heal-ing, There I find com-fort And there I am blest.
e-vil can harm me, Rest-ing in Je-sus I'm safe ev-er-more.

Un-der His wings, Un-der His wings Who from His love can sev-er?

Un-der His wings My soul shall a-bide, Safely a-bide for-ev-er.

Under His Wings

1896

He shall cover you with His feathers, and under His wings you shall take refuge ...
Psalm 91:4

In the days following World War II, when Communists were overrunning China, the endangered missionaries found comfort knowing that in a world dominated by the "Iron Curtain" and the "Bamboo Curtain" they could rest under the "Feather Curtain" of God.*

Psalm 91:4 says, "He shall cover you with His feathers, and under His wings you shall take refuge." The biblical patriarch, Boaz, referred to Ruth as a woman who had come under the Lord's wings for refuge (Ruth 2:12). Later Ruth's great-grandson, King David, perhaps recalling that story, asked the Lord in Psalm 17:8: "Keep me as the apple of Your eye; hide me under the shadow of Your wings." And in Psalm 57, he cried, "Be merciful to me, O God, be merciful to me! For my soul trusts in You; and in the shadow of Your wings I will make my refuge, until these calamities have passed by."

A thousand years later, David's great descendant, Jesus of Nazareth, said to the people of Jerusalem, "O Jerusalem, Jerusalem, the one who kills the prophets and stones those who are sent to her! How often I wanted to gather your children together, as a hen gathers her chicks under her wings . . ."

All these comforting word-pictures were woven together in the hymn, "Under His Wings," written by William Orcutt Cushing, who was born into a Unitarian home in 1823. He labored for over twenty years as a Christian pastor in New York with the Disciples of Christ, but the death of his wife and severe problems with his voice forced him out of the pastorate. In near despair, he asked God to give him something to do for the kingdom. It came into his heart to begin writing hymns, and in subsequent years, he produced more than 300 of them, including "Ring the Bells of Heaven," "When He Cometh," "Down in the Valley," and "Under His Wings."

If you find yourself in near despair with the worries and fears of life, close your eyes and visualize the warm safety of the "Feather Curtain of God."

Under His wings I am safely abiding,
Though the night deepens and tempests are wild,
Still I can trust Him; I know He will keep me,
He has redeemed me, and I am His child.

---

*See Isobel Kuhn, *Green Leaf in Drought* (Singapore: 1997), p. 37.

Count Your Blessings

Johnson Oatman, Jr.

Edwin O. Excell

1. When up-on life's bil-lows You are tem-pest tossed,
2. Are you ev-er bur-dened With a load of care,
3. When you look at oth-ers With their lands and gold,
4. So a-mid the con-flict Wheth-er great or small,

When you are dis-cour-aged Think-ing all is lost,
Does the cross seem heav-y You are called to bear.
Think that Christ has prom-ised You His wealth un-told.
Do not be dis-cour-aged God is o-ver all.

Count your man-y bless-ings Name them one by one,
Count your man-y bless-ings Ev-'ry doubt will fly,
Count your man-y bless-ings Mon-ey can-not buy,
Count your man-y bless-ings An-gels will at-tend,

And it will sur-prise you What the Lord hath done.
And you will be sing-ing As the days go by.
Your re-ward in heav-en Nor your home on high.
Help and com-fort give you To your jour-ney's end.

Count Your Blessings

1897

Every good gift and every perfect gift is from above, and comes down from the Father of lights, with whom there is no variation or shadow of turning. James 1:17

I t's impossible to be thankful and, at the same time, grumpy, cantankerous, critical, or ill-tempered. That's a lesson Johnson Oatman wanted to teach young people in his song, "Count Your Blessings."

Johnson was born in New Jersey just before the Civil War. His father had a powerful voice which some people claimed was the best singing voice in the East. That's why, as a boy, Johnson, Jr., always wanted to stand beside his father in church.

When Johnson was a young man, he stood alongside his father in another way. He became a partner in Johnson Oatman & Son, his dad's mercantile business. At age 19, Johnson joined the Methodist Episcopal Church and was ordained into the ministry. He often preached, but Johnson never entered the fulltime pastorate, for he enjoyed the business world and found it paid his bills, giving him freedom to minister without cost.

In 1892, with his father's voice undoubtedly ringing in his memory, Johnson began writing hymns. He averaged 200 hymns and gospel songs a year—5,000 during the course of his lifetime, among them: "Higher Ground," "No, Not One," "The Last Mile of the Way," and this one, "Count Your Blessings," which was published in a song book for young people in 1897. It reflected Johnson's optimistic faith, and has been a lesson to many ever since.

⌇⌇

Martin Luther wrote in his book, *Table Talk:* "The greater God's gifts and works, the less they are regarded." We tend to exhibit a degree of thanksgiving in reverse proportion to the amount of blessings we've received. A hungry man is more thankful for his morsel than a rich man for his heavily-laden table. A lonely woman in a nursing home will appreciate a visit more than a popular woman with a party thrown in her honor.

If the birds only burst into song once a year, we'd all pay close attention. But because they are singing every morning, we scarcely bother to listen.

Now is a good time to lay this book aside and deliberately thank God for something you've never before mentioned in thanksgiving. Count your blessings. Name them one by one.

And it will surprise you what the Lord has done.

O to Be Like Thee!

Thomas O. Chisholm

William J. Kirkpatrick

1. O to be like Thee! Bless-ed Re-deem-er, This is my con-stant
2. O to be like Thee! Full of com-pas-sion, Lov-ing, for-giv-ing,
3. O to be like Thee! Low-ly in spir-it, Ho-ly and harm-less,
4. O to be like Thee! While I am plead-ing, Pour out Thy Spir-it,

long-ing and prayer; Glad-ly I'll for-feit all of earth's treas-ures,
ten-der and kind. Help-ing the help-less, cheer-ing the faint-ing.
pa-tient and brave; Meek-ly en-dur-ing cru-el re-proach-es,
fill with Thy love. Make me a tem-ple deemed to re-ceive You:

Je-sus, Thy per-fect like-ness to wear.
Seek-ing the wan-dering sin-ner to find!
Will-ing to suf-fer oth-ers to save.
Fit me for life and heav-en a-bove.

O to be like Thee!

O to be like Thee, Bless-ed Re-deem-er, pure as Thou art! Come in Thy

sweet-ness, come in Thy full-ness; Stamp Thine own im-age deep on my heart.

O to Be Like Thee!

1897

As for me, I will see Your face in righteousness; I shall be satisfied when I awake in Your likeness. Psalm 17:15

This is one of the earliest poems of Thomas Chisholm, author of "Great is Thy Faithfulness" and "Living for Jesus." He was born in a log cabin in Kentucky, and came to Christ at age twenty-seven during a revival meeting conducted by Dr. H. C. Morrison. He later became editor of Morrison's paper, *The Pentecostal Herald*. "O to Be Like Thee" was written shortly after Thomas' conversion, as he yearned for increasing Christlikeness in his experience.*

The words were discovered and set to music by William James Kirkpatrick, who wrote the music to many popular gospel songs and is remembered as one of the finest Christian composers of the late 1800s and early 1900s.

Kirkpatrick was born in Pennsylvania, and was taught music at an early age by his father, a schoolteacher. He took to music naturally, and later his parents provided the best training available. Young William studied under Pasquale Rondinella, Leopold Meignen, and T. Bishop. As a teen, he moved to Philadelphia and joined the Wharton Street Methodist Episcopal Church. By twenty-one, he was editing his first songbook, *Devotional Melodies*, and dreaming of becoming a world-class violinist.

William fell in love and married in 1861, at the onset of the Civil War. He enlisted as a fife-major in the 91st Regiment of the Pennsylvania Volunteers. He served but a short time before returning to Philadelphia, where he worked in a furniture store to support his new wife. All the while, he was devoting his extra time to music.

In 1880, he began editing collections of songbooks, and over the next forty years he published more than one hundred collections of hymns. William's own compositions flowed from his love for Christ, his musical talents, and his bouts of personal sorrow. His wife died in 1878, and in his grief he poured himself into his music. He married again in 1893, and the second Mrs. Kirkpatrick died around 1910. He then married the widow of hymnwriter John Sweney.

William Kirkpatrick is best remembered for his popular hymn tunes, such as:

"Blessed Be the Name" • "The Cradle Song"
"He Hideth My Soul" • "Lead Me to Calvary"
"Lord, I'm Coming Home"
"Redeemed, How I Love to Proclaim It"
"Singing I Go" • "'Tis So Sweet to Trust in Jesus"
"We Have an Anchor"

---

*For more on Thomas Chisholm, see the story behind "Living for Jesus" in this book, and the hymn story for "Great Is Thy Faithfulness" in *Then Sings My Soul*, Volume 1.

Face to Face

Carrie E. Breck

Grant C. Tullar

1. Face to face with Christ my Sav - ior, Face to face what will it be
2. On - ly faint-ly now I see Him, With the dark - ling veil be - tween;
3. What re - joic-ing in His pres - ence When are ban-ished grief and pain;
4. Face to face! O bliss-ful mo - ment! Face to face to see and know;

When with rap-ture I be - hold Him, Je - sus Christ who died for me?
But a bless-ed day is com - ing When His glo - ry shall be seen.
When the crook-ed ways are straight-ened And the dark things shall be plain.
Face to face with my Re - deem - er, Je - sus Christ who loves me so.

Face to face I shall be - hold Him, Far be - yond the star - ry sky;

Face to face in all His glo - ry, I shall see Him by and by!

Face to Face

1898

Behold, He is coming with clouds, and every eye will see Him ... Revelation 1:7

T his hymn came about because of a rocking chair, a jar of jelly, and a timely coincidence.

Grant Colfax Tullar was so named because he was born in 1869, when Ulysses S. Grant and Schuyler Colfax were President and Vice-President of the United States. He was raised by an austere set of relatives, his mother having died when he was two, and he spent his youth working in woolen mills and shoe stores. When he was 19, he was converted at a Methodist camp meeting and eventually became the music leader for evangelistic campaigns and a successful music publisher.

One Sunday in the late 1890s, Grant was leading the music for a revival in Rutherford, New Jersey. After spending the afternoon in visitation, he returned to the pastor's house where Rev. and Mrs. Charles Mead had spread leftovers on the table so everyone could make a hurried supper before the evening service. A nearly empty jar of jelly was on the table, and, knowing how Grant loved jelly, it was passed straight to him.

"So, this is all for me, is it?" he said, smiling. That little phrase, "all for me," prompted an idea. He rose, went over the piano, and on the spot composed the words and melody of a hymn entitled "All for me the Savior suffered; / All for me He bled and died." Rev. Mead reportedly sang it at church that very night.

The next morning, Grant received a packet of poems in the mail from Mrs. Frank A. Breck. Among them was a poem that said: "Face to face with Christ my Savior; / Face to face what will it be?"

As Grant read and reread the poem, he realized that the words perfectly fit the music he had written the day before. He sensed the Hand of God in this "coincidence," and, discarding his own poem, replaced it with the one by Mrs. Breck.

Carrie Elizabeth (Mrs. Frank) Breck was a homemaker and mother of five in Portland, Oregon, who wrote hymns in the midst of housework. "I penciled verses under all conditions," she once explained, "over a mending basket, with a baby on my arm, and sometimes even when sweeping or washing dishes, my mind moved in poetic meter." Frail in health, however, she often recorded her poems in a notebook while resting in her favorite rocking chair.

When We All Get to Heaven

Eliza E. Hewitt

Emily D. Wilson

1. Sing the won-drous love of Je - sus, Sing His mer - cy and His grace;
2. While we walk the pil - grim path - way, Clouds will o - ver - spread the sky;
3. Let us then be true and faith - ful, Trust - ing, serv - ing ev - er - y day;
4. On - ward to the prize be - fore us! Soon His beau - ty we'll be - hold;

In the man - sions bright and bless - ed, He'll pre - pare for us a place.
But when trav - 'ling days are o - ver, Not a shad - ow, not a sigh.
Just one glimpse of Him in glo - ry Will the toils of life re - pay.
Soon the pearl - y gates will o - pen, We shall tread the streets of gold.

When we all get to heav - en, What a day of re-
When we all What a

joic - ing that will be! When we all see
day of re - joic - ing that will be! When we all

Je - sus, We'll sing and shout the vic - tor - y.
shout, and shout the vic - to - ry.

When We All Get to Heaven

1898

"And I will give you the keys of the kingdom of heaven, and whatever you bind on earth will be bound in heaven, and whatever you loose on earth will be loosed in heaven." Matthew 16:19

Eliza Edmunds Hewitt was one of the premier women hymnwriters of the late 1800s and the early 1900s. She wrote the popular hymn, "Singing I Go Along Life's Road," which was to have such a profound influence of soloist George Beverly Shea.* She is also the author of "Will There Be Any Stars in My Crown?" "My Faith Has Found a Resting Place," "Sunshine in My Soul," "More About Jesus," and this hymn, "When We All Get To Heaven."

It came to her as she studied John 14, where Jesus told His disciples, "Let not your heart be troubled; you believe in God, believe also in Me. In My Father's house are many mansions; if it were not so, I would have told you. I go to prepare a place for you."

But this wasn't Eliza's only hymn about heaven. Though now seldom-sung, one of her most unique songs is entitled, "The Everlasting Hymn," in which she imagines the majesty of worshipping the Lord as we gather around Him in the heavenly places, vibrantly echoing the biblical song of the angels:

> *Holy, holy, holy; / Angel voices singing;*
> *Holy, holy, holy, / Through high heaven ringing.*
> *From that temple, pure and bright, / Bathed in streams of crystal light,*
> *Hear the everlasting hymn, / Holy, holy, holy.*
>
> *Holy, holy, holy; / Grandest music swelling;*
> *Holy, holy, holy, / All sweet notes excelling.*
> *Those who conquered by His might, / Wearing now their crowns of light,*
> *Join the everlasting hymn, / Holy, holy, holy.*
>
> *Holy, holy, holy; / Come, let us adore Him;*
> *Holy, holy, holy, / Humbly bow before Him.*
> *Wisdom, glory, love and might, / With the seraphim unite*
> *In the everlasting hymn, / Holy, holy, holy.*

That's what we'll be singing—when we all get to heaven.

---

*See the story behind "I'd Rather Have Jesus."

Tell Mother I'll Be There

Charles M. Fillmore

Charles M. Fillmore

1. When I was but a lit-tle child how well I rec-ol-lect
2. Though I was of-ten way-ward, she was al-ways kind and good;
3. When I be-came a prod-i-gal, and left the old roof-tree,
4. One day a mes-sage came to me, it bade me quick-ly come

How I would grieve my moth-er with my fol-ly and ne-glect;
So pa-tient, gen-tle, lov-ing. when I act-ed rough and rude;
She al-most broke her lov-ing heart in mourn-ing af-ter me;
If I would see my moth-er ere the Sav-ior took here home;

And now that she was gone to heav'n I miss her ten-der care:
My child-hood griefs and tri-als she would glad-ly with me share:
And day and night she prayed to God to keep me in His care:
I prom-ised her be-fore she died for heav-en to pre-pare:

O Sav-ior, tell my moth-er I'll be there! (I'll be there!)
O Sav-ior, tell my moth-er I'll be there! (I'll be there!)
O Sav-ior, tell my moth-er I'll be there! (I'll be there!)
O Sav-ior, tell my moth-er I'll be there! (I'll be there!)

Tell Mother I'll Be There

<u>1898</u>

As one whom his mother comforts, so I will comfort you. Isaiah 66:13

cannot subscribe to the idea that luck had very much to do with making me President of the United States," William McKinley once said. "I have never been in doubt since I was old enough to think intelligently that I would sometime be made President."

That may be, but it isn't what his mother had intended.

William was born in 1843, in Ohio, seventh of the nine children of William and Nancy McKinley. His father ran a pig-iron foundry. His mother devoted her time to serving the Lord in her local Methodist church. She taught a Bible class and served as superintendent of the Sunday school. She boasted to friends that her son, William, would one day be a Methodist bishop. (When he became the twenty-fifth President of the United States, she said, "Well, that's all right, too.")

There was always a special bond between William and his mother, and during the winter of 1897, she became seriously ill. President McKinley installed a special telegraph wire connecting the White House to his mother's home in Canton, Ohio. He also kept a special train ready for the trip. One night, the elderly woman called for her son, and the nurses wired, "Mr. President, we think you had better come." He flashed back the answer, TELL MOTHER I'LL BE THERE. He arrived in time, and Mrs. McKinley died in his arms.

When the story was reported in the newspapers, a Midwestern hymnwriter named Charles M. Fillmore was deeply touched. He felt those words expressed the perfect sentiment for wayward children who needed to one day meet their mothers in heaven. "Tell Mother I'll Be There" became one of the most popular invitational hymns of the early twentieth century, and evangelist Charles Alexander once claimed it had "converted more men than any other song."

Four years after his mother's death, President McKinley was attending a reception in Buffalo, New York. At 4:07 PM, as he reached to shake another hand, two .32 bullets entered his chest at point-blank range, and he fell backwards into the arms of Secret Service agents. As he lay bleeding, he managed to tell his guards not to hurt the assassin and to be very careful how they broke the news to his wife. He died a week later, just six months after his second inauguration.

Higher Ground

Johnson Oatman, Jr.

Charles H. Gabriel

1. I'm press-ing on the up-ward way, New heights I'm gain-ing ev-ery
2. My heart has no de-sire to stay Where doubts a-rise and fears dis-
3. I want to live a-bove the world, Though Sa-tan's darts at me are
4. I want to scale the ut-most height And catch a gleam of glo-ry

day; Still pray-ing as I'm on-ward bound, "Lord, plant my
may; Though some may dwell where these a-bound, My prayer, my
hurled; For faith has caught the joy-ful sound, The song of
bright; But still I'll pray 'til heaven I've found "Lord, lead me

feet on high-er ground."
aim is high-er ground.
saints on high-er ground.
on to high-er ground."

Lord, lift me up and let me

stand By faith on heav-en's ta-ble-land, A high-er

plain than I have found: Lord, plant my feet on high-er ground.

Higher Ground

1898

I press toward the goal for the prize of the upward call of God in Christ Jesus.
Philippians 3:14

 his hymn-prayer, loosely based on Paul's testimony in Philippians 3, was written by Johnson Oatman, author of "Count Your Blessings" and "No, Not One!" Oatman wrote thousands of other hymns, most of which have fallen into the ocean of oblivion.

That's too bad, for Oatman was one of the special gospel songwriters whose hymns focused primarily on Christian growth and personal victory. Behind his hymns was this thought: It isn't enough to know Christ; we need to know Him better and more deeply. This is reflected in "Higher Ground" and in many of Oatman's other songs.

His hymn, "Alone with God," for example, visualizes the sweetness of soul-solitude during one's daily "quiet times" of Bible study and prayer.

> *When storms of life are round me beating,*
> *When rough the path that I have trod,*
> *Within my closet door retreating,*
> *I love to be alone with God.*

Perhaps the song that best expressed Oatman's own experience with Christ was his bright and blithesome hymn, "I'm Living on the Hallelujah Side"—

> *Tho' the world may sweep around me with her dazzle and her dreams,*
> *Yet I envy not her vanities and pride,*
> *For my soul looks up to heaven, where the golden sunlight gleams,*
> *And I'm living on the hallelujah side.*

> *Not for all earth's golden millions would I leave this precious place,*
> *Tho' the tempter to persuade me oft has tried,*
> *For I'm safe in God's pavilion, happy in His love and grace,*
> *And I'm living on the hallelujah side.*

> *Here the sun is always shining, here the sky is always bright;*
> *'Tis no place for gloomy Christians to abide,*
> *For my soul is filled with music and my heart with great delight,*
> *And I'm living on the hallelujah side.*

Nearer, Still Nearer

Lelia N. Morris

Lelia N. Morris

1. Near-er, still near-er, close to Thy heart, Draw me, my
2. Near-er, still near-er, noth-ing I bring, Naught as an
3. Near-er, still near-er, Lord, to be Thine! Sin, with its
4. Near-er, still near-er, while life shall last, 'Til safe in

Sav-ior, so pre-cious Thou art! Fold me, O fold me
of-fering to Je-sus, my King; On-ly my sin-ful,
fol-lies I glad-ly re-sign, All of its plea-sures,
glo-ry my an-chor is cast; Through end-less a-ges,

close to Thy breast, Shel-ter me safe in that "Ha-ven of
now con-trite heart, Grant me the cleans-ing Thy blood doth im-
pomp, and its pride; Give me but Je-sus, my Lord cru-ci-
ev-er to be, Near-er, my Sav-ior, still near-er to

Rest," Shel-ter me safe in that "Ha-ven of Rest."
part, Grant me the cleans-ing Thy blood doth im-part.
fied, Give me but Je-sus, my Lord cru-ci-fied.
Thee, Near-er, my Sav-ior, still near-er to Thee.

Nearer, Still Nearer

1898

Now our salvation is nearer than when we first believed. Romans 13:11

elia Naylor Morris wrote over one thousand gospel songs, but she shunned the limelight, preferring to be known as Mrs. C. M. Morris, a nondescript homemaker. For forty-seven of her forty-eight years of married life, she lived in the same simple house in McConnelsville, Ohio.

Lelia had been born in the spring of 1862 in the mountains of Ohio near the West Virginia border, just as her father was leaving for the Civil War. When he returned in 1866, the family moved to Malta, Ohio; and when he died, her mother opened a millinery shop in McConnelsville.

As a child, Lelia went forward to the altar several times, seeking salvation. Finally a man came and laid his hand on her head, saying, "Why, little girl, God is here and ready to forgive your sins." That marked her conversion at age ten. Shortly thereafter, she began playing the organ at prayer meetings.

At age nineteen, Lelia married Charles H. Morris, and the young couple joined the Methodist Episcopal Church, becoming active in congregational work, revivals, and camp meetings. Lelia sang in the choir and worked in the Sunday school and women's ministries. The Morris home became a community center of sorts. Charles and Lelia had more books than anyone else in town, and students frequently dropped by to work on school assignments.

In 1892, at a Methodist camp meeting at Mountain Lake Park, Maryland, Lelia had a dramatic Pentecost-like experience. She later said she had read books about the cleansing power of the Holy Spirit, but thought such anointings were only for preachers and bishops. "I did not suppose it was for me. . . . I was so glad when I found that I might have the Holy Spirit in my life. So I opened my heart and let the Holy Spirit come in."

Shortly afterward, back home, she was sitting at her sewing machine when she realized she was composing a hymn of her own. It soon became a pattern. Day after day, as she worked at home, the words and melody of a hymn would compose themselves in her mind. She would go to the piano, work on it, and hide it away. Thus she accumulated a large collection of personal hymns, one of the first of which was "Nearer, Still Nearer."

Let Jesus Come into Your Heart

Lelia N. Morris

Lelia N. Morris

Let Jesus Come into Your Heart

1898

Let not your heart be troubled; you believe in God, believe also in Me. John 14:1

fter a Pentecost-like experience at the Methodist Camp Meeting at Mountain Lake Park, Maryland, Lelia Morris began writing hymns at her sewing machine. As she devoted more and more time to the Methodist Holiness movement, her hymns became increasingly popular.

One of her finest hymns came early in her songwriting experiences. One Sunday in 1898, while working at the Methodist Camp Meeting at Mountain Lake Park, Maryland, Lelia assisted at the altar of the morning service. The subject of the sermon was repentance, and a large number of people came forward to confess their sins.

One woman was in obvious spiritual anguish. Lelia went to pray with her. So did song leader, Dr. Henry Gilmour, author of "The Haven of Rest." The preacher, L. H. Baker, was also present, and all three converged on the woman.

"Just now your doubting give o'er," said Lelia.

"Just now reject Him no more," added Dr. Gilmour.

"Just now throw open the door," said Rev. Baker.

"Let Jesus come into your heart," concluded Lelia.

After the service had closed, Lelia took those phrases back to her room and worked them into the hymn, "Let Jesus Come into Your Heart," with its popular chorus:

> *Just now, your doubtings give o'er;*
> *Just now, reject Him no more;*
> *Just now, throw open the door;*
> *Let Jesus come into your heart.*

As long as she lived, Lelia served the Lord with tireless zeal. But in 1913, her eyesight began failing. Her son built a huge blackboard with oversized staff lines so she could continue composing, but alas—within a year she was totally blind. Of course, that didn't stop her. Lelia composed hymns in her mind and remembered them until her daughter, Fanny, came for her annual visit. Then she would dictate them all—dozens of them each year—while Fanny wrote down the words and music.

Her life's attitude is best described in another of her popular hymns that reflected her attitude toward growing older, "Sweeter as the Years Go By."

> *Sweeter as the years go by, sweeter as the years go by,*
> *Richer, fuller, deeper, Jesus' love is sweeter,*
> *Sweeter as the years go by.*

There Is Power in the Blood

Lewis E. Jones

Lewis E. Jones

There Is Power in the Blood

1899

Inasmuch as there is none like You, O LORD (You are great, and Your name is great in might). Jeremiah 10:6

Both the words and music of this old hymn were written during a camp meeting at Mountain Lake Park, Maryland by Lewis Jones. Jones, a California native, graduated from Moody Bible Institute and spent his vocational life with the Young Men's Christian Association (YMCA). On the side, he wrote hymns. This, his best known, is particularly effective in resisting the "wiles of the devil."

One day as missionary Dick Hillis preached in a Chinese village, his sermon was suddenly interrupted by a piercing cry. Everyone rushed toward the scream, and Dick's coworker, Mr. Kong, whispered that an evil spirit had seized a man. Dick, having not previously encountered demon possession, didn't believe him.

Just then, a woman rushed toward them. "I beg you help me!" she cried. "An evil spirit has again possessed the father of my children and is trying to kill him."

The two evangelists entered the house, stepping over a filthy old dog lying in the doorway. The room was charged with a sense of evil. "An evil spirit has possessed Farmer Ho," Kong told the onlookers. "Our God, the 'Nothing-He-Cannot-Do One' is more powerful than any spirit, and He can deliver this man. First, you must promise you will burn your idols and trust in Jesus, son of the Supreme Emperor."

The people nodded. Kong asked Dick to begin singing the hymn, "There is Power in the Blood." With great hesitation, Dick began to sing, "Would you be free from your burden of sin. . . ."

"Now," continued Kong, "in the name of Jesus we will command the evil spirit to leave this man." Kong began praying fervently. Suddenly, the old dog in the doorway vaulted into the air, screeching, yelping, whirling in circles snapping wildly at his tail. Kong continued praying, and the dog abruptly dropped over dead.

Instantly Dick remembered Luke 8, the demons of the Gadarenes who invisibly flew into the herd of swine. As Kong finished praying, Farmer Ho seemed quiet and relaxed, and soon he was strong enough to burn his idols. At his baptism shortly afterward, he testified, "I was possessed by an evil spirit who boasted he had already killed five people and was going to kill me. But God sent Mr. Kong at just the right moment, and in Jesus I am free."*

---

*This story is related in *Steel in His Soul: The Dick Hillis Story* by Jan Winebrenner (Chicago: Moody Press, 1985), chapter 6, "The Day the Dog Died."

O That Will Be Glory

Charles H. Gabriel

Charles H. Gabriel

1. When all my la-bors And tri-als are o'er, And I am safe On that beau-ti-ful shore, Just to be near The dear Lord I a-dore

2. When by the gift Of His in-fi-nite grace, I am ac-cord-ed In heav-en a place, Just to be there And to look on His face

3. Friends will be there I have loved long a-go; Joy like a riv-er A-round me will flow. Yet, just a smile From my Sav-ior I know,

Will through the a-ges Be glo-ry for me. O that will be glo-ry for me, Glo-ry for me, glo-ry for me! When by His grace

O that will be glo-ry for me, Glo-ry for me, glo-ry for me!

I shall look on His face. That will be glo-ry, Be glo-ry for me.

O That Will Be Glory

1900

For in this we groan, earnestly desiring to be clothed with our habitation which is from heaven. 2 Corinthians 5:2

This song came from the pen of Charles H. Gabriel, who was one of America's most prolific writers of gospel songs at the turn of the century. Charles had grown up in a musical family in Iowa, and his mom encouraged his musical inclinations. When Charles told her he was going to write a song that would one day be world-famous, she replied, "My boy, I would rather have you write a song that will help somebody than see you President of the United States."

Several decades later, in 1900, Charles, 44, wrote a song inspired by his friend Ed Card, director of the Sunshine Rescue Mission in Saint Louis. Ed often punctuated his sermons with the word, "Glory!", and at the end of his prayers, he usually said, "And that will be glory for me!"

Using those expressions, Gabriel wrote "O, That Will Be Glory for Me."

Not long afterward, this song came to the attention of the famous music director, Charles M. Alexander. Alexander and J. Wilber Chapman had been the first men to entirely circle the globe holding evangelistic campaigns. He was a gifted, popular, and enthusiastic worship leader, beloved around the world. His blessing on a song could make it a "hit."

But when Alexander saw "O, That Will Be Glory," he didn't think too highly of it. "That man has wasted a page for I do not believe that song will be sung much," he said to himself as he tossed it aside.

Several months later, Alexander attended a Convention where "The Glory Song" was sung with great vivacity. It affected him so deeply that he was soon teaching it to his friends and co-workers. When he joined Dr. R. A. Torrey for a series of evangelistic rallies in Australia, this became their theme song.

Alexander was surprised to hear telephone operators and hotel maids singing this song, even workmen in the streets and executive in their offices. It was translated into a myriad of languages. In Great Britain, it was sung again and again in Alexander's evangelistic rallies. Other evangelists such as Gipsy Smith caught on and started using it. It became enormously popular around the world, the most popular gospel song of its era.

And Charles Gabriel . . . well, he couldn't have been happier if he had been elected President of the United States.

Deeper, Deeper

Charles P. Jones

Charles P. Jones

1. Deep-er, deep-er in the love of Je-sus Dai-ly let me go;
2. Deep-er, deep-er bless-ed Ho-ly Spir-it, Take me deep-er still,
3. Deep-er, deep-er tho' it cost hard tri-als, Deep-er let me go!
4. Deep-er, high-er, ev-'ry day in Je-sus, Till all con-flicts past,

High-er, high-er in the school of wis-dom, More of grace to know.
Till my life is whol-ly lost in Je-sus, And His per-fect will.
Root-ed in the ho-ly love of Je-sus, Let me fruit-ful grow.
Finds me con-qu'ror, and in His own im-age Per-fect-ed at last.

O, deep - - - er yet, I pray, And
O deep - er yet, I pray, deep - er yet, I pray, And

high - - er ev-'ry day, And wis - - - er, bless-ed
high-er ev-'ry day, high-er ev-'ry day, And wis-er, bless-ed Lord,

Lord, In Thy pre-cious, ho-ly Word.
wis - er bless-ed Lord,

Deeper, Deeper

Can you search out the deep things of God? Can you find out the limits of the Almighty? Job 11:7

One of America's first African-American hymnists, Charles Price Jones, was born in Rome, Georgia, at the end of the Civil War. His father died when he was young, but Charles later said, "I love his memory. I had not sense enough when young to appreciate his worth. But the years have taught me his true value."

After his mother's death when he was seventeen, Charles wandered across the South, ending up in Arkansas, where he found Christ as Savior. He immediately began witnessing of his newfound faith, and soon he was formally licensed to preach. He married in 1891, and became a popular preacher. Yet he felt something was missing.

"I was pastor of the Tabernacle Baptist Church, Selma, Alabama, and my ministry with that church . . . seemed to be accepted and much loved. But as I read my Bible and observed conditions, I felt that we were not, as a brother once said to me, 'toting fair with Jesus.' I began then to seek Him with all my heart for that power that would make my life wholly His. . . . I fasted and prayed three days and nights. He then sanctified me sweetly in His love. . . . The earnestness of the Spirit was mine. I was sealed in Him unto the day of Redemption. The blessing of God rested upon me—all on the merits of Christ. . . . For in myself I felt more unworthy and undone than ever. It was the nearness, the eminence, the reality of the presence of God that exalted my spirit and filled me with joy, the joy of the Holy Ghost."

In 1895, Jones became pastor of the Mt. Helm Baptist Church in Jackson, Mississippi, and there his "Holiness" teachings created a storm. "I was looked on as a fanatic by some; by others as weak in the brain," he said. While trying to minister amid a storm of criticism, Charles suffered a personal tragedy when his four-year-old daughter was burned in a fire and died. Soon thereafter, he was dismissed as pastor of Mt. Helm and began holding services in an empty store where he preached from the counter. But his attitude was victorious, as expressed in his great hymn, written during this period: "O deeper yet, I pray, and higher every day."

Does Jesus Care?

Frank E. Graeff

J. Lincoln Hall

1. Does Je-sus care When my heart is pained Too deep-ly for mirth and
2. Does Je-sus care when my way is dark With a name-less dread and
3. Does Je-sus care When I've tried and failed To re-sist some temp-ta-tion
4. Does Je-sus care When I've said good-bye To the dear-est on earth to

song; As the bur-dens press And the cares dis-tress, And the
fear? As the day-light fades In-to deep night shades, Does He
strong; When for my deep grief I find no re-lief, Though my
me, And my sad heart aches Till it near-ly breaks, Is it

way grows wea-ry and long?
care e-nough to be near?
tears flow All the night long?
aught to Him? Does He see?

O yes, He cares; I

know He cares, His heart is touched with my grief; When the

days are wea-ry, The long nights drea-ry, I know my Sav-ior cares. He cares.

Does Jesus Care?

1901

Casting all your care upon Him, for He cares for you. 1 Peter 5:7

I n his book, *Lectures to My Students,* Charles Haddon Spurgeon devoted a chapter to "The Minister's Fainting Fits," warning his students of the dangers of discouragement and depression in the ministry. The chapter begins: "Fits of depression come over the most of us . . . The strong are not always vigorous, the wise not always ready, the brave not always courageous, and the joyous not always happy."

That observation is perfectly illustrated by Rev. Frank Graeff, the Methodist minister who wrote this hymn. Frank was born in 1860, in northeastern Pennsylvania. When he entered the ministry, one of his greatest assets was his cheerful disposition. While pastoring in the Philadelphia area, he was dubbed the "Sunshine Minister" because of his radiant personality. He had a special way with children, who were drawn to his simple faith and perpetual smile.

But as Spurgeon said, "the joyous are not always happy." A series of heartbreaks shattered his spirits, and Frank Graeff found himself in the unfamiliar valley of deep depression and despondency. His gloom became as great as the bliss he had previously enjoyed. At length, he collapsed into the Everlasting Arms and found himself singing Joseph Scriven's old hymn:

> *What a friend we have in Jesus, | All our sins and griefs to bear |*
> *What a privilege to carry, | Everything to God in prayer . . .*

The truth of 1 Peter 5:7 suddenly took hold of him: ". . . casting all your care upon Him, for He cares for you." Out of that experience, Frank wrote "Does Jesus Care?" with its series of commonly asked questions, followed by this resounding reply:

> *O yes, He cares; I know He cares; | His heart is touched with my grief;*
> *When the days are weary, the long nights dreary, | I know my Savior cares.*

How *do* we cast our cares on the One who cares for us? The secret is found in the word CAST:

- **C**ommit your burden to the Lord. Give it over to Him who cares even more than you do, and who has the power to do what you cannot.
- **A**sk for His help in prayer. Philippians 4 tells us to be anxious about nothing, but in everything, by prayer and supplication, to let our needs be known to the Lord.
- **S**earch the Scriptures. God has a promise for every need.
- **T**rust Him. For He *does* care for you.

This Is My Father's World

Maltbie D. Babcock

Traditional English Melody

1. This is my Fa-ther's world, And to my lis-t'ning ears;
2. This is my Fa-ther's world; The birds their car-ols raise.
3. This is my Fa-ther's world, O let me ne'er for-get

All na-ture sings and round me rings The mu-sic of the spheres.
The morn-ing light, the lil-y white, De-clare their Mak-er's praise;
That though the wrong seems oft so strong, God is the Rul-er yet.

This is my Fa-ther's world; I rest me in the thought
This is my Fa-ther's world; He shines in all that's fair;
This is my Fa-ther's world; The bat-tle is not done;

Of rocks and trees, of skies and seas; His hand the won-ders wrought.
In the rust-ling grass I hear Him pass, He speaks to me ev-ery-where.
Je - sus, who died, shall be sat-is-fied, And earth and heav'n be one.

This Is My Father's World

1901

. . . For the world is Mine, and all its fullness. Psalm 50:12b

Maltbie Babcock was arguably the most remarkable student Syracuse University had ever seen. Hailing from an aristocratic family, he was a brilliant scholar with a winning personality. Tall and steel-muscled, he was an outstanding athlete, expert swimmer, and captain of the baseball team. He also directed the university's orchestra, played several instruments, and composed original compositions. A proficient vocalist, he directed the university glee club. He entertained other students by drawing and doing impersonations. On the side, he was an avid fisherman.

He would have been successful in any profession, but God called him to the ministry; and after further training at Auburn Theological Seminary, he became pastor of the First Presbyterian Church in Lockport, New York. It was a beautiful area—midway between Lake Erie and Lake Ontario, not far from Niagara Falls—and Maltbie enjoyed hiking and running in the hills outside town. Telling his secretary, "I'm going out to see my Father's world," he would run or hike a couple of miles into the countryside where he'd lose himself in nature.

It was during his pastorate at Lockport that he wrote a sixteen-stanza poem, each verse beginning with the words, "This is My Father's World."

In 1886, Maltbie was called to the Brown Memorial Church in Baltimore. While there, he traveled widely and was in great demand on college campuses. He was a fresh, engaging speaker who never failed to stimulate students. In 1899, he moved to the Brick Presbyterian Church in New York City. Here he found it more difficult to take off on his hikes. The work load was enormous, but Maltbie faced it stoically, writing:

> *Be strong! We are not here to play, to dream, to drift,*
> *We have hard work to do and loads to lift;*
> *Shun not the struggle. Face it. 'Tis Gods gift. Be strong!*

When he was 42, his church presented him with a special gift—a pilgrimage to the "Holy Land." With great excitement, Maltbie departed by ship. While enroute at Naples, Italy, he was seized with a deadly bacterial fever and died at the International Hospital on May 18, 1901.

After his death, his wife compiled his writings into a book entitled *Thoughts for Everyday Living*, published in 1901. Included was Maltbie's "This Is My Father's World."

I Would Not Be Denied

Charles P. Jones

Charles P. Jones

1. When pangs of death seized on my soul, Un - to the Lord I cried,
2. As Ja - cob in the days of old, I wres - tled with the Lord;
3. Old Sa - tan said my Lord was gone And would not hear my prayer,

Till Je - sus came and made me whole, I would not be de - nied.
And in - stant with a cour - age bold, I stood up - on His Word.
But praise the Lord the work is done, And Christ the Lord is here.

I would not be de - nied, I would not be de - nied,
de - nied, de - nied,

Till Je - sus came and made me whole, I would not be de - nied.
de - nied.

I Would Not Be Denied

1901

Then Jacob was left alone; and a Man wrestled with him until the breaking of day. Genesis 32:24

hen Charles Price Jones was evicted from his church in Jackson, Mississippi, because of his "Holiness" doctrine, many of the members followed him to an old store where Jones preached from the counter. The congregation soon built their own building.

Using his new church as a base, Jones began traveling widely, preaching as far west as Los Angeles. Churches were started in cities like Chicago, St. Louis, Cleveland, and San Diego. When he was dismissed from his Baptist denomination because of his holiness doctrines, Jones (along with C. M. Mason) formed the young churches into a new denomination, "The Church of God in Christ."

It wasn't easy. All his life, Jones faced religious misunderstanding and racial prejudice. In 1905, a gang of white men with dogs burned his church in Jackson to the ground. On two occasions in Mississippi, shots were fired into his congregations as he preached. In Jackson, a mob approached the house where Jones was staying, intending to harm him. They backed down only when the owner of the house met them nose-to-nose on the porch, saying, "You can't come in unless you walk over my dead body." A conflict over speaking in tongues tore his young denomination in two, leading to a painful split with C. M. Mason, and the founding of "The Church of Christ (Holiness), USA."

But out of these backbreaking trials came heart-touching hymns. Jones' secretary said, "In those days of persecution many of those lovely, inspiring, encouraging, and heart-strengthening songs were born in the heart of our pastor. Sometimes when they were given to him in the night, he would have us join him through the hours and sing. Often we remained in the church until midnight."

"I Would Not Be Denied" was written on one such occasion as Jones studied the story of Jacob wrestling with the Lord in Genesis 32. "I prayed in every closet," Jones said, "behind every door; wherever I could hide I went to my knees begging for mercy. But no comfort came. . . . Satan tempted me to despair. (But finally) my mourning became a song. When all the trial was over, thinking of it all one day while alone communing with God and thanking Him for His mercy to me, my soul felt that it must express itself in song; and so was born 'I Would Not Be Denied.'"

Near to the Heart of God

Cleland B. McAfee

Cleland B. McAfee

1. There is a place of qui - et rest, Near to the heart of God;
2. There is a place of com - fort sweet, Near to the heart of God;
3. There is a place of full re - lease, Near to the heart of God;

A place where sin can - not mo - lest, Near to the heart of God.
A place where we our Sav - ior meet, Near to the heart of God.
A place where all is joy and peace, Near to the heart of God.

O Je - sus, blest Re - deem - er, Sent from the heart of God,

Hold us, who wait be - fore Thee, Near to the heart of God.

Near to the Heart of God

1903

. . . He will gather the lambs with His arm, and carry them in His bosom . . .
Isaiah 40:11

ark University in Parkville, Missouri, with 38 campuses across the United States, boasts of an enrollment of over 17,000 students. It was begun in 1875, with only 17 students, by John A. McAfee, and by Colonel George Park, the colorful founder of Parkville, who donated the land.

McAfee had five sons and a daughter who all became involved in the college. The fourth son, Cleland, graduated from what was then Park College; after studying at Union Theological Seminary, he returned to Park as chaplain and choir director. Cleland's daughter, Katharine, later told how her father came to write the great hymn, "Near to the Heart of God":

My father's father, John A. McAfee, was one of the founders and the first president of Park College in Missouri. In the last years of the past century, his five sons (Lowell, Howard, Lapsley, Cleland, Ernest) and his only daughter (Helen) were all living in Parkville, serving the college. My father was the college preacher and director of the choir, and it was his custom, when communion services came, to write the words and music of a response which his choir could sing and which would fit into the theme of his sermon.

One terrible week, just before a communion Sunday, the two little daughters of my Uncle Howard and Aunt Lucy McAfee died of diphtheria within twenty-four hours of each other. The college family and town were stricken with grief. My father often told us how he sat long and late thinking of what could be said in word and song on the coming Sunday . . .

So he wrote ("Near to the Heart of God"). The choir learned it at the regular Saturday night rehearsal, and afterward they went to the Howard McAfee's home and sang it as they stood under the sky outside the darkened, quarantined house. It was sung again on Sunday morning at the communion service.

"Near to the Heart of God" was published in October, 1903, in *The Choir Leader*. In later years, Cleland pastored in the Presbyterian denomination, taught at McCormick Theological Seminary in Chicago, and helped direct the Presbyterian foreign missions program. He is the author of a number of textbooks including, *The Greatest English Classic: A Study of the King James Version and Its Influence*, and *Ministerial Practices: Some Fraternal Suggestions*, published in 1928.

God Leads Us Along

G. A. Young

G. A. Young

1. In shad-y green pas-tures, so rich and so sweet, God leads His dear
2. Some-times on the mount where the sun shines so bright, God leads His dear
3. Though sor-rows be-fall us and Sa-tan op-pose, God leads His dear
4. A - way from the mire and a-way from the clay, God leads His dear

chil-dren a - long; Where the wa-ter's cool flow bathes the wea-ry one's feet,
chil-dren a - long; Some - times in the val - ley, in dark-est of night,
chil-dren a - long; Through grace we can con-quer, de - feat all our foes,
chil-dren a - long; A - way up in glo - ry, e - ter-ni-ty's day

God leads His dear chil - dren a - long. Some thru the wa-ters, some thru the

flood, Some thru the fire, but all thru the blood; Some thru great sor-row, but

God gives a song, In the night sea-son, and all the day long.

God Leads Us Along

1903

He leads me beside the still waters. He restores my soul. Psalm 23:2, 3

George Young, a carpenter, and his wife dedicated their lives to following the Lord, wherever He would lead. "He does the leading," they often said, "and we do the following." God led them to the rural Midwest and they traveled from church to church in revival efforts. Their finances were always tight, but "through the many years we never went hungry!" Mrs. Young said years later. "Oh, sometimes we didn't have too much of this world's goods but . . . we always had so much of Jesus."

Finally they saved enough to buy a small piece of land on which George built a cottage. Though small, it was the fulfillment of a life's dream, and when they moved in they dedicated the house to God and sang the Doxology. But some time later, when the Youngs were away on a ministry trip, a thug who had been offended by George's preaching set the house afire. Returning home, the Youngs found a heap of ashes. All their worldly goods and cherished possessions were gone.

As George gazed at the ruins, he recounted the precious possessions fire could never destroy—his family, his relationship with Christ, his ministry, his eternal home. There and then, the words to "God Leads Us Along" began forming in his mind. Within a few days, he had written all three stanzas.

Years later, Dr. Harold Lillenas, seeking to track down George's widow, drove to the small Kansas town where she resided. Stopping for directions, he was alarmed to hear that Mrs. Young was living in the run-down Country Poor House. Lillenas was deeply troubled that the widow of the author of such a hymn about God's guidance should spend her final days in the Poor House. But when he finally found her, Mrs. Young explained, "One day God took my sweet husband home. Oh, how I missed him for we had always served the Lord together. In my heart, I wondered—where will God now lead me? Dr. Lillenas, God led me here! I'm so glad He did, for you know, about every month someone comes into this place to spend the rest of their days, and, Dr. Lillenas, so many of them don't know my Jesus. I'm having the time of my life introducing them to Jesus! Dr. Lillenas, isn't it wonderful how God leads?"

God Will Take Care of You

Civilla D. Martin

W. Stillman Martin

1. Be not dis-mayed what-e'er be-tide, God will take care of you;
2. Thro' days of toil, when heart doth fail, God will take care of you;
3. All you may need He will pro-vide, God will take care of you;
4. No mat-ter what may be the test, God will take care of you;

Be - neath His wings of love a - bide, God will take care of you.
When dan - gers fierce your path as - sail, God will take care of you.
Noth - ing you ask will be de - nied, God will take care of you.
Lean, wea - ry one, up - on His breast, God will take care of you.

God will take care of you. Thro' ev - ery day, o'er all the way,

He will take care of you; God will take care of you.

God Will Take Care of You

1904

Bless the LORD, O my soul, and forget not all His benefits: who forgives all your iniquities, who heals all your diseases. Psalm 103:2–3

J. C. Penney, who descended from a long line of Baptist preachers, was well on his way to establishing a successful career when the 1929 Great Depression threw him into crisis. His business deals turned sour, and Penney became overwhelmed with anxiety and insomnia. He developed a painful case of shingles and was hospitalized, but tranquilizers and drugs only made things worse. His mental state deteriorated until, as he later said, "I was broken nervously and physically, filled with despair, unable to see even a ray of hope. I had nothing to live for. I felt I hadn't a friend left in the world, that even my family turned against me."

But one morning he heard singing coming from the little hospital chapel. The words of the song said, "Be not dismayed whate'er betide / God will take care of you."

Entering the chapel, he listened to the song, to the Scripture reading, and to the prayer. "Suddenly—something happened. I can't explain it. I can only call it a miracle. I felt as if I had been instantly lifted out of the darkness of a dungeon into warm, brilliant sunlight." All worry left him as he realized more fully than he had ever imagined just how much the Lord Jesus Christ cared for him. From that day J. C. Penney was never plagued with worry, and he later recalled those moments in the chapel as, "the most dramatic and glorious twenty minutes of my life." He later became one of America's greatest retail merchants.

On a Sunday in 1904, Civilla Martin was in Lestershire, New York, where her husband, Walter, was compiling a collection of hymns for the Practical Bible Training School. They were planning to travel to another town that day, for Martin had a preaching assignment. Civilla woke up sick, and Martin was about to cancel his plans, when their young child piped up and said: "Oh, Daddy, you don't have to stay home because of mother—God will take care of us."

Martin proceeded to the train station and fulfilled his appointment. When he returned, Civilla handed him the words of "God Will Take Care of You," which she had written in his absence. Going to his little organ, Martin composed the music, and it was first published in the songbook he was compiling for the school.

Jesus Is All the World to Me

Jesus Is All the World to Me

1904

There is one God, the Father, of whom are all things, and we for Him; and one Lord Jesus Christ, through whom are all things, and through whom we live. 1 Corinthians 8:6

You can take the boy out of the town, but you can't take the town out of the boy. Will L. Thompson grew up in East Liverpool, Ohio, in the mid-1800s. A few hours away by horseback were the grimy steel mills of Pittsburgh, Pennsylvania; but East Liverpool was known for a happier trade—its pottery. Will's parents, Josiah and Sarah Thompson, were local entrepreneurs who had helped transform the area into a pottery manufacturing region.

Will showed early signs of his dad's entrepreneurial spirit; and, being from a financially comfortable family, he was also able to devote time to his other passion—music. By age sixteen, he had already published two songs, "Liverpool Schottische" and "Darling Minnie Gray."

After musical training in Boston and Germany, Will tried to sell his music to major publishers. When they didn't offer him enough money, he published them himself. He printed copies of his most popular song, "Gathering Shells by the Sea," and sent them to minstrel organizations throughout the country. Soon "Gathering Shells" was one of America's most popular songs, just behind Stephen Foster's "Old Folks at Home" in popularity.

With his earnings, Will established his own music publishing business in Chicago, "Will L. Thompson & Co." Having arrived at financial success, Will decided to devote himself exclusively to Christian music. He wrote the great invitational hymn, "Softly and Tenderly Jesus Is Calling," the rousing gospel song "There's a Great Day Coming," and this beautiful hymn, "Jesus Is All the World to Me."

Despite being wealthy, famous, widely traveled, and in great demand, Will never wanted to leave his hometown. He opened a music business in East Liverpool.* He became a prominent land developer and owned property throughout the town. He was a generous philanthropist, supporting heavily the local YMCA and the Emmanuel Presbyterian Church. He served as the first president of the local library. He also donated acreage for a park that bears his name to this day, stipulating that no alcoholic beverages be allowed in the park and no sports permitted there on Sundays.

He regularly hitched up his two-horse wagon on which he placed a portable piano, and he traveled throughout the area singing his hymns in churches and public squares.

Will Thompson died in 1909; but in 2002, the grateful citizens of East Liverpool inducted him into the Lou Holtz/Upper Ohio Valley Hall of Fame.

---

*The store Thompson built still stands at the corner of Fourth and Washington Streets and now houses the Pottery City Galleries Antique Mall.

507

His Eye Is on the Sparrow

Civilla D. Martin

Charles H. Gabriel

1. Why should I feel dis - cour - aged? Why should the shad - ows come?
2. When - ev - er I am tempt - ed, When - ev - er clouds a - rise,

Why should my heart be lone - ly And long for heaven and home When
When song gives place to sigh - ing, When hope with - in me dies, I

Je - sus is my por - tion? My con - stant friend is He: His
draw the clos - er to Him; From care He sets me free; His

eye is on the spar - row, And I know He watch - es me; His
eye is on the spar - row, And I know He watch - es me; His

eye is on the spar - row, And I know He watch - es me.
eye is on the spar - row, And I know He watch - es me.

His Eye Is on the Sparrow

1905

Are not two sparrows sold for a copper coin? And not one of them falls to the ground apart from your Father's will. Matthew 10:29

ost people have a hobby of some sort to provide a healthy diversion from the rigors of work. Long ago, there was a woodworker in Nazareth who counted bird-watching among His diversions. We can make that assumption, because Jesus later referred frequently to bird-life in His sermons, saying things like:

- "Are not two sparrows sold for a copper coin? And not one of them falls to the ground apart from your Father's will" (Matthew 10:29).
- "Look at the birds of the air, for they neither sow nor reap nor gather into barns; yet your heavenly Father feeds them. Are you not of more value than they?" (Matthew 6:26)
- "Consider the ravens . . ." (Luke 12:26).
- "Do not fear . . . you are of more value than many sparrows" (Luke 12:7).

It was this theme that caused the author of "God Will Take Care of You," to write, a year later, another great hymn on God's care: "His Eye Is on the Sparrow."

Civilla Durfee Martin was a Canadian by birth, born on August 21, 1869, in Nova Scotia. She became a school and music teacher, but when she married Dr. Walter Martin, an evangelist, she gave up teaching to travel with him and assist in his meetings.

This is her account of the writing of this song:

Early in the spring of 1905, my husband and I were sojourning in Elmira, New York. We contracted a deep friendship for a couple by the name of Mr. and Mrs. Doolittle—true saints of God. Mrs. Doolittle had been bedridden for nigh twenty years. Her husband was an incurable cripple who had to propel himself to and from his business in a wheel chair. Despite their afflictions, they lived happy Christian lives, bringing inspiration and comfort to all who knew them. One day while we were visiting with the Doolittles, my husband commented on their bright hopefulness and asked them for the secret of it. Mrs. Doolittle's reply was simple: "His eye is on the sparrow, and I know He watches me." The beauty of this simple expression of boundless faith gripped the hearts and fired the imagination of Dr. Martin and me. The hymn "His Eye Is on the Sparrow" was the outcome of that experience.

The day after writing the song, she mailed it to the famous Gospel composer, Charles Gabriel, who penned the music.

Nothing Between

Charles A. Tindley

Charles A. Tindley

1. Noth-ing be-tween my soul and the Sav - ior, Naught of this world's de -
2. Noth-ing be-tween, like world - ly plea-sure: Hab - its of life, though
3. Noth-ing be-tween, like pride or sta - tion: Self or friends shall
4. Noth-ing be-tween, e'en man - y hard tri - als, Though the whole world a -

lu - sive dream; I have re - nounced all sin - ful plea - sure,
harm - less they seem, Must not my heart from Him ev - er sev - er,
not in - ter - vene; Though it may cost me much trib - u - la - tion,
gainst me con - vene, Watch - ing with prayer and much self - de - ni - al,

Je - sus is mine! There's noth - ing be - tween.
He is my all! There's noth - ing be - tween.
I am re - solved! There's noth - ing be - tween.
Tri - umph at last, with noth - ing be - tween.

Noth - ing be - tween my

soul and the Sav - ior, So that His bless - ed face may be seen;

Noth-ing pre-ven-ting the least of His fa-vor: Keep the way clear! Let noth-ing be-tween.

Nothing Between

1905

Nor height nor depth, nor any other created thing, shall be able to separate us from the love of God which is in Christ Jesus our Lord. Romans 8:39

Charles Tindley was born into slavery in 1851. "My father was poor as it relates to this world's goods," Charles wrote, "but was rich in the grace of God. He was unable to send me to school or to keep me with him at his little home. It therefore became my lot to be hired out. . . . The people with whom I lived were not all good. Some of them were very cruel. . . . I used to find bits of newspaper on the roadside . . . in order to study the ABCs from them. During the day I would gather pine knots, and when the people were asleep at night I would light these pine knots, and . . . with fire-coals, mark all the words I could make out. I continued in this way, and without any teacher, until I could read the Bible."

One day Charles slipped into church and sat in the back. When the preacher asked any child who could read the Bible to come forward, Charles went to the front. He later recalled the odd looks people gave him and overheard someone refer to him as "the boy with the bare feet." From that moment, Charles resolved to gain an education.

After emancipation, he moved to Philadelphia, and it was there, in a Methodist church, that he gave his life to Christ. His entrance into "full-time" ministry began humbly—as the church janitor.

"My first plan was to buy every book I could," he explained. "Then I entered by correspondence all the schools to which my limited means would afford . . . Thus while I was unable to go through the schools, I was able to let the schools go through me."

In 1885, he applied for ordination. One of the other candidates asked him, "How do you expect to pass your examination? The other candidates and I have diplomas. What do you hold?"

"Nothing but a broom," was Tindley's reply. But the boy with the broom went on to become a world-famous pastor, preacher, and hymnist.

One evening as he studied, according to most accounts of the story, a piece of paper, caught by the wind, flew across Charles' lamp, causing a shadow to fall over his writing. Pausing, Charles considered the power of a sin to darken his soul, and out of that came his great hymn: "Nothing Between."

Stand by Me

Charles A. Tindley

Charles A. Tindley

1. When the storms of life are rag-ing, Stand by me;
2. In the midst of trib-u-la-tion, Stand by me;
3. In the midst of faults and fail-ures, Stand by me;
4. When I'm grow-ing old and fee-ble, Stand by me;

When the storms of life are rag-ing, Stand by me.
In the midst of trib-u-la-tion, Stand by me.
In the midst of faults and fail-ures Stand by me.
When I'm grow-ing old and fee-ble, Stand by me.

When the world is toss-ing me Like a ship up-on the sea,
When the hosts of hell as-sail, And my strength be-gins to fail,
When I do the best I can, And my friends mis-un-der-stand,
When my life be-comes a bur-den, And I'm near-ing chill-y Jor-dan,

Thou Who rul-est wind and wa-ter, Stand by me.
Thou Who nev-er lost a bat-tle, Stand by me.
Thou Who know-est all a-bout me, Stand by me.
O Thou Lil-y of the Val-ley, Stand by me.

Stand by Me

He calms the storm, So that its waves are still. Psalm 107:29

I n 1902, Charles A. Tindley was elected pastor of the Bainbridge Street Methodist Church in Philadelphia—the church in which he was converted and where he had once served as janitor. There were one hundred thirty members, but under Tindley's powerful preaching, the numbers grew, making it necessary to relocate. The congregation purchased a building from a white Presbyterian church and moved in, changing the name to East Calvary Methodist Episcopal Church.

As large numbers of African-Americans flooded into Philadelphia during World War I to take jobs vacated by whites who had left for the war, East Calvary Church mushroomed in growth. Tindley stood on the street corners, sharing Christ and doing evangelistic work. "Up and down this area, Tindley walked and talked about God's saving grace," wrote one biographer. "Sometimes individually and sometimes in small clusters . . . Counseling and consoling, Tindley moved among the unchurched. Many . . . cabbies . . . were often aroused by Tindley for a shared moment of prayer. He came to be known as 'Our Preacher.'"

He organized benevolence ministries, and started a home-loan program so that his poor parishioners could begin saving for houses. He established soup kitchens and opened the church to the homeless in cold weather.

Charles Tindley was a striking man, standing six-foot-three and possessing a strong, deep voice. Multitudes were attracted to Christ through his preaching, and the church was expanded until it held over three thousand people. Even then, Tindley had to encourage members not to attend all the services so that guests could come.

At the congregation's insistence, the church was renamed "Tindley Temple"; but in the wee hours of the Sunday appointed for the dedication, his wife, Daisy, died suddenly, and Tindley was unable to attend the opening.

Such a prominent ministry also invites attacks, criticism, misunderstanding, and heavy burdens. Tindley once said, "It was when I was overburdened with criticisms, abuse, and hard and many oppositions—some of them from those whom I took to be my best friends—I wrote 'Stand by Me.'"

When the storms of life are raging, stand by me;
When the storms of life are raging, stand by me.
When the world is tossing me like a ship upon the sea
Thou Who rulest wind and water, stand by me.

We'll Understand It Better By and By

Charles A. Tindley

Charles A. Tindley

We'll Understand It Better By and By

1905

Consider what I say, and may the Lord give you understanding in all things.
2 Timothy 2:7

You are an unlettered ignoramus. You know you are not educationally fit to be a bishop." Those words were spoken by a Methodist minister to Charles Tindley, author of "Stand by Me," "I Will Not Be Denied," "Nothing Between," and "We'll Understand It Better By and By." Charles was being considered for a Methodist bishopric, a position sought by the rival minister. Just before the election, an anonymous letter falsely accused Tindley of immorality.

As a prominent, powerful African-American preacher in Philadelphia, Charles often suffered racially motivated persecution. He once said in a sermon, "Previous conditions of servitude, in the eyes of our enemies, have left its ineffaceable marks of inferiority upon every human being whose veins contain one drop of Negro blood."

His worst heartaches, however, arose within his own family. The deepest blows were the death of his wife, Daisy, on the eve of the dedication of the Tindley Temple Methodist Church, and the death of one of his sons in World War I. Eventually Charles remarried; but several of his grown children, still living at home, didn't get along with their stepmother. Charles finally sent them packing.

Atop those pressures were the financial burdens of a large church made up of poverty-stricken masses. "All of us know we are without jobs," he told his congregation when they were struggling to meet the church's bills. "We don't own big bank accounts. We don't even know what tomorrow will bring. But we do have hope. We do have God. We do have salvation. We do have faith." It was in this spirit that he wrote this great old gospel hymn for his church. One additional stanza says:

> *We are often destitute of the things that life demands,*
> *Want of food and want of shelter, thirsty hills and barren lands;*
> *We are trusting in the Lord, and according to God's Word,*
> *We will understand it better by and by.*

Tindley served Christ faithfully until he was in his eighties. One day in 1933, he showed up at the hospital. "How are you, Reverend?" asked the hospital director. "What can we do for you?"

"I have come to die," said Tindley. He declined rapidly, and passed away on July 26, 1933. All Philadelphia mourned, but he was buried in an unmarked grave, for his church did not have funds for a memorial.

The Way of the Cross Leads Home

The Way of the Cross Leads Home

1906

Go your way, sell whatever you have and give to the poor, and you will have treasure in heaven; and come, take up the cross, and follow Me. Mark 10:21

I know that My Redeemer Liveth," "Anywhere with Jesus," "The Touch of His Hand on Mine," and "The Way of the Cross Leads Home" were all written by a Midwestern woman named Jessie Brown Pounds.

Jessie was born in 1861 in Hiram, Ohio, outside Cleveland. Her father, Rev. Holland Brown, was a pioneer preacher among the Disciples of Christ. Her mother, Jane Abell Brown, loved children's literature and encouraged Jessie from kindergarten to write poetry.

Jessie began writing poems and articles for Christian magazines when she was fifteen, and for over thirty years she wrote hymns and religious poetry for Charles H. Fillmore, which he set to music. Like Jessie, Fillmore was a member of the Christian Church (Disciples of Christ), and the two became a prolific gospel-songwriting team.

In 1897, Jessie, thirty-eight, married Rev. John E. Pounds, pastor of the Central Christian Church in Indianapolis. One Sunday a few weeks after her wedding, she woke up feeling unwell. Her husband went to church without her, and in the quietness of the morning, Jessie began thinking of heaven. Taking a pen she scribbled out a poem titled "Beautiful Isle of Somewhere." It became a favorite hymn of President William McKinley and was sung at his funeral after he was assassinated in Buffalo, New York.

Somewhere the sun is shining, somewhere the songbirds dwell;
Hush, then, thy sad repining, God lives, and all is well.

Somewhere, somewhere, Beautiful Isle of Somewhere!
Land of the true, where we live anew, Beautiful Isle of Somewhere!

In all, Jessie wrote nine books, fifty cantata librettos, and over four hundred hymns. We don't know the background behind "The Way of the Cross Leads Home," but many have speculated that it was inspired by a popular story and sermon illustration that was circulating during those days.

The geographical heart of London is Charing Cross, which is referred to locally simply as "the Cross." A London police officer came upon a lost child who was unable to tell him where he lived. Finally, amid sobs and tears, the child simply said, "If you will take me to the Cross, I think I can find my way home from there."

"I must needs go home by the way of the cross," wrote Jessie Pounds. "There's no other way but this."

Have Thine Own Way, Lord

Adelaide A. Pollard

George C. Stebbins

1. Have Thine own way, Lord! Have Thine own way!
2. Have Thine own way, Lord! Have Thine own way!
3. Have Thine own way, Lord! Have Thine own way!
4. Have Thine own way, Lord! Have Thine own way!

Thou art the Pot - ter, I am the clay.
Search me and try me, Mas - ter, to - day!
Wound - ed and wea - ry, help me, I pray!
Hold o'er my be - ing ab - so - lute sway!

Mold me and make me af - ter Thy will,
Whit - er than snow, Lord, wash me just now,
Pow - er, all pow - er sure - ly is Thine!
Fill with Thy Spir - it till all shall see,

While I am wait - ing, yield - ed and still.
As in Thy pres - ence hum - bly I bow.
Touch me and heal me, Sav - ior di - vine!
Christ on - ly, al - ways, liv - ing in me!

Have Thine Own Way, Lord
1907

. . . as the clay is in the potter's hand, so are you in My hand . . . Jeremiah 18:6

Hope differed makes the heart sick," says Proverbs 13:12. Yet "*dis*appointments are *His* appointments." God uses setbacks to renew our focus on Him, to strengthen our faith, and to divert us to other opportunities. In this case, a bitter disappointment led to one of our greatest invitational hymns.

Its author, Adelaide Pollard, was born in Iowa during the Civil War. Her parents named her Sarah, but when she was old enough, she changed her name to "Adelaide," not liking the name "Sarah." After attending the Boston School of Oratory (Emerson College), she moved to Chicago to teach in a girls' school.

While in Chicago and struggling with frail health, she was attracted to the strange ministry of John Alexander Dowie, a Scottish-born faith healer who was drawing international attention. In 1901, Dowie announced he was the Elijah who would precede the Coming of Christ. Purchasing 6,800 acres of land outside Chicago, he began building "Zion City," which, despite a strong start, ended in failure. Adelaide, however, was apparently healed of diabetes through Dowie's ministry.

Afterward, she became very involved in the work of an evangelist named Sanford, who was predicting the imminent return of Christ. In New England, where she had moved to assist Sanford, she felt God was calling her to Africa as a missionary. But, to her intense disappointment, she was unable to raise her financial support. Heartsick, Adelaide, in her forties at the time, attended a prayer meeting. That night an elderly woman prayed, "It doesn't matter what you bring into our lives, Lord. Just have your own way with us."

That phrase rushed into Adelaide's heart, and the verses began shaping in her mind. At home that evening, she read again the story of the potter and the clay in Jeremiah 18. By bedtime she had written out the prayer, "Have Thine Own Way."

Adelaide did eventually make it to Africa, but the outbreak of World War I sent her to Scotland and, later, back to America where she wrote poems, spoke to groups, and ministered freely.

In the middle of December, 1934, Adelaide, 72, purchased a ticket at New York's Penn Station. She was heading to Pennsylvania for a speaking engagement. While waiting for the train, she was stricken with a seizure and shortly thereafter died.

Joyful, Joyful, We Adore Thee

Henry van Dyke

Ludwig van Beethoven

1. Joy-ful, joy-ful, we a-dore Thee, God of glo-ry Lord of love;
2. All Thy works with joy sur-round Thee, Earth and heaven re - flect Thy rays;
3. Thou art giv-ing and for-giv-ing. Ev - er bless-ing, ev - er blest,
4. Mor-tals join the might-y cho - rus, Which the Morn-ing Stars be-gan.

Hearts un-fold like flow'rs be - fore Thee, Open-ing to the sun a-bove.
Stars and an-gels sing a-round Thee, Cen-ter of un-bro-ken praise.
Well-spring of the joy of liv-ing, O-cean depth of hap-py rest!
Fa - ther love is reign-ing o'er us, Broth-er love binds man to man.

Melt the clouds of sin and sad-ness; Drive the dark of doubt a-way;
Field and for-est, vale and moun-tain, Flow-ery mea-dow, flash-ing sea,
Thou our Fa - ther, Christ our Broth - er, All who live in love are Thine.
Ev - er sing-ing, march we on-ward, Vic-tors in the midst of strife;

Giv - er of im - mor-tal glad-ness, Fill us with the light of day!
Chant-ing bird and flow-ing foun-tain, Call us to re - joice in Thee.
Teach us how to love each oth - er; Lift us to the joy di-vine.
Joy - ful mu - sic lifts us sun-ward, In the tri-umph song of life.

Joyful, Joyful, We Adore Thee

1907

For I know the thoughts that I think toward you, says the LORD, thoughts of peace and not of evil, to give you a future and a hope. Jeremiah 29:11

nce when recovering from a bout of depression, I found this hymn very therapeutic. "Melt the clouds of sin and sadness, drive the dark of doubt away," it says. "Giver of immortal gladness, fill us (me) with the light of day." Notice how every phrase of this prayer is bursting with exuberance: The Lord is our "wellspring of the joy of living," our "ocean depth of happy rest," and we ask Him to, "Lift us to the joy divine."

The author of the hymn, Henry Jackson van Dyke, was born in Pennsylvania in 1852, and became pastor of the Brick Presbyterian Church in New York City.* Henry later became professor of English literature at Princeton, and the author of a number of books, including the still popular "The Other Wise Man." He went on to occupy a number of eminent positions, including:

- American Ambassador to the Netherlands and Luxenbourg (appointed by his friend, Woodrow Wilson)
- Lieutenant Commander in the United States Navy Chaplains Corps during World War I
- Moderator of the General Assembly of the Presbyterian Church
- Commander of the Legion of Honor
- President of the National Institute of Arts and Letters
- Chairman of the committee that compiled the Presbyterian *Book of Common Worship*

In 1907, Henry van Dyke was invited to preach at Williams College in Massachusetts. At breakfast one morning, he handed the college president a piece of paper, saying, "Here is a hymn for you. Your mountains (the Berkshires) were my inspiration. It must be sung to the music of Beethoven's 'Hymn of Joy.'"

When he was later asked about his hymn, van Dyke replied: "These verses are simple expressions of common Christian feelings and desires in this present time—hymns of today that may be sung together by people who know the thought of the age, and are not afraid that any truth of science will destroy religion, or any revolution on earth overthrow the kingdom of heaven. Therefore this is a hymn of trust and joy and hope."

---

*His resignation from Brick Church in 1899 paved the way for Maltbie Babcock to be called as pastor. See the story behind "This Is My Father's World."

Go, Tell It on the Mountain

John W. Work Jr.

American Folk Song

Go, tell it on the moun-tain, O-ver the hills and ev-ery-where;

Go, tell it on the moun-tain, That Je-sus Christ is born!

1. While shep-herds kept their watch-ing O'er si-lent flocks by night, Be-
2. The shep-herds feared and trem-bled When lo! A-bove the earth Rang
3. Down in a low-ly man-ger The hum-ble Christ was born, And

hold through-out the heav-ens There shone a ho-ly light.
out the an-gel cho-rus That hailed our Sav-ior's birth.
brought us God's sal-va-tion That bless-ed Christ-mas morn.

Go, Tell It on the Mountain
1907

Then the shepherds returned, glorifying and praising God for all the things that they had heard and seen, as it was told them. Luke 2:20

During the bitter days of slavery, black workers on American plantations, solaced themselves with song and created a unique form of American hymnology—the Negro spiritual. It was the Jubilee Singers of Fisk University in Nashville, Tennessee, that took the plantation songs of the Negro slaves to the entire world. One of the last "spirituals" to be uncovered and published was this unique Christmas carol, "Go, Tell It on the Mountain."

How did it come about?

John Wesley Work Jr. was born in Nashville, on or about August 6, 1871. His father was choir director for a Nashville church who often wrote his own arrangements. John grew up singing in his dad's choirs, and when he enrolled in Fisk University, he became active in its music program, though his primary subjects were history and Latin. Returning to Fisk to work on his master's degree, John was eventually hired as professor of Latin and Greek. But his greatest love was the preservation and performance of the Negro spiritual.

Many of the spirituals had been published, but "Go, Tell It on the Mountain" was largely unknown, though it had been performed by the Jubilee Singers since 1879. Some of the original stanzas were obscure, for spirituals, by definition, were unwritten songs passed from plantation to plantation and from generation to generation. The chorus, however, was crystal clear and highlighted the theme for the whole: "Go, tell it on the mountain / Jesus Christ is born."

Intrigued by the chorus and melody, John wrote two new stanzas for this song, and it became his custom before sunrise on Christmas morning to take students caroling from building to building, singing, "Go, Tell It on the Mountain." It was first published in 1907 in *Work's Folk Songs of the Negro as Sung on the Plantations*.

John Work has been called the first black collector of Negro folk songs, a pursuit continued by his two sons, John Wesley Work II and Frederick J. Work. Both young men served on the faculty of Fisk University, working with the Jubilee Singers and collecting and publishing African-American spirituals and folk music.

"Go Tell It on the Mountain" is classic in that genre. To black slaves in antebellum America, the birth of a liberating Savior was a message to be heralded from the highest mountains.

It still is, for us all.

Will the Circle Be Unbroken?

Ada Ruth Habershon

Charles H. Gabriel

1. There are loved ones in the glo - ry, Whose dear forms you of - ten miss;
2. In the joy - ous days of child-hood, Oft they told of won-drous love,
3. You re - mem - ber songs of heav - en Which you sang with child - ish voice
4. You can pic - ture hap - py ga-th'rings Round the fire - side long a - go,

When you close your earth - ly sto - ry, Will you join them in their bliss?
Point - ed to the dy - ing Sav - ior Now they dwell with Him a - bove.
Do you love the hymns they taught you, Or are songs of earth your choice?
And you think of tear - ful part - ings, When they left you here be - low:

Will the cir - cle be un - bro - ken, By and by, Lord, by and by?

In a bet - ter home a - wait - ing, In the sky, in the sky?

Will the Circle Be Unbroken?

1908

And the heavens will praise Your wonders, O LORD; Your faithfulness also in the assembly of the saints. Psalm 89:5

ne of my choice possessions is a little black-and-white photograph taken when I was a toddler in the early 1950s. It's a picture of my father's family, standing by a Christmas tree. My dad is beside his mother, surrounded by his six brothers and sisters. I'm a tiny fellow being held in my Uncle George's arms.

I look at the picture wistfully now, for my dad, my grandmother, and all my uncles and aunts are gone; and I think of that picture whenever I hear this song, because it poses a poignant question. As one of the verses puts it:

> *One by one their seats were emptied,*
> *One by one they went away;*
> *Here the circle has been broken—*
> *Will it be complete one day?*

Many people consider this an Appalachian folk hymn, because the Carter Family, the founding family of country music, popularized it. A. P. Carter wrote the bluegrass version sometime between 1931 and 1939; and the Carter Family's version became so well known that he is sometimes credited with composing the song.

The words, however, were actually written by a brilliant London Bible teacher named Ada Ruth Habershon, the youngest daughter of a godly doctor, S. O. Habershon. Ada was a precocious child and a tender Christian, and even as a teen she was an avid Bible student. When D. L. Moody and Ira Sankey toured England in 1884, they were so impressed with Ada, then twenty-three, they invited her to visit America and teach the Bible at Moody's Conference Center in Northfield, Massachusetts. Her lectures on the Old Testament were later published, along with a number of other books, some of which are still in print. They include *Study of the Types, Study of the Miracles, Study of the Parables, Study of the Tabernacle,* and *Types in the Old Testament.*

In 1901, when Ada was forty and suffering from an illness, she began writing poetry. Four years later, when the powerful evangelistic team of R. A. Torrey and Charles M. Alexander visited England, Alexander asked her to write some gospel songs. Within a year, she had sent him two hundred!

Ada Habershon never married, and she passed away in 1918, at the age of fifty-seven. But her books continue to be studied to this day and her hymns are still sung around the world.

One Day

J. Wilbur Chapman

Charles H. Marsh

1. One day when heav - en was filled with His prais - es,
2. One day they led Him up Cal - va - ry's moun - tain,
3. One day they left Him a - lone in the gar - den,
4. One day the grave could con - ceal Him no long - er,
5. One day the trum - pet will sound for His com - ing,

One day when sin was as black as could be,
One day they nailed Him to die on the tree;
One day He rest - ed, from suf - fer - ing free;
One day the stone rolled a - way from the door;
One day the skies with His glo - ry will shine;

Je - sus came forth to be born of a vir - gin,
Suf - fer - ing an - guish, de - spised and re - ject - ed,
An - gels came down o'er His tomb to keep vig - il;
Then He a - rose, o - ver death He had con - quered,
Won - der - ful day, my be - lov - ed one's bring - ing!

Dwelt a - mong men, my Ex - am - ple is He!
Bear - ing our sins, my Re - deem - er is He!
Hope of the hope - less, my Sav - ior is He!
Now is as - cend - ed, my Lord ev - er - more!
Glo - ri - ous Sav - ior, this Je - sus is mine!

One Day

1908

And she will bring forth a Son, and you shall call His name JESUS, for He will save His people from their sins. Matthew 1:21

his was written by one of America's greatest evangelists, J. Wilbur Chapman. Under D. L. Moody's ministry, Chapman received absolute assurance of his salvation. And it was Moody who encouraged him to enter full-time evangelism.

Chapman wrote a number of books and pastored several churches. His hymn, "Our Great Savior," is one of my favorites.* A leader among American Presbyterians, Chapman was elected Moderator of the Presbyterian General Assembly in 1918, but he passed away on Christmas Day that year. He was only fifty-nine years old.

One of Chapman's young musicians, Charles Marsh, was a gifted pianist who wrote the music for "One Day." He later described the legal wrangling over this song:

It was about 1908 or 1909 that Dr. Chapman was invited to conduct a Bible Conference at Stony Brook, Long Island, and he took me with him. It was at Stony Brook that he gave me the poem "One Day" and another entitled "All Hail the Power." I set them both [to music] that summer and as I remember, they were copyrighted in my name. Within a year or two Dr. Parley E. Zartmann (Dr. Chapman's assistant) persuaded me to sell my interest in the songs to him. I wanted to go to college, so I left my association with Dr. Chapman, much as I enjoyed it. Soon after that, Dr. Chapman joined forces with Charles M. Alexander and the next time I saw "One Day" in print, it had at the bottom "Charles M. Alexander, owner of the copyright." In the meantime, Dr. Zartmann had sold the two songs to Hope Publishing Company. I don't know who won out in the mess that was raging at the time, but I do think Dr. Zartmann and the Hope Publishing Company were in the right and that Alexander had simply appropriated the song because of Dr. Chapman's having written the words.

Well, nothing can keep a good hymn down—especially one that presents such an all-inclusive view of the Savior's great work for us. As the refrain says:

> *Living, He loved me; dying, He saved me;*
> *Buried, He carried my sins far away;*
> *Rising, He justified, freely forever;*
> *One day He's coming—O glorious day!*

---

*See this story in *Then Sings My Soul*, Volume 1.

He Keeps Me Singing

Luther B. Bridgers

Luther B. Bridgers

1. There's with-in my heart a mel-o-dy. Je-sus whis-pers sweet and low:
2. All my life was wrecked by sin and strife; Dis-cord filled my life with pain.
3. Feast-ing on the rich-es of His grace, Rest-ing 'neath His shel-t'ring wing,
4. Tho' some-times He leads thro' wa-ters deep, Tri-als fall a-cross my way,
5. Soon He's com-ing back to welcome me Far be-yond the star-ry sky.

"Fear not, I am with thee; peace, be still," In all of life's ebb and flow.
Je-sus swept a-cross the bro-ken strings, Stirred the slumb-'ring chords a-gain.
Al-ways look-ing on His smil-ing face, That is why I shout and sing.
Tho' some-times the path seems rough and steep, See His foot-prints all the way.
I shall wing my flight to worlds un-known; I shall reign with Him on high.

Je - sus, Je - sus, Je - sus, Sweet-est name I know,

Fills my ev-'ry long - ing, Keeps me sing-ing as I go.

He Keeps Me Singing

1910

And the ransomed of the Lord shall return, and come to Zion with singing, with everlasting joy on their heads. . . . Isaiah 35:10

T hough battered by life, the patriarch Job declared that God is able to give us "songs in the night" (Job 35:10). When the Psalmist, Asaph, felt overwhelmed, he consoled himself with God's "song in the night" (Psalm 77:6). God is strong enough to keep us singing, even in the night seasons.

North Carolina native Luther Bridgers began preaching at age seventeen while attending Asbury College in Kentucky. Afterward, he developed a reputation as an effective pastor/evangelist/church planter. The Lord gave him a wonderful wife and three precious boys.

In 1910, when Luther was twenty-six and the future seemed bright, he took his family to his wife's home in Harrodsburg, Kentucky, southwest of Lexington. They were going to stay with her parents while Luther was on a preaching trip.

One evening a nearby neighbor, unable to sleep, rose in the night and glanced out his window. He was horrified to see flames. Racing across the field, he gave the alarm, but by that time the house was fully engulfed. Luther's in-laws evidently escaped, but his wife and sons perished.*

During the long, slow recovery from overwhelming grief, Luther suffered deep and almost suicidal depression, according to some sources. But he recalled the Bible's promise of "songs in the night," and several months later he wrote both the words and the music for this gospel song about God's ability to keep him singing. Notice how he alludes to his tragedy in verse 4:

Though sometimes He leads through waters deep, | Trials fall across the way,
Though sometimes the path seems rough and steep, | See His footprints all the way.

Jesus, Jesus, Jesus, Sweetest Name I know,
Fills my every longing, Keeps me singing as I go.

In 1914, Luther married again and became a general evangelist for the Methodist Episcopal Church South, a ministry that kept him occupied for the next eighteen years (with a brief interruption after World War I when he traveled to Belgium, Czechoslovakia, and Russia, doing evangelistic work).

After 1932, he served as pastor in churches in Georgia and North Carolina, and retired in Gainesville, Georgia, in 1945. He passed away in Atlanta in 1948.

---

*Dr. Alfred B. Smith, the "Dean of Gospel Music," says that Luther himself was at his in-laws that night and had to be restrained by neighbors from re-entering the collapsing inferno.

Our Great Savior

J. Wilbur Chapman

Rowland W. Prichard

1. Je - sus! What a friend for sin - ners! Je - sus lov - er of my soul!
2. Je - sus! What a strength in weak - ness! Let me hide my - self in Him;
3. Je - sus! What a help in sor - row! While the bil - lows o'er me roll,
4. Je - sus! What a guide and keep - er! While the tem - pest still is high,
5. Je - sus! I do now re - ceive Him; More than all in Him I find.

Friends may fail me, foes as - sail me; He, my Sav - ior, makes me whole.
Tempt - ed tried and some - times fail - ing, He, my strength my vic - tory wins.
E - ven when my heart is break - ing, He, my Com - fort helps my soul.
Storms a - bout me, night o'er - takes me, He, my pi - lot hears my cry.
He hath grant - ed me for - give - ness; I am His and He is mine.

Hal - le - lu - jah! what a Sav - ior! Hal - le - lu - jah! what a Friend!

Sav - ing, help - ing, keep - ing, lov - ing, He is with me to the end.

Our Great Savior

1910

. . . you shall know no God but Me; For there is no Savior besides Me. Hosea 13:4

During his teen years, John Wilbur Chapman attended two Sunday schools each week in his hometown of Richmond, Indiana. He went to one church each Sunday morning, and in the afternoon he would go to Grace Methodist Episcopal Church. It was in the latter that he first publicly professed Christ as His Savior at age seventeen. A guest speaker gave the lesson that afternoon, then asked for those to stand who wanted to become Christians. Chapman later wrote:

> I think every boy in my class rose to his feet with the exception of myself . . . My Sunday School teacher (Mrs. C. C. Binkley), with tears in her eyes, leaned around back of the other boys, and looking straight at me, as I turned toward her, said, "Would it not be best for you to rise?" And when she saw I still hesitated, she put her hand under my elbow and lifted me up just a little bit, and I stood on my feet. I can never describe my emotions . . . Through all these years I have never forgotten it was my teacher who influenced me thus to take a stand—it was her personal touch that gave me courage to rise before the church and confess my Savior.

Wilber Chapman went on to become an outstanding pastor, writer, hymnist, and denominational leader. But he is best remembered for his evangelism. Multitudes of people were converted in his crusades (with songleader Charles M. Alexander) in the United States, Canada, Hawaii, the Fiji Islands, Australia, Tasmania, New Zealand, the Philippines, China, Japan, Ceylon, England, Scotland, Ireland, and Wales. It was in 1910 in the midst of his endeavors that he wrote the hymn "Our Great Savior," celebrating the varied and wonderful roles Christ plays in our lives: "Jesus! What a friend of sinners . . . . Jesus! What a Strength in weakness . . . . Jesus! What a Help in Sorrow . . . . Jesus! What a Guide and Keeper . . . Hallelujah! What a Savior."

This hymn is sung to the exhilarating tune HYFRYDOL, which is a Welsh word meaning "good cheer." It was composed around 1830 by Rowland W. Pritchard, a choir director born in north Wales, and has since become widely used with a number of hymn texts. It was Robert Harkness, the gifted pianist in Chapman's evangelistic campaigns, who took Chapman's words and wedded them to Pritchard's music.

Dwelling in Beulah Land

C. Austin Miles

C. Austin Miles

1. Far a-way the noise of strife up-on my ear is fall-ing,
2. Far be-low the storm of doubt up-on the world is beat-ing,
3. Let the storm-y breez-es blow, their cry can-not a-larm me;
4. View-ing here the works of God, I sink in con-tem-pla-tion.

Then I know the sins of earth be-set on ev-ery hand;
Sons of men in bat-tle long the en-e-my with-stand;
I am safe-ly shel-tered here, pro-tect-ed by God's hand;
Hear-ing now His bless-ed voice, I see the way He planned;

Doubt and fear and things of earth in vain to me are call-ing,
Safe am I with-in the cas-tle of God's Word re-treat-ing,
Here the sun is al-ways shin-ing, here there's naught can harm me,
Dwell-ing in the Spir-it, here I learn of full sal-va-tion,

None of these shall move me from Beu-lah Land.
Noth-ing then can reach me, 'tis Beu-lah Land.
I am safe for-ev-er in Beu-lah Land.
Glad-ly will I tar-ry in Beu-lah Land.

Dwelling in Beulah Land

1911

I will both lie down in peace, and sleep; For You alone, O LORD, make me dwell in safety. Psalm 4:8

This peppy song about heaven was written by pharmacist-turned-publisher, C. Austin Miles, born on January 7, 1868, in Lakehurst, New Jersey. He had wanted to train for the ministry, but circumstances forced him to take a job with a pharmacy at age sixteen. Soon Miles found himself attending the Philadelphia College of Pharmacy and the University of Pennsylvania, after which he settled down as a druggist for several years.

It all changed when he wrote his first gospel song, "List 'Tis Jesus' Voice." After Hall-Mack Publishing Company of Philadelphia published it, Miles abandoned drugs for hymns. For nearly four decades, he was employed by the Hall-Mack Publishing Company as music editor, even after it merged with the Rodeheaver Company. In a way, of course, he hadn't changed vocations at all, just venue. He was now filling prescriptions for the soul.

Interestingly, Miles wrote many of his hymns in the darkroom. He was an amateur photographer, and he found he could read his Bible in the glow of the special light in the darkroom. While waiting for photographs to develop, Miles would read the Scriptures and pray them into songs. One day, for example, while waiting for some film to develop, he poured over John 20, the story of Mary coming to Christ's tomb on Easter morning. Out of his meditation came the song, "In the Garden."

Miles also wrote the popular gospel hymn, "If Jesus Goes with Me I'll Go Anywhere," and the exuberant song that says, "There's a new name written down in Glory—and it's mine, O yes, it's mine!"

In his spare time, Miles was in demand as a song leader at conferences, churches, conventions, and camp meetings. He also published some of his compositions as poetry, his best-known work being "The World's Greatest Need."

THE WORLD'S GREATEST NEED

A little more kindness and a little less greed;
A little more giving and a little less need;
A little more smile and a little less frown;
A little less kicking a man when he's down;
A little more "we" and a little less "I"
A little more laughs and a little less cry;
A little more flowers on the pathway of life;
And fewer on graves at the end of the strife.

Rise Up, O Men of God

William P. Merrill

William H. Walter

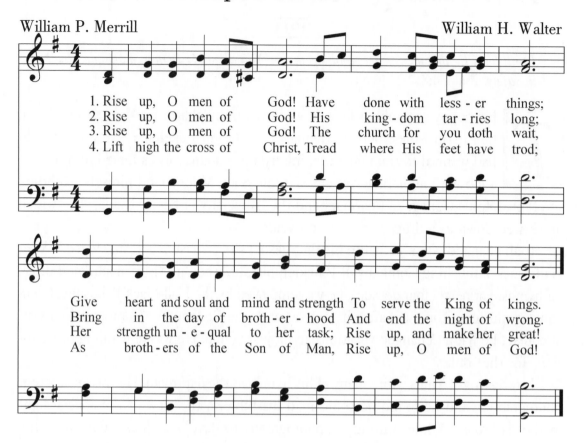

1. Rise up, O men of God! Have done with less - er things;
2. Rise up, O men of God! His king - dom tar - ries long;
3. Rise up, O men of God! The church for you doth wait,
4. Lift high the cross of Christ, Tread where His feet have trod;

Give heart and soul and mind and strength To serve the King of kings.
Bring in the day of broth - er - hood And end the night of wrong.
Her strength un - e - qual to her task; Rise up, and make her great!
As broth - ers of the Son of Man, Rise up, O men of God!

Rise Up, O Men of God

1911

Who will rise up for me against the evildoers? Who will stand up for me against the workers of iniquity? Psalm 94:16

his hymn was written somewhere on Lake Michigan, on a steamship heading toward Chicago. Its author was William Merrill, who was nearing the end of his pastorate in Chicago before moving east to assume the leadership of New York's famous Brick Church.

Merrill had come to Christ at age eleven. As a young man, he attended Rutgers College and Union Theological Seminary and was ordained into the Presbyterian ministry in 1890. He pastored churches in Philadelphia, then in Chicago.

In 1911, he became pastor of the Brick Presbyterian Church, where he remained until his retirement in 1938.* He wrote ten books and several hymns, the best known of which was "Rise Up, O Men of God."

He once explained how the hymn was written. While pastoring in Chicago, he was associated with a Presbyterian publication known as *The Continent.* Its editor, Nolan R. Best, approached him, suggesting the need for a strong hymn challenging men to rise up for Christ, especially in light of the Brotherhood Movement within the Presbyterian Church. Shortly afterward, Merrill read an article by Gerald Stanley Lee entitled, "The Church of Strong Men."

"I was on one of the Lake Michigan steamers going back to Chicago for a Sunday at my own church," Merrill later wrote, "when suddenly this hymn came up, almost without conscious thought or effort." It first appeared in *The Continent* on February 16, 1911, and the next year was published in *The Pilgrim Hymnal.*

William Merrill was also instrumental in starting the Church Peace Union, now known as the Carnegie Council on Ethics and International Affairs. In 1914, the steel magnate, Andrew Carnegie, wanted to establish an organization seeking to end war forever. They planned to gather on August 1, 1914, on the shore of Lake Constance in southern Germany. But when Germany invaded Belgium, trains carrying delegates were halted and turned back and other delegates were arrested by German authorities. The arrival of the First World War crushed Carnegie's dreams of banning war; but the Church Peace Union continued its work, and William Merrill served as its first president. Today on Manhattan's Upper East Side, two adjoining townhouses, named for William Merrill, serve as headquarters for the Carnegie Council's popular public speaker series.

---

*Other famous pastor/hymnists of Brick Church include Henry Van Dyke ("Joyful, Joyful, We Adore Thee) and Maltbie Babcock ("This Is My Father's World"). These stories are told in the first volume of *Then Sings My Soul.*

In the Garden

C. Austin Miles

C. Austin Miles

1. I come to the gar - den a - lone, While the dew is still on the
2. He speaks, and the sound of His voice is so sweet, the birds hush their
3. I'd stay in the gar - den with Him, Though the night a - round me be

ros - es; And the voice I hear, fall - ing on my ear, The
sing - ing, And the mel - o - dy that He gave to me, With -
fall - ing, But He bids me go; through the voice of woe, His

Son of God dis - clos - es.
in my heart is ring - ing. And He walks with me, And He
voice to me is call - ing.

talks with me, And He tells me I am His own; And the

joy we share as we tar - ry there, None oth - er has ev - er known.

In the Garden

1912

. . . she turned around and saw Jesus standing there . . . John 20:14

 he art of meditating on Scripture involves using one's imagination. Instead of simply reading a passage, we must read it, close our eyes, and visualize the scene, perhaps even putting ourselves in the picture. That's what the author of this hymn did.

C. Austin Miles was a pharmacist who began writing gospel songs and eventually became an editor of hymnals and songbooks, as well as a popular music director at camp meetings, conventions, and churches. His hobby was photography, and he found his darkroom perfect for developing, not just his photographs, but his devotional life. In its privacy and strange blue glow, Miles could read his Bible in total privacy.

One day in March, 1912, while waiting for some film to develop, he opened the Bible to his favorite chapter, John 20, the story of the first Easter. Miles later said: "As I read it that day, I seemed to be part of the scene . . . My hands were resting on the Bible while I stared at the light blue wall. As the light faded, I seemed to be standing at the entrance of a garden, looking down a gently winding path, shaded by olive branches. A woman in white, with head bowed, hand clasping her throat as if to choke back her sobs, walked slowly into the shadows. It was Mary. As she came to the tomb, upon which she placed her hand, she bent over to look in and hurried away. John, in flowing robe, appeared, looking at the tomb; then came Peter, who entered the tomb, followed slowly by John.

"As they departed, Mary reappeared, leaning her head upon her arm at the tomb. She wept. Turning herself, she saw Jesus standing; so did I. I knew it was He. She knelt before Him, with arms outstretched and looking into his face, cried, 'Rabboni!'

"I awakened in full light, gripping my Bible, with muscles tense and nerves vibrating. Under the inspiration of this vision I wrote as quickly as the words would be formed the poem exactly as it has since appeared. That same evening I wrote the music."

In addition to "In the Garden," Austin Miles is the author of several other gospel songs, including "A New Name in Glory," "Dwelling in Beulah Land," and "If Jesus Goes with Me I'll Go Anywhere."

What If It Were Today?

Lelia N. Morris

Lelia N. Morris

1. Je - sus is com - ing to earth a - gain, What if it were to - day?
2. Sa - tan's do-min - ion will then be o'er, O that it were to - day!
3. Faith - ful and true would He find us here If He should come to - day?

Com - ing in pow - er and love to reign, What if it were to - day?
Sor - row and sigh - ing shall be no more, O that it were to - day!
Watch - ing in glad - ness and not in fear, If He should come to - day?

Com - ing to claim His cho - sen bride, All the re - deemed and pu - ri - fied,
Then shall the dead in Christ a - rise, Caught up to meet Him in the skies;
Signs of His com - ing mul - ti - ply, Morn - ing light breaks in east - ern sky,

O - ver this whole earth scat - tered wide, What if it were to - day?
When shall these glo - ries meet our eyes? What if it were to - day?
Watch, for the time is draw - ing nigh, What if it were to - day?

What If It Were Today?

1912

And if I go and prepare a place for you, I will come again and receive you to Myself; that where I am, there you may be also. John 14:3

Christians of every generation have longed for Christ to return in their lifetime. *The Didache*, one of the earliest documents in church history, says, *Let not your lamps be quenched, nor your loins unloosed; but be ready, for you know not the hour in which our Lord will come.* St. Cyril wrote in the fourth century, *But let us wait and look for the Lord's coming upon the clouds from heaven. Then shall angelic trumpets sound.*

Augustine felt the Lord would return somewhere around the year AD 1000. In the 1300s, John Wycliffe, the "Morning Star of the Reformation," studied the "signs of the times" and concluded that the end of the world and the Second Coming of Christ should be expected immediately. In the sixteenth century, John Calvin preached: *We must hunger after Christ until the dawning of that great day when our Lord will fully manifest the glory of His kingdom.* Today His return seems closer than ever.

It's not surprising, then, that the Return of Christ has been the theme of hundreds of hymns through the ages. "What If It Were Today?" was written by Ohio homemaker, Lelia Morris, whose story has already been told in connection with her hymns, "Nearer, Still Nearer" and "Let Jesus Come into Your Heart." It was one of the most popular Second Coming songs of the last hundred years. But look at a much older hymn about the Second Coming.

John Newton, the London pastor who wrote "Amazing Grace," showed the other side of the Lord's return with his hymn "Day of Judgment! Day of Wonders!" It provides an important contrast to Lelia Morris' uplifting strains.

Day of judgment! Day of wonders!
Hark! the trumpet's awful sound,
Louder than a thousand thunders,
Shakes the vast creation round!
How the summons shall the sinner's heart confound!

At His call the dead awaken,
Rise to life from earth and sea;
All the powers of nature shaken
By His look, prepares to flee.
Careless sinner, what will then become of thee!

Love Lifted Me

James Rowe

Howard E. Smith

1. I was sink-ing deep in sin, Far from the peace-ful shore, Ver-y deep-ly
2. All my heart to Him I give; Ev-er to Him I'll cling, In His bless-ed
3. Souls in dan-ger, look a-bove; Je-sus com-plete-ly saves. He will lift you

stained with-in, Sink-ing to rise no more. But the Mas-ter of the sea
pres-ence live, Ev-er His prais-es sing. Love so might-y and so true
by His love Out of the an-gry waves. He's the Mas-ter of the sea,

Heard my de-spair-ing cry, From the wa-ters lift-ed me-Now safe am I.
Mer-its my soul's best songs; Faith-ful, lov-ing ser-vice, too, To Him be-longs.
Bil-lows His will o-bey. He your Sav-ior wants to be, Be saved to-day.

Love lift-ed me! Love lift-ed me! When noth-ing
e-ven me, e-ven me,

1. else could help, Love lift-ed me;.
2. Love lift-ed me.

Love Lifted Me

1912

My hands also I will lift up to Your commandments, Which I love, And I will meditate on Your statutes. Psalm 119:48

T he two huddled together, working line by line, bar by bar, composing this hymn in tandem. The words were jotted down by James Rowe, and the music was hammered out at the piano by his friend, Howard E. Smith, whose hands were so twisted from arthritis that his friends wondered how he could play the piano at all. But there they were, James pacing back and forth while Howard banged away the melody. When they finished, the world had "Love Lifted Me."

James Rowe was a New Year's baby, born in Devonshire, England, on the first day of 1865. His father, John Rowe, was a copper miner. As a young man, James went to work for the Irish government, but when he was in his mid-twenties, he decided to immigrate to the United States. He settled down in Albany, New York, got married, and found a job with the railroad. He later became superintendent of the Hudson River Humane Society in Albany before eventually becoming a full-time writer. He composed hymns and edited music journals for several publishers. His last years were spent in Wells, Vermont, where he supported himself by writing messages for greeting card publishers, working alongside his daughter who was an artist.

During his lifetime, James claimed to have written more than 19,000 song texts. James Rowe and Howard Smith created "Love Lifted Me" in Saugatuck, Connecticut, in 1912, and sold the copyright to Charles Tillman, who transferred it to Robert Coleman in 1915 for one hundred dollars.

Several of James' other hymns are well known, including "I Choose Jesus," "I Would Be Like Jesus," and "Sweeter as the Days Go By." Among his lesser-known songs is one entitled, "God Holds the Future in His Hands."

Dread not the things that are ahead,
The burdens great, the sinking sands,
The thorns that o'er the path are spread,
God holds the future in His hands.

God holds the future in His hands
And every heart He understands.
On Him depend, He is your Friend,
He holds the future in His hands.

Brighten the Corner Where You Are

Ina Duley Ogdon

Charles H. Gabriel

1. Do not wait un-til some deed of great-ness you may do, Do not
2. Just a-bove are cloud-ed skies that you may help to clear, Let not
3. Here for all your tal-ent you may sure-ly find a need, Here re-

wait to shed your lights a-far; To the man-y du-ties Ev-er near you
nar-row self your way de-bar; Tho' in-to one heart a-lone may fall your
flect the Bright and Morn-ing Star, E-ven from your hum-ble hand The bread of

Now be true, Bright-en the cor-ner Where you are.
song of cheer, Bright-en the cor-ner Where you are. Bright-en the cor-ner
life may feed. Bright-en the cor-ner where you are.

Where you are! Bright-en the cor-ner Where you are! Some-one far from

har-bor You may guide A-cross the bar, Bright-en the cor-ner Where you are.

Brighten the Corner Where You Are

1913

You are the light of the world. Matthew 5:14a

I n August, 1874, a Methodist minister named John Heyl Vincent organized a Sunday school training camp beside beautiful Lake Chautauqua in upstate New York. Families came for two-week summer camps that combined recreation, entertainment, and Sunday school training sessions. It was an enormous hit, and over the next several decades, the "Chautauqua Circuit" spread to other areas and quickly outgrew its Sunday school origins.

Performers, musicians, lecturers, and motivational speakers traveled the country, staying about a week in these summer camps. Enormous audiences gathered to enjoy Broadway hits, popular plays, and stars from the Metropolitan Opera. Speakers like William Jennings Bryan drew thousands, and Theodore Roosevelt called the Chautauqua Circuit, "the most American thing in America."*

In 1912, Ina Duley Ogdon received an invitation to be a Chautauqua Circuit speaker. Having long felt God's calling on her life, she was tremendously excited by the possibilities of motivating thousands of people for the cause of Christ. But as she was packing for the tour, her father was seriously injured in a wreck in one of the new-fangled "horseless carriages." Ina, deeply distressed, cancelled her travel plans to care for him.

Though bitterly disappointed, she was able to surrender the disappointment to God and trust His purposes. Making up her mind to be a blessing wherever she was, she concluded that even if she couldn't minister to thousands, she could be a blessing to one—her father—and to those around him. She sat down and wrote:

Do not wait until some deed of greatness you may do, | Do not wait to shed your light afar,
To the many duties ever near you now be true, | Brighten the corner where you are.

After this poem was set to music by Charles H. Gabriel, it was discovered by Homer Rodeheaver, the song director for Billy Sunday's evangelistic campaigns. He was so taken by the song that he made it the theme song of his ministry, and for twenty-two years, "Brighten the Corner" opened every Billy Sunday meeting. In the process, it became one of gospel music's most popular and uplifting songs.

Instead of speaking to thousands, Ina Duley Ogdon has ministered to millions.

---

*Today, the Library of Congress has a collection of 7,949 publicity brochures, promotional advertisements, and talent circulars for some 4,546 performers who were part of the Chautauqua Circuit.

The Old Rugged Cross

George Bennard   George Bennard

1. On a hill far a - way Stood an old rug-ged cross; The em - blem of
2. Oh, that old rug-ged cross, So de - spised by the world, Has a won-drous at -
3. To the old rug-ged cross I will ev - er be true, It's shame and re -

suf - fering and shame. And I love that old cross Where the dear-est and best,
trac - tion for me; For the dear Lamb of God, Left His glo - ry a - bove,
proach glad- ly bear; Then He'll call me some day To my home far a - way,

For a world of lost sin - ners was slain.
To bear it to dark Cal - va - ry. So I'll cher - ish the old rug - ged
Where His glo - ry for - ev - er I'll share.

cross, Till my tro - phies at last I lay down; I will cling to the

old rug - ged cross, And ex - change it some day for a crown.

The Old Rugged Cross

1913

For God so loved the world that He gave His only begotten Son, that whoever believes in Him should not perish but have everlasting life. John 3:16

George Beverly Shea recalls seeing George Bennard, author of this hymn, many times at Winona Lake Bible Conference in Indiana. "Though a preacher—a good one—he would sometimes sing," wrote Mr. Shea. "His voice was not trained or out of the ordinary, but he had great feeling and expression and could really put over any hymn. I remember how moved I was the first time I heard him sing his own 'The Old Rugged Cross . . . .' What a distinguished looking man—slight of build, short, with glasses, the most memorable thing about him was his long, white hair."

George Bennard was born in Youngstown, Ohio, shortly after the end of the Civil War. His father, a coal miner, moved the family to Iowa, and there George came to Christ through the ministry of the Salvation Army. He felt impressed to train for the ministry, but his plans were disrupted when his father's death left him responsible for his mother and sisters. He was sixteen years old. Instead of theological school, he worked by day and devoted his spare time to books.

Eventually George's obligations lessened, and he was able to move to Chicago, marry, and begin in ministry with the Salvation Army. Later he was ordained by the Methodist Episcopal church and became a traveling evangelist.

On one occasion, after a difficult season of ministry, George realized he needed to better understand the power of the Cross of Christ. He later said, "I was praying for a full understanding of the Cross . . . I read and studied and prayed . . . The Christ of the Cross became more than a symbol . . . It was like seeing John 3:16 leave the printed page, take form, and act out the meaning of redemption. While watching this scene with my mind's eye, the theme of the song came to me."

It took several months for the words to formulate in his mind. As he preached through the Midwest, George would carry the words with him, working on them, polishing them, and sometimes singing them in his meetings. It always struck a chord with his audiences.

At last, his hymn finished, George went to the home of his friends, Rev. and Mrs. L. O. Boswick, and sang it for them. After the last note, he looked at them and asked, "Will it do?"

The Boswicks were so moved that they helped pay the fees to have it printed, and it soon began appearing in hymnbooks across America.

To Canaan's Land I'm on My Way

William M. Golden

William M. Golden

1. To Ca-naan's land I'm on my way, Where the soul (of man) nev-er dies;
2. A rose is bloom-ing there for me, Where the soul (of man) nev-er dies;
3. A love-light beams a-cross the foam, Where the soul (of man) nev-er dies;
4. I'm on my way to that fair land, Where the soul (of man) nev-er dies;

My dark-est night will turn to day, Where the soul (of man) nev-er dies.
And I will spend e-ter-ni-ty, Where the soul (of man) nev-er dies.
It shines to light the shores of home, Where the soul (of man) nev-er dies.
Where there will be no part-ing hand, Where the soul (of man) nev-er dies.

No sad fare-wells, no tear-dimmed eyes,
Dear friends, there'll be no sad fare-wells, There'll be no tear-dimmed eyes,

Where all is love, and the soul nev-er dies.
Where all is peace and joy and love, and the soul of man nev-er dies.

To Canaan's Land
I'm on My Way

1914

Now may the God of peace Himself sanctify you completely; and may your whole spirit, soul, and body be preserved blameless at the coming of our Lord Jesus Christ.
1 Thessalonians 5:23

When William Golden wrote this song in 1914, he called it "To Canaan's Land I'm on My Way." Hank Williams later recorded it under the title, "Where the Soul of Man Never Dies," and it became a hit. It's been sung by many gospel groups, but it was Duane Allen, lead singer for the Oak Ridge Boys, who gave me this wonderful story.

"In 1976, the Oak Ridge Boys were invited to Russia," Duane said. "The Communists were still in charge and the Iron Curtain was in place. Before we made the trip, the Soviets demanded the lyrics of all our songs for approval.

"Shortly after the tour began, we realized we needed more songs. At that time we didn't have country music hits. We only had our gospel music, and it was difficult to get those songs approved by the Communists.

"I wanted to use 'Where the Soul of Man Never Dies,' because we'd won a Grammy for it. But fearing it would be rejected by the censors, I submitted it under the original title, 'To Canaan's Land I'm On My Way.' The Soviets took the lyrics into a room, and half an hour later they called me in.

"We could sing the song, they said, if we changed the first line. They didn't know what 'Canaan' was. That word wasn't in their dictionaries. They asked if we would sing: 'To *Disneyland* I'm on my way . . .' They knew all about Disneyland.

"I was appalled, but after thinking a moment, I asked if we could sing, 'To *that fair land* I'm on my way.' That satisfied them, and it became one of our biggest hits of the tour.

"That evening after the concert," Duane added, "they loaded us onto a military bus for departure, and as we were getting ready to leave an old woman ran up and knocked on the glass. When I pulled down the window, she pitched in a note that fell to my feet. I bent over and picked it up, then turned to wave goodbye. To my horror, she was being dragged off and beaten by the authorities. Opening the note, I read her words, which I've never forgotten: 'Keep singing about Jesus,' said the note. 'There are still those over here who love His message.'"

Since Jesus Came Into My Heart

Rufus H. McDaniel

Charles H. Gabriel

1. What a won-der-ful change in my life has been wrought, Since Je - sus came
2. I have ceased from my wan-d'ring and go-ing a - stray, Since Je - sus came
3. I'm pos - sessed of a hope that is stead-fast and sure, Since Je - sus came
4. I shall go there to dwell in that Cit - y, I know, Since Je - sus came

in - to my heart! I have light in my soul, For which long I have sought,
in - to my heart; And my sins, which were man - y, are all washed a - way,
in - to my heart; And no dark clouds of doubt now my path - way ob - scure,
in - to my heart; And I'm hap - py, so hap - py, as on - ward I go,

Since Je - sus came in - to my heart.
Since Je - sus came in, came

heart, Since Je - sus came in - to my heart, Floods of joy o'er my
in - to my heart, Since Je - sus came in, came in - to my heart,

soul Like the sea bil - lows roll, Since Je - sus came in - to my heart.

Since Jesus Came Into My Heart

1914

Let not your heart be troubled; you believe in God, believe also in Me. John 14:1

Rufus McDaniel, born in rural Ohio in 1850, was licensed to preach when he was only nineteen. He was soon afterward ordained into the Christian Church and married. His blessings were tripled by the births of Clarence, Minnie, and Herschel. Clarence, the firstborn, followed in his father's footsteps and became a minister in the Christian denomination. The daughter, Minnie, married an Ohio boy and lived nearby in Dayton. It was Herschel who broke his dad's heart by his untimely death in 1913.

After Rufus had buried his son, he realized anew that joy and contentment cannot be based on human affection or external gift. They flow from an endless relationship with our Lord Jesus Christ. Out of that experience, he wrote, "Since Jesus Came Into My Heart."

Rufus went on to pastor churches in southern Ohio for many years before retiring to Dayton to be near his daughter. He wrote over a hundred hymns, but this is the only one that has endured. It, too, would have been lost to us but for the great evangelist Billy Sunday, who counted it among his favorites.

This notice appeared among the obituaries in the *Dayton Daily News* on February 13, 1940:

Rev. McDaniel, noted writer of hymns, dies.

The Rev. Rufus H. McDaniel, 90, retired Congregational Christian minister, died at 9 a.m. Tuesday at the home of the daughter, Mrs. Frank R. Liesenhoff . . . He had been ailing for some time, but had been seriously ill about one week. The Rev. McDaniel, who celebrated his ninetieth birthday on Jan. 29, composed and published more than one hundred hymns that have been used by all denominations, yet he received nothing in the way of cash remuneration. He was the guest on Ken Randolph's program over WHIO the day after he had celebrated his eighty-ninth birthday, and sang "Since Jesus Came Into My Heart," a hymn he wrote many years ago and which is now one of the best known of its type in evangelistic circles.

Ivory Palaces

Henry Barraclough

Henry Barraclough

1. My Lord has gar-ments so won-drous fine, And myrrh their tex - ture fills;
2. His life had al - so its sor-rows sore, For al - oes had a part;
3. His gar-ments too were in cas - sia dipped, With heal - ing in a touch;
4. In gar-ments glo - ri - ous He will come, To o - pen wide the door;

Its fra-grance reached to this heart of mine, With joy my be - ing thrills.
And when I think of the cross He bore, My eyes with tear-drops start.
Each time my feet in some sin have slipped, He took me from its clutch.
And I shall en - ter my heav'n - ly home, To dwell for - ev - er-more.

Out of the i - vo-ry pal - a - ces, In - to a world of woe,

On - ly His great, e - ter - nal love Made my Sav-ior go.

Ivory Palaces

1915

All Your garments are scented with myrrh and aloes and cassia, Out of the ivory palaces, by which they have made You glad. Psalm 45:8

Billy Graham enjoys telling the story behind this hymn which was written near his home. Billy and Ruth Graham live in a rambling log cabin at the end of a steep, winding road outside Asheville, North Carolina. At the bottom of the hill is Montreat Conference Center that, for a hundred years, has served as a major conference grounds for the Presbyterian Church (USA).

In the summer of 1915, evangelist J. Wilbur Chapman was preaching at Montreat Conference Center. He brought his famous song leader, Charles M. Alexander, and his young pianist, Henry Barraclough.

Barraclough, twenty-four, had begun studying organ and piano at age five in his native England. As a young man, he worked in insurance, and then became secretary for a Member of Parliament. When Chapman met him and recognized his musical talents, he invited him to join his team as pianist. With great excitement, Barraclough traveled to Montreat as part of an evangelistic tour.

One evening, Chapman spoke of Psalm 45, and the eighth verse of the psalm was Dr. Chapman's text: "All thy garments shall smell of myrrh, and aloes, and cassia, out of the ivory palaces . . ." Chapman was speaking on one of his favorite themes, having previously written a book entitled *Ivory Palaces of the King*. On this evening in Montreat, he spoke with such tender passion that the young pianist was deeply moved.

After the service, some of Chapman's team took a drive through the mountains and stopped at a country store. Sitting in the front seat of the car, Barraclough scribbled down the words to "Ivory Palaces." Returning to the conference hotel, he developed his hymn through the night, and the next morning it was sung as a duet at the conference by Mrs. Alexander and Albert Brown.

Mr. Graham adds an additional link in the story, as well. It was Albert Brown, one of the original singers, who, years later, introduced Graham to song leader Cliff Barrows at the Ben Lippen Conference Center in Asheville. Thus began another great evangelistic partnership that has lasted over fifty years.*

---

*Some of the information for this story came from "Ivory Palaces: A Hymn Story by Billy Graham," in *Crusader Hymns and Hymn Stories* (Minneapolis: The Billy Graham Evangelistic Association, 1967), pp. 25–26.

The Love of God

F. M. Lehman

F. M. Lehman

1. The love of God is great-er far, Than tongue or pen can ev-er tell,
2. When years of time shall pass a-way And earth-ly thrones and king-doms fall,
3. Could we with ink the o-cean fill And were the skies of parch-ment made,

It goes be-yond the high-est star And reach-es to the low-est hell;
When men, who here re-fuse to pray, On rocks and hills and moun-tains call;
Were ev-'ry stalk on earth a quill And ev-'ry man a scribe by trade.

The guilt-y pair, bowed down with care, God gave His Son to win;
God's love so sure shall still en-dure, All mea-sure-less and strong;
To write the love of God a-bove Would drain the o-cean dry;

His err-ing child He rec-on-ciled And par-doned from his sin.
Re-deem-ing grace to A-dam's race The saints' and an-gels' song.
Nor could the scroll con-tain the whole Tho stretched from sky to sky.

The Love of God

Praise the LORD! Oh, give thanks to the LORD, for He is good! For His mercy endures forever. Psalm 106:1

T his hymn was written in a citrus packing house in Pasadena, California, by a German-born Christian named Frederick M. Lehman. At age four, Frederick and his family had immigrated to America, settling down in Iowa. Converted to Christ at age eleven while walking through a crabapple orchard, Frederick eventually entered the ministry and pastored churches in the Midwest. But his greatest love was gospel music, and he compiled five songbooks and published hundreds of songs.

In 1917, his finances had gone sour, and he found himself working in a packing factory in Pasadena, moving thirty tons of lemons and oranges a day. One morning as he arrived at work, a song was forming in his mind. He had been thinking about the limitlessness of God's love, and during breaks he sat on an empty lemon crate and jotted down words with a stubby pencil.

Arriving home that evening, he went to the old upright piano and began putting notes to his words. He finally had a melody and two stanzas, but almost all gospel songs of that era had at least three stanzas. At length, he thought of some lines he had recently heard in a sermon:

> *Could we with ink the ocean fill and were the skies of parchment made,*
> *Were every stalk on earth a quill, and every man a scribe by trade,*
> *To write the love of God above would drain the ocean dry,*
> *Nor could the scroll contain the whole though stretched from sky to sky.*

That verse perfectly formed the third stanza, but who had written it? As Frederick heard the story, it was composed on the wall of an insane asylum by an unknown inmate. Perhaps someone did find it there, but we now know the words originally came from the pen of an eleventh-century Jewish poet in Germany named Meir Ben Isaac Nehorai.

Frederick lived the rest of his life in California, writing a number of hymns before his death in 1953. One of his most popular gospel songs, now outdated and forgotten, was based on the wonder of a new-fangled invention that was sweeping over America. It was called "The Royal Telephone."

> *Central's never "busy," always on the line;*
> *You may hear from heaven almost any time. . . .*
> *Telephone to glory, O what joy divine!*
> *I can feel the current moving on the line. . . .*

Living for Jesus

Thomas O. Chisholm

C. Harold Lowden

1. Liv-ing for Je - sus, a life that is true.
2. Liv-ing for Je - sus Who died in my place,
3. Liv-ing for Je - sus, wher - ev - er I am.
4. Liv-ing for Je - sus, through earth's lit - tle while,

Striv - ing to please Him in all that I do.
Bear - ing on Cal - v'ry, my sin and dis - grace.
Do - ing each du - ty in His ho - ly name.
My dear - est trea - sure, the light of His smile.

Yield - ing al - le - giance, glad heart - ed and free.
Such love con - strains me, to an - swer His call,
Will - ing to suf - fer af - flic - tion or loss.
Seek - ing the lost ones, He died to re - deem.

This is the path - way of bless - ing for me.
Fol - low His lead - ing and give Him my all.
Deem - ing each tri - al a part of my cross.
Bring - ing the wea - ry to find rest in Him.

Living for Jesus

1917

And I give them eternal life, and they shall never perish; neither shall anyone snatch them out of My hand. John 10:28

I n the 1950s, a frail figure would be seen on the boardwalks of Ocean Park, New Jersey. Though modest and shy, he was warmly greeted as he ducked in and out of shops and cafés. Behind his back people would whisper. "See that man? He's the author of 'Great Is Thy Faithfulness,' 'Living for Jesus,' and 'O to Be Like Thee.'"

His name was Thomas Obadiah Chisholm, and he had settled into the Methodist Home for the Aged in Ocean Park to enjoy his sunset years.

Thomas was born in 1866, in a log cabin in Franklin, Kentucky. His education was sparse, yet at age sixteen he began teaching in the same one-room schoolhouse he had attended as a child. Four years later, the local newspaper, *The Franklin Advocate,* offered him a job.

When Thomas was twenty-seven, the founder and president of Asbury College, Dr. H. C. Morrison, came to Franklin to preach. During that revival, Thomas found Christ as his Savior, and Dr. Morrison soon asked him to become office editor and business manager for the *Pentecostal Herald,* headquartered in Louisville.

In 1903, Thomas applied for ordination in the Methodist church and accepted the pastorate of a church in Scottsville, Kentucky. He labored there a single year before his health collapsed, forcing him to move to Winona Lake, Indiana, where his family had property. There he supported himself by selling insurance.

Thomas wrote poems for personal therapy, some of which were published and came to the attention of pastor/musician C. Harold Lowden of New Jersey. One day in 1915, Lowden composed a song for the children in his church. He called it the "Sunshine Song," and used it during a Children's Day service. Two years later, as Lowden prepared to publish a songbook, he wanted to use his tune but felt the words were lacking. He contacted Thomas, asking him to compose new words.

"[Thomas] returned it to me," Lowden later wrote, "saying he didn't have the slightest idea as to the method used in writing words to music. Immediately, I sent the material back to him, telling him I believed God led me to select him."

Since Thomas couldn't read music, he asked his daughter to hum the melody over and over until he understood it enough to compose suitable words. Thus was born "Living for Jesus." It was published in Lowden's collection of hymns, *Uplifting Songs,* in 1917.

Saved!

Oswald Jeffrey Smith

Roger M. Hickman

1. Saved! Saved! Saved! My sins are all for-giv'n,
2. Saved! Saved! Saved! By grace and grace a-lone.
3. Saved! Saved! Saved! O joy be-yond com-pare!

Christ is mine! I'm on my way to heav'n,
Oh, what won - drous love to me was shown,
Christ my life, and I His con - stant care,

Once a guilt - y sin - ner, lost, un - done,
In my stead Christ Je - sus bled and died.
Yield - ing all and trust - ing Him a - lone,

Now a child of God, Saved thro' His Son.
Bore my sins, for me was cru - ci - fied.
Liv - ing now each mo - ment as His own.

Saved!
1917

And she will bring forth a Son, and you shall call His name JESUS, for He will save His people from their sins. Matthew 1:21

anadian Oswald J. Smith came to Christ as a teen during an evangelistic campaign by R. A. Torrey and Charles Alexander. He enrolled in Bible College at eighteeen to be a missionary, but was later turned down for service due to poor health. So he began preaching and writing hymns.

In his autobiography, he wrote, "Never will I forget the thrill that was mine when I saw the first printed copies of two of my hymns. It was in 1914 when I was twenty-four. The music was by Dr. D. B. Towner, and it was he who sent them to me. My whole being was electrified as I gazed at them. The ecstasy of that moment will never be erased. I was then in South Chicago. But in those early days only a few of my hymns ever really saw the light of day. I wrote scores, but for years it was a struggle with many discouraging experiences."

One of his earliest hymns was "Saved!" published in 1918. "It was born in Toronto in the year 1917," wrote Smith, "when I was twenty-seven. The music was written by Roger M. Hickman. Arthur W. McKee was the first to introduce it. To hear the great Massey Hall audience sing this hymn during the Paul Rader campaign was an experience never to be forgotten. It is known and sung throughout America."

> *Saved! I'm saved thro' Christ, my all in all;*
> *Saved! I'm saved whatever may befall;*
> *He died upon the cross for me,*
> *He bore the awful penalty;*
> *And now I'm saved eternally—*
> *I'm saved! Saved! Saved!*

As a hymn writer, Oswald Smith may have struggled for recognition, but as a pastor he made his mark. Having been rejected for overseas service, he started a church in 1928 in Toronto to send out missionaries. It was known as the Cosmopolitan Tabernacle (now the Peoples Church). It became one of the strongest churches in Canada and one of the greatest missionary churches in the world.

Later in life when his hymns became more widely used (including the popular songs, "Then Jesus Came" and "The Song of the Soul Set Free"), Smith wrote, "I have never written in a mechanical way just for the sake of writing. As I rule I wait until I am passing through some great crisis, and then I cannot help writing. And because they have been born out of personal experiences, they appeal to others."*

---

*Oswald J. Smith, *The Story of My Life* (London: Marshall, Morgan, & Scott, 1962), pp. 109–112.

Wonderful Grace of Jesus

Haldor Lillenas

Haldor Lillenas

1. Won-der-ful grace of Je - sus, Great-er than all my sin.
2. Won-der-ful grace of Je - sus, Reach-ing to all the lost.
3. Won-der-ful grace of Je - sus, Reach-ing the most de - filed.

How shall my tongue de - scribe it? Where shall its praise be - gin?
By it I have been par - doned, Saved to the ut - ter - most.
By its trans - form - ing pow - er Mak - ing Him God's dear child.

Tak - ing a - way my bur - den, Set - ting my spir - it free.
Chains have been torn a - sun - der, Giv - ing me lib - er - ty.
Pur - chas - ing peace and heav - en For all e - ter - ni - ty.

For the won - der - ful grace of Je - sus reach - es me.
For the won - der - ful grace of Je - sus reach - es me.
And the won - der - ful grace of Je - sus reach - es me.

Wonderful Grace of Jesus

<u>1918</u>

Through Him we have received grace . . . Romans 1:5a

Worship leaders around the world owe a debt of gratitude to Lillenas Publishing Company, which was started by the author of this hymn, Haldor Lillenas. He was born in the fjord district of Norway in 1885, and, as a child, immigrated to the United States with his family. From his youth, Haldor had a musical bent, a talent that served him well when he entered the ministry in 1910 in the newly established Church of the Nazarene.

Between his sermons and visits, Haldor took musical studies by correspondence and soon began writing gospel songs. In 1919, he published his first book, and three years later he organized his own publishing house in Indianapolis, Indiana, where he was serving as pastor of the First Church of the Nazarene. For the next decade, Haldor preached, traveled, wrote hymns, and published songbooks.

In 1930, the Nazarene Publishing House in Kansas City, Missouri, became interested in expanding its fledgling efforts in the field of music. They agreed to purchase Lillenas Publishing Company provided that Haldor himself would move to Kansas City and manage it. He remained in that role until he retired in 1950, then served in an advisory capacity until his death in Aspen, Colorado, in 1959. Today Lillenas Publishing Company is one of the largest church music publishers in the world, owning more than 20,000 song copyrights.

"Wonderful Grace of Jesus" is the best known of the 4,000 hymns Haldor himself wrote. He later gave this account of how it came to be composed:

In 1917, Mrs. Lillenas and I built our first little home in the town of Olivet, Illinois. Upon its completion, we had scarcely any money left to furnish the little home. Having no piano at the time, and needing an instrument of some kind, I managed to find, at one of the neighbor's home, a little wheezy organ which I purchased for $5.00. With the aid of this instrument, a number of my songs were written which are now popular, including "Wonderful Grace of Jesus." It was sung by the great chorus, in 1918, at the Northfield, Massachusetts Bible Conference, being introduced for the first time by Homer Hammontree.

Not yet having started his own publishing house, he sold his soon-to-be-famous hymn for $5.00—just enough to pay for the organ on which it was composed.

Lead Me to Calvary

Jennie Evelyn Hussey

William J. Kirkpatrick

1. King of my life, I crown Thee now, Thine shall the glo - ry be;
2. Show me the tomb where Thou wast laid, Ten - der - ly mourned and wept;
3. Let me, like Ma - ry, through the gloom, Come with a gift to Thee;
4. May I be will - ing, Lord, to bear, Dai - ly my cross for Thee;

Lest I for - get Thy thorn crowned brow, Lead me to Cal - va - ry.
An - gels in robes of light ar - rayed, Guard - ed Thee whilst Thou slept.
Show to me now the emp - ty tomb, Lead me to Cal - va - ry.
E - ven Thy cup of grief to share, Thou hast borne all for me.

Lest I for - get Geth - sem - a - ne, Lest I for - get Thine ag - o - ny,

Lest I for - get Thy love for me, Lead me to Cal - va - ry.

Lead Me to Calvary

1921

And when they had come to the place called Calvary, there they crucified Him . . .
Luke 23:33

J ennie Hussey was born in Henniker, New Hampshire, on February 8, 1874, and lived most of her life in a farmhouse where four generations of her Quaker ancestors had lived. Much of her time was devoted to her helpless, invalid sister, but Jennie wasn't known to complain or grumble. She displayed a cheerful personality. Whenever weary, she would open her Bible and turn to the story of Calvary, finding there fresh strength.

Jennie eventually became disabled with deformative arthritis, but her attitude remained positive. "Please, Lord," she said, "make me willing to bear my cross daily without complaining because you bore yours for me." It was out of that experience that she wrote "Lead Me to Calvary," with its last verse:

May I be willing, Lord, to bear daily my cross for Thee;
Even Thy cup of grief to share—Thou hast borne all for me.

When Jennie was baptized in the First Baptist Church of Concord, New Hampshire, she told the pastor, "I've spent so much of my life hidden away in the country, and I'd like to have the opportunity before God takes me home to tell everybody (that) I love Jesus." Her request was fulfilled in this famous hymn, along with approximately one hundred fifty others that she wrote.

Jennie spent her last years in the Home for the Aged in Concord, New Hampshire, and passed away in 1958. Her remains were taken the seventeen miles back to Henniker, where she was buried in the Quaker Cemetery.

There's an interesting P.S. to her story. Civil War buffs know Jennie Hussey as the author of a famous poem called "The War Dog." It's the true story of a stray mutt named Sallie who became attached to one of the soldiers from Pennsylvania and followed him into battle. When her master fell in battle, the dog refused to leave his body. Sallie was "adopted" as the mascot of the 11th Regiment of Pennsylvania Volunteers, and she stayed with her soldiers until she was shot and killed at the Battle of Hatcher's Run, Virginia, in 1864. A cast bronze replica of Sallie stands today in Gettysburg National Military Park.

Sallie was a lady; she was a soldier too—
She marched beside the colors, our own red, white, and blue.
It was in the days of our Civil War that she lived her life so true. . . .

Only Believe

Only Believe

1921

As soon as Jesus heard the word that was spoken, He said to the ruler of the synagogue, "Do not be afraid; only believe." Mark 5:36

W ritten very clearly upon my mind is the memory of the night I was converted when a boy of nine years," testified evangelist Paul Rader in a 1930s-era sermon at Chicago's Moody Memorial Church. Paul was traveling with his preacher-dad in Cheyenne, Wyoming, and a revival was in progress. "A few soldiers from a nearby fort were at the altar, and more grown folks, but no children," said Paul. But God was dealing mightily with the boy, and that evening back at their lodgings his father led him to Christ.

"The days I spent with my father as we traveled together while he preached to the men of the plains, hundreds of miles from any railroad, gave my soul a firm grasp of the simple gospel as he saw it," said Paul. "There came to me a great desire in those days to preach the gospel. . . ."

Paul enrolled in a university in Colorado. During class one day, a professor questioned the reliability of the Bible. "I stayed at the close of the class," Paul later said, "and with cutting sarcasm he gave me to understand that my simple faith in the Bible came from my ignorance."

Paul's crisis of faith eventually soured him to Scripture. "I then gave up and quit preaching. . . I vowed I would never preach again." Leaving school, Paul, who was a splendid athlete, became a boxer, then a boxing promoter, then the public relations agent for an oil company—but God wasn't through with him.

Sometime about 1912, "I was walking the streets of New York when God spoke to my heart in a tender pleading way, just as He used to do when I was a boy. I almost ran to my room and dropped on my knees beside the bed. . . . Three days and nights the fight with self lasted. At four on the third morning I took the splendid Bible given me . . . and threw it in the air above the bed, letting it light and settle into stillness. I had promised God that when the old Book became still on the bed I would give up and obey Him at any cost."

Paul Rader went on to become one of the most visionary, progressive, effective, and influential evangelists of the early twentieth century—and, appropriately, the author of:

Only believe, only believe;
All things are possible, only believe.

I'd Rather Have Jesus

Rhea F. Miller

George Beverly Shea

1. I'd rath-er have Je-sus than sil-ver or gold; I'd rath-er be
2. I'd rath-er have Je-sus than men's ap - plause; I'd rath-er be
3. He's fair-er than lil-ies of rar-est bloom; He's sweet-er than

His than have rich-es un-told; I'd rath-er have Je-sus than
faith-ful to His dear cause; I'd rath-er have Je-sus than
hon-ey from out the comb; He's all that my hun-ger-ing

hous - es or lands. I'd rath-er be led by His nail-pierced hand.
world-wide fame. I'd rath-er be true to His ho - ly name.
spi - rit needs. I'd rath-er have Je-sus and let Him lead.

Than to be the king of a vast do - main Or be held in sin's dread sway.

I'd rath-er have Je-sus than an-y-thing This world af-fords to-day.

I'd Rather Have Jesus

1922

For what profit is it to a man if he gains the whole world and loses his own soul?
Matthew 16:26a

George Beverly Shea, "America's beloved gospel singer," has traveled with the Billy Graham evangelistic team since 1946. He was born in 1909 in Winchester, Ontario, where his dad served as pastor of the Wesleyan Methodist Church. Bev's mother, the church organist, had a piano that came from England; and, seated in front of its keys, she became a sort of "human alarm clock" for the family. Every weekday morning, striking an E-flat chord, she would sing Eliza Hewitt's old song:

> *Singing I go along life's road, | Praising the Lord, praising the Lord,*
> *Singing I go along life's road, | For Jesus has lifted my load.*

On Sundays, she chose a different selection, Isaac Watts' hymn:

> *Lord, in the morning Thou shalt hear | My voice ascending high;*
> *To Thee will I direct my prayer, | To Thee lift up mine eye.*

When Bev was 21 he began working for the Mutual Insurance Company of New York, assisting medical examiners in obtaining information relating to the applicant's health history. Among those who came into the office was Fred Allen, host of a coast-to-coast radio talent show. Learning that Bev liked to sing, Mr. Allen arranged an audition, and a few weeks later Bev found himself singing "Go Down Moses" to a nationwide audience on the National Broadcasting Company. Though he lost the contest to a yodeler, he received fifteen dollars and a taste of widespread fame.

One Sunday shortly afterward, Bev sat down at his mother's organ to practice for the morning church service. His eyes fell on a clipping she had left for him there, a poem written in 1922 by Mrs. Rhea F. Miller. As Bev read the words, they spoke to him about his own aims and ambitions in life. An appropriate melody came easily, practically composing itself.

When Bev's mother came in from the kitchen, he played and sang it for her. Wrapping both arms around him, she placed a wet cheek against his. In church that morning, Bev sang "I'd Rather Have Jesus" publicly for the first time. It later became a sort of "signature song" expressing his own decisions in life.

> *I'd rather have Jesus than men's applause, | I rather be faithful to His dear cause;*
> *I'd rather have Jesus than worldwide fame, | I'd rather be true to His holy name . . .*

Turn Your Eyes Upon Jesus

Helen H. Lemmel

Helen H. Lemmel

1. O soul, are you wea-ry and trou-bled? No light in the
2. Thro' death in-to life ev-er-last-ing He passed, and we
3. His word shall not fail you He prom-ised; Be-lieve Him, and

dark-ness you see? There's light for a look at the Sav-ior, And
fol-low Him there; O-ver us sin no more hath do-min-ion For
all will be well; Then go to a world that is dy-ing, His

life more a-bun-dant and free!
more than con-qu'rors we are!
per-fect sal-va-tion to tell!

Turn your eyes up-on Je-sus,

Look full in His won-der-ful face, And the things of

earth Will grow strange-ly dim In the light of His glo-ry and grace.

Turn Your Eyes Upon Jesus

1922

. . . let us run with endurance the race set before us, looking unto Jesus, the author and finisher of our faith . . . Hebrews 12:1–2

Helen Howarth Lemmel was born in England in 1863, into the home of a Wesleyan minister who immigrated to America when Helen was a child. She loved music, and her parents provided the best vocal teachers they could find. Eventually Helen returned to Europe to study vocal music in Germany. In time, she married a wealthy European, but he left her when she became blind, and Helen struggled with multiple heartaches during midlife.

At age 55, Helen heard a statement that deeply impressed her: "So then, turn your eyes upon Him, look full into His face and you will find that the things of earth will acquire a strange new dimness."

"I stood still," Helen later said, "and singing in my soul and spirit was the chorus, with not one conscious moment of putting word to word to make rhyme, or note to note to make melody. The verses were written the same week, after the usual manner of composition, but nonetheless dictated by the Holy Spirit."

Pastor Doug Goins of Palo Alto, California, and his parents, Paul and Kathryn Goins, both 82, of Sun City, Arizona, knew Helen in Seattle. "She was advanced in years and almost destitute, but she was an amazing person," said Doug. "She made a great impression on me as a junior high child because of her joy and enthusiasm. Though she was living on government assistance in a sparse bedroom, whenever we'd ask how she was doing, she would reply, 'I'm doing well in the things that count.'"

One day, the Goins invited her to supper. "We had never entertained a blind person before," recalled Kathryn, "and it was interesting. Despite her infirmities, she was full of life. I remember how amused we were when, following supper, she said, 'Now if you will lead me to the bathroom, I'll sit on the throne and reign.'"

"But she was always composing hymns," said Kathryn. "She had no way of writing them down, so she would call my husband at all hours and he'd rush down and record them before she forgot the words."

Helen had a small plastic keyboard by her bed. There she would play, sing, and cry. "One day God is going to bless me with a great heavenly keyboard," she'd say. "I can hardly wait!"

Helen Lemmel, who wrote nearly 500 hymns during her lifetime, died in Seattle in 1961, thirteen days before her 98th birthday.

Great Is Thy Faithfulness

Thomas O. Chisholm

William M. Runyan

1. Great is Thy faith - ful - ness, O God my Fa - ther,
2. Sum - mer and win - ter And spring-time and har - vest,
3. Par - don for sin And a peace that en - dur - eth,

There is no shad - ow Of turn - ing with Thee;
Sun, moon and stars In their cours - es a - bove;
Thine own dear pres - ence To cheer and to guide;

Thou chang - est not, Thy com - pas - sions they fail not;
Join with all na - ture In man - i - fold wit - ness
Strength for to - day And bright hope for to - mor - row,

As Thou hast been Thou for - ev - er wilt be.
To Thy great faith - ful - ness, Mer - cy and love.
Bless - ings all mine, With ten thou - sand be - side!

Great Is Thy Faithfulness

1923

Your mercy, O LORD, is in the heavens; your faithfulness reaches to the clouds.
Psalm 36:5

The author of this hymn, Thomas Obediah Chisholm, was born in a log cabin in Kentucky. At age 16, he began teaching school, despite the paucity of his own education. He came to Christ at age 27 under the ministry of evangelist H. C. Morrison. But Chisholm's health was unstable, and he alternated between bouts of illness and gainful employment in which he did everything from journalism to insurance to evangelistic work. Through all the ups and downs, he discovered new blessings from God every morning. The third chapter of Lamentations 3 became precious to him: *His compassions fail not. They are new every morning; Great is Your faithfulness* (Lamentations 3:22–23).

Thomas later admitted there was no dramatic story behind the writing of "Great is Thy Faithfulness." While serving the Lord in Vineland, New Jersey, Thomas sent several poems to his friend, musician William Runyan, who was so moved by this one that he prayed earnestly for special guidance in composing the music. Runyan was in Baldwin, Kansas, at the time, and the hymn was published in 1923 in Runyan's private song pamphlets.

"It went rather slowly for several years," Thomas recalled. Then Dr. Will Houghton of the Moody Bible Institute of Chicago discovered it, and would say in chapel, "Well, I think we shall have to sing 'Great is Thy Faithfulness." It became an unofficial theme song for the Institute; and when Houghton died, it was sung at his funeral.

Still, it remained relatively unknown until popularized around the world by George Beverly Shea and the choirs at the Billy Graham Crusades.

Thomas spent his retirement years in a Methodist Home for the Aged in Ocean Park, New Jersey, where he was frequently seen walking by the ocean and along town streets. Tom Rich, a resident of Ocean Park, recalls his pleasant demeanor as he dropped by the diner, sat on park benches, and fellowshipped with friends at Ocean Park's summer Bible conferences.

Thomas died in Ocean Park in 1960. During his lifetime he wrote 1,200 poems and hymns. In addition to "Great is Thy Faithfulness," he is the author of the well-known "O To Be Like Thee," and the hymn, "Living for Jesus."

Living for Jesus, a life that is true,
Striving to please Him in all that I do;
Yielding allegiance, glad hearted and free,
This is the pathway of blessing for me.

In My Heart There Rings a Melody

Elton M. Roth

Elton M. Roth

1. I have a song that Je-sus gave me, It was sent from heav'n a-bove; There nev-er was a sweet-er mel-o-dy, 'Tis a mel-o-dy of love.
2. I love the Christ who died on Cal-v'ry, For He washed my sins a-way; He put with-in my heart a mel-o-dy, And I know it's there to stay.
3. 'Twill be my end-less theme in glo-ry, With the an-gels I will sing; 'Twill be a song with glo-rious har-mo-ny, When the courts of heav-en ring.

In my heart there rings a mel-o-dy, There rings a mel-o-dy with heav-en's har-mo-ny; In my heart there rings a mel-o-dy, There rings a mel-o-dy of love.

In My Heart There Rings a Melody

1923

Let the word of Christ dwell in you richly in all wisdom, teaching and admonishing one another in psalms and hymns and spiritual songs, singing with grace in your hearts to the Lord. Colossians 3:16

The great evidence of being "Spirit-filled" is singing, according to Ephesians 5:18, 19: "Be filled with the Spirit, speaking to one another in psalms and hymns and spiritual songs, singing and making melody in your heart to the Lord." That's the theme of this happy little gospel chorus with its irresistible melody. It's been a favorite for many years around the world.

Its author, Elton Menno Roth, was born during the Thanksgiving season of 1891. He led his first church choir when he was only fourteen. After attending Moody Bible Institute and Fort Wayne Bible School in his native state of Indiana, he studied music in Europe. Elton became a singing evangelist and song leader for evangelistic meetings. In the 1930s, he formed a popular singing group called the Ecclesia Choir that performed across the country. He was also a noted instructor of music at a number of Christian schools and colleges. Los Angeles became his home in his latter years, and he passed away there at age sixty on the last day of 1951.

"I Have a Song That Jesus Gave Me" was one of the first of the one hundred or so hymns written by Elton Roth. He composed this hymn in 1923 while conducting evangelistic meetings in Texas. "One hot summer afternoon," he wrote, "I took a little walk to the cotton mill just outside of town. On my way back through the burning streets . . . I became weary with the oppressive heat, and paused at a church on the corner. The door being open, I went in. There were no people in the pews, no minister in the pulpit. Everything was quiet, with a lingering of the sacred presence. I walked up and down the aisle and began singing, 'In My Heart There Rings a Melody,' then hurried into the pastor's study to find some paper. I drew a staff and sketched the melody, remaining there for an hour or more to finish the song, both words and music. That evening I introduced it by having over two hundred boys and girls sing it at the open-air meeting, after which the audience joined in the singing. I was thrilled as it seemed my whole being was transformed by the song."

Little Is Much When God Is in It

Kittie Louise Suffield

Kittie Louise Suffield

1. In the har-vest field now rip-ened, There's a work for all to do;
2. Does the place you're called to la-bor Seem so small and lit-tle known?
3. When the con-flict here is end-ed And our race on earth is run;

Hark, the voice of God is call-ing, To the har-vest call-ing you.
It is great if God is in it And He'll not for-get His own.
He will say if we are faith-ful, Wel-come home, My child well done.

Lit-tle is much when God is in it, La-bor not for wealth or fame;

There's a crown and you can win it, If you go in Je-sus' name.

Little Is Much When God Is in It

c. 1924

A little one shall become a thousand, and a small one a strong nation. I the LORD, will hasten it in its time. Isaiah 60:22

One snow-blanketed night, Canadian Fred Suffield awoke to an urgent pounding on his door. A half-frozen man reported that a train had stalled in the blizzard, and the passengers were in danger of freezing to death. Lighting a lantern, Fred followed the man to the site and led the travelers back to his house. Later one of the passengers, Kittie, wrote a thank you note. Fred replied, and Kittie wrote back. Their correspondence led to courtship and to marriage.

Some time later, Fred and Kittie attended a church in Ottawa pastored by Rev. A. J. Shea, and there they gave their lives to the Lord. As the couple grew in Christ, they entered the ministry of evangelism. One summer they invited Shea's teenage son, George Beverly, to spend a month with them in Westport, Ontario, holding evangelistic meetings. One night, accompanied by Kittie on the piano, Bev attempted to sing, but his voice cracked on the high notes, and he sat down mortified, vowing never to sing again.

Kittie wouldn't hear of it, suggesting he sing in a lower key. He did, and he kept on singing, and singing, and singing.

Many years passed, and in June of 2000, Billy Graham came to Nashville, Tennessee, for a four-night mission. My wife and I were privileged to attend a reception for the Graham team just before the meetings began, and George Beverly Shea, 92 at the time, rose to sing. His rich baritone voice broke into a song that had been written 73 years before by Fred and Kittie: "Little Is Much When God Is in It."

I thought it a strange choice of hymn. We were on the verge of the greatest evangelistic effort in Nashville's history, headlined by the most famous evangelist in the world. And Bev Shea's song was about the littleness of our efforts. But later I realized how perfectly the song fit. Compared to this great mission to untold multitudes, our own individual ministries seemed small and insignificant. But God uses little things in great ways. A tiny acorn may produce a forest. A spark may ignite a revival. A small church might produce the next far-famed evangelist.

Don't be discouraged if your place seems small. You're doing more good than you know.

Jesus Is the Sweetest Name I Know

Lela B. Long

Lela B. Long

1. There have been names that I have loved to hear, But nev-er has there
2. There is no name in earth or heav'n a-bove, That we should give such
3. And some day I shall see Him face to face To thank and praise Him

been a name so dear To this heart of mine as the name di-vine, The
hon-or and such love As the bless-ed name; let us all ac-claim That
for His won-drous grace Which He gave to me when He made me free; The

pre-cious, pre-cious name of Je-sus.
won-drous, glo-rious name of Je-sus. Je-sus is the sweet-est name I
bless-ed Son of God called Je-sus.

know, And He's just the same as His love-ly name, And that's the rea-son

why I love Him so; O Je-sus is the sweet-est name I know.

Jesus Is the Sweetest Name I Know

1924

Repent, and let every one of you be baptized in the name of Jesus Christ for the remission of sins; and you shall receive the gift of the Holy Spirit. Acts 2:38

We're indebted to gospel songwriter and historian, Al Smith, for the story of this hymn by Lela B. Long. Smith collected it firsthand from Dr. P. W. Philpot, who told him:

"While I was pastor of Moody Church in Chicago, I received a frantic phone call about 2 o'clock in the morning from the Stephens Hotel. The voice on the line pleaded with me to come, for a young lady was very ill and very disturbed. At the hotel I found a very sick young lady who from outward appearances did not have long to live. I spent some time talking with her and was eventually able to lead her to the Lord. As I left, her family thanked me and assured me they would keep me informed as to her progress. Late the next day, having not heard from them and anxious to know how she was, I phoned the hotel and was informed that they had checked out and were en route to California, which was their home. For the remaining years of my stay in Chicago, I did not again receive any communication from them. I then moved to California where I became pastor of the Church of the Open Door in Los Angeles.

"One Sunday afternoon after the service, who should come to see me but the three people I had met at the hotel in Chicago those many years before. They told me that their leaving Chicago had been so sudden they had forgotten to advise me. That past week they had seen a church ad in the paper and had come to thank me for my help and to apologize for not advising me sooner of what had transpired. The young lady especially thanked me for leading her to Christ and testified to the fact that her life had been wonderfully changed and that now she was using a special talent the Lord had given her in music, for Him. The talent was writing gospel songs. With that she handed me a manuscript of a new song saying, 'I have written this especially for you in remembrance of the day that you introduced me to the most wonderful person I have ever known.' As I opened the manuscript I saw a beautifully written song she had titled, 'Jesus Is the Sweetest Name I Know.'"*

---

*Condensed from Alfred B. Smith's *Treasury of Hymn Histories*.

Precious Lord, Take My Hand

Thomas A. Dorsey

George N. Allen

1. Pre - cious Lord, take my hand, Lead me on, help me
2. When my way grows drear, Pre - cious Lord, lin - ger

stand; I am tired, I am weak, I am worn;
near; When my life is al - most gone,

Thru the storm, thru the night, Lead me on to the
Hear my cry, hear my call, Hold my hand lest I

light, Take my hand, pre-cious Lord, lead me home.
fall; Take my hand, pre-cious Lord, lead me home.

Precious Lord, Take My Hand

1932

Be strong and of good courage, do not fear nor be afraid of them; for the LORD your God, He is the One who goes with you. He will not leave you nor forsake you.
Deuteronomy 31:6

Some people think this great old gospel song was written by the famous big bandleader Tommy Dorsey. It wasn't; the author was named Thomas Andrew Dorsey, and he was the son of a Black revivalist preacher.

Thomas was born in a small town in Georgia in 1899. When he was about eleven, the Dorseys moved to Atlanta where Thomas was quickly enamoured with the blues and began playing piano at a vaudeville theater. Later the family moved to Chicago where he attended classes at the College of Composition and Arranging. Soon he was on stage under the name "Georgia Tom," playing barrelhouse piano in one of Al Capone's Chicago speakeasies and leading jazz bands.

Thomas was converted at the National Baptist Convention in Chicago in 1921, and began writing gospel songs and trying to get them published. It was discouraging at first. He later said, "I borrowed five dollars and sent out 500 copies of my song, 'If You See My Savior,' to churches throughout the country . . . It was three years before I got a single order. I felt like going back to the blues."

He didn't, and gradually his reputation grew and his work became known.

In August, 1932, while leading music in St. Louis, he was handed a telegram bearing the words, "Your wife just died." He rushed to a phone to call home, but all he could hear over the line was "Nettie is dead! Nettie is dead!" A friend drove him through the night, and he arrived home to learn that his baby boy had also died.

"I began to feel that God had done me an injustice," Thomas later said. "I didn't want to serve Him anymore or write any more gospel songs." But the next Saturday, while alone in a friend's music room, he had a "strange feeling" inside—a sudden calm and a quiet stillness. "As my fingers began to manipulate over the keys, words began to fall in place on the melody like drops of water falling from the crevice of the rock:

Precious Lord, take my hand
Lead me on, let me stand
I am tired, I am weak, I am worn . . ."

Today Thomas A. Dorsey is remembered as the "Father of Gospel Music" and the author of hundreds of gospel songs including his equally famous, "Peace in the Valley."

I'll Fly Away

Albert E. Brumley

Albert E. Brumley

I'll Fly Away

1932

Therefore you now have sorrow; but I will see you again and your heart will rejoice, and your joy no one will take from you. John 16:22

I *could* tell you this old Southern hymn was written by a sacred soul on his knees with Psalm 90 open before him: "The days of our lives are seventy years; and if by reason of strength they are eighty years, yet their boast is only labor and sorrow; for it is soon cut off, and we fly away."

The truth, however, is a little plainer.

Albert E. Brumley was born on a cotton farm near Spiro, Oklahoma, in 1905. The medium of radio was gaining popularity as he grew up, and one of the most requested songs was a sad ballad called "If I Had the Wings of an Angel" which said:

> *Now if I had the wings of an angel,*
> *Over these prison walls I would fly,*
> *I'd fly to the arms of my poor darling,*
> *And there I'd be willing to die.*

One hot Oklahoma day, Albert was in the fields picking cotton and singing this song. The thought of flying away suddenly seemed quite appealing to him, and he began composing "I'll Fly Away" on the spot. "I was dreaming of flying away from that cotton field when I wrote 'I'll Fly Away,'" he later said. The middle verse of Albert's song echoes the old prison ballad when it says:

> *When the shadows of this life have grown, I'll fly away;*
> *Like a bird from prison bars has flown, I'll fly away.*

Of course, "I'll Fly Away" is about far more than escaping cotton fields. It expressed Brumley's personal hope of eternal life through Jesus Christ. It was one of a number of gospel songs he wrote during those days, but all of them were stashed away in drawers and boxes, unpublished.

Two years later, Albert married Goldie Schell, whom he met while teaching a singing school in Powell, Missouri. With her encouragement, Albert mailed "I'll Fly Away" to the Hartford Music Company. It was published in 1932, and shortly afterward, Albert was hired by Hartford for $12.50 a month. He spent thirty-four years writing for the Hartford and Stamps/Baxter companies before forming the Albert E. Brumley & Sons Music Company. In all, Albert wrote over eight hundred songs and became one of the most respected names in the development of twentieth-century Southern gospel music.

He Lives

Alfred H. Ackley

Alfred H. Ackley

1. I serve a ris-en Sav-ior. He's in the world to-day.
2. In all the world a-round me I see His lov-ing care;
3. Re-joice, re-joice, O Chris-tian. lift up your voice and sing.

I know that He is liv-ing; what-ev-er men may say.
And tho' my heart grows wea-ry I nev-er will de-spair.
E-ter-nal hal-le-lu-jahs to Je-sus Christ the King.

I see His hand of mer-cy. I hear His voice of cheer,
I know that He is lead-ing thro' all the storm-y blast.
The hope of all who seek Him, the help of all who find.

And just the time I need Him. He's al-ways near.
The day of His ap-pear-ing will come at last.
None oth-er is so lov-ing, So good and kind.

A. H. Ackley

He Lives

1933

He is not here; for He is risen, as He said. Matthew 28:6a

W hy should I worship a dead Jew?" That question—and a dreadful sermon—inspired this hymn.

Alfred Henry Ackley was born in Pennsylvania in 1887.* He showed great promise as a child, and his musician-father personally tutored him before sending him to New York City to study music. From there, it was on to the Royal Academy of Music in London. Alfred then returned to the States to attend Westminster Seminary in Maryland, and he was ordained into the Presbyterian ministry in 1914. After pastoring a church in his home state of Pennsylvania, Alfred was called to a congregation in California.

It was there in 1932, that Alfred met a Jewish man to whom he began witnessing. But the man resisted the Christian faith, saying, "Why should I worship a dead Jew?"

That statement played on Alfred's mind as he prepared his Easter Sunday message. Rising early to prepare for the day, Alfred flipped on the radio as he shaved and was astonished to hear a famous liberal preacher in New York say: "Good morning—it's Easter! You know, folks, it really doesn't make any difference to me if Christ be risen or not. As far as I am concerned, His body could be as dust in some Palestinian tomb. The main thing is, His truth goes marching on!"

Alfred wanted to fling the radio across the room. "It's a lie!" he exclaimed. His wife rushed into the bathroom, asking, "Why are you shouting so early in the morning?"

"Didn't you hear what that good-for-nothing preacher said?" Alfred replied.

That morning, Ackley preached with great vigor on the reality of Christ's Resurrection, and he did the same at the evening service. But later that night, he was still exercised over his friend's question and the morning's radio sermon. "Listen here, Alfred Ackley," his wife said at last. "It's time you did that which you can do best. Why don't you write a song about it and then maybe you'll feel better?"

Alfred went to his study, opened the Bible, and re-read the Resurrection account from Mark's Gospel. A thrill went through him, and he began writing the words to "He Lives." A few minutes later, he was at the piano putting it to music, not dreaming it would become one of the church's most triumphant Easter hymns.

---

*Alfred's older brother, Bentley, was also a renowned gospel songwriter who traveled with the Billy Sunday/Homer Rodeheaver evangelistic team as pianist. Bentley later became a composer and editor with the Rodeheaver Publishing Company, writing over 3,000 hymns and gospel songs.

Beyond the Sunset

Virgil P. Brock

Blanche Kerr Brock

1. Be-yond the sun-set, O bliss-ful morn-ing, When with our
2. Be-yond the sun-set, no clouds will gath-er, No storms will
3. Be-yond the sun-set a hand will guide me, To God the
4. Be-yond the sun-set, O glad re-un-ion, With our dear

Sav - ior, heav'n is be - gun. Earth's toil-ing end - ed, O glo - rious
threat-en, no fears an - noy. O day of glad-ness, O day un -
Fa - ther, whom I a - dore. His glo-rious pres-ence, His words of
loved ones who've gone be - fore. In that fair home-land, we'll know no

dawn - ing. Be - yond the sun - set, when day is done.
end - ing, Be - yond the sun - set, e - ter - nal joy.
wel - come, Will be my por - tion on that fair shore.
part - ing, Be - yond the sun - set for - ev - er - more.

Beyond the Sunset

1936

And God will wipe away every tear from their eyes; there shall be no more death, nor sorrow, nor crying. There shall be no more pain, for the former things have passed away. Revelation 21:4

Homer Rodeheaver's name will live as long as gospel music is sung. He began his career as song director for the Billy Sunday campaigns, then went on to establish a publishing company that produced hundreds of the era's most popular gospel songs. Both Billy Sunday and Homer Rodeheaver settled down in beautiful Winona Lake, Indiana, home of a renowned Bible conference center and seminary. The Rodeheavers built an expansive home on Rainbow Point which became a center of fellowship for Christians traveling through the area.

During the summer of 1936, the Rodeheaver School of Music was in session at Winona Lake Bible Conference, and "Rody" invited all the faculty members to Rainbow Point for the evening. Among them were the well-known Christian musicians, Virgil Brock and his wife, Blanche Kerr Brock.

On this particular evening, the sunset was fabulous. As the faculty members talked about the splendor of the setting sun against the lake, one of them—a blind man named Horace Burr, Virgil's cousin—exclaimed, "My, that sure is a wonderful sunset. Thanks so much for picturing it for me. I would have missed a lot if you folks hadn't been here to describe it."

When someone commented on Horace's "seeing," he replied, "I *can* see. I see through other people's eyes, and I think I often see more; I see beyond the sunset."

By and by the conversation shifted to the subject of heaven. Someone asked if we can really visualize what lies beyond death's door. Recalling Horace's words, Virgil replied, "Horace Burr has never seen the glory of an earthly sunset, yet was blessed as we tried to describe it to him. In the same way we, as Christians, have never seen what is beyond, but God in His love and promise has told us in the Bible of the glory that is awaiting us beyond the sunset."

Back in their own lodgings later that evening, Virgil and Blanche re-lived the evening. Sitting down together at an old piano, they began putting together words and music. "To us it seemed as if a bright light of truth had streamed into our hearts and lives and had become a song," Virgil later said.

The song was completed that evening and dedicated to Horace and Grace Burr.

Search Me, O God

J. Edwin Orr

Maori Melody

1. Search me, O God, and know my heart to-day;
2. I praise Thee, Lord, for cleans-ing me from sin;
3. Lord, take my life, and make it whol-ly Thine;
4. O Ho-ly Ghost, re-vi-val comes from Thee;

Try me, O Sav-ior, know my thoughts, I pray.
Ful-fill Thy Word, and make me pure with-in.
Fill my poor heart with Thy great love di-vine.
Send a re-vi-val, start the work in me.

See if there be some wick-ed way in me;
Fill me with fire where once I burned with shame;
Take all my will, my pas-sion, self and pride;
Thy Word de-clares Thou wilt sup-ply our need;

Cleanse me from ev-ery sin and set me free.
Grant my de-sire to mag-ni-fy Thy name.
I now sur-ren-der, Lord in me a-bide.
For bless-ings now, O Lord, I hum-bly plead.

Arranged by Mark Hill

Search Me, O God

1936

Search me, O God, and know my heart; Try me, and know my anxieties; And see if there is any wicked way in me, and lead me in the way everlasting. Psalm 139:23–24

When I was a student at Columbia International University in South Carolina, a small, peppery, gray-haired Irishman came to lecture. He was brisk and plain-spoken, and his subject was revival. J. Edwin Orr had studied the history of revivals like no one else; as it happened, I had just read one of his many books on the subject.

When I requested an appointment, he agreed to see me in the lobby of the men's dormitory. Perhaps it was his shyness, but he seemed uncomfortable chatting with me. Instead of looking in my direction and engaging in conversation, he gazed straight ahead and answered my questions with short replies. After several fruitless exchanges, I decided to ask him one last thing.

"Dr. Orr, besides praying for revival, what can I do to help bring it about?" Without a moment's pause, he glanced in my direction gave me an answer I've never forgotten: "You can let it begin with you."

That was exactly the point of this hymn, which he had written years before, in 1936, during an intense springtime revival convention in the town of Ngaruawahia, on the North Island of New Zealand. There had been an attitude of unusual expectancy about the meetings, and prayer meetings proliferated across the city. Many students were coming to Christ, and the area began overflowing with the testimonies of those being saved and renewed in Christ.

One day Dr. Orr heard four Aborigine girls sing a beautiful song entitled, "The Song of Farewell," the first words being, "Now is the hour when we must say good-bye." Unable to get the lovely Polynesian tune out of his mind, Dr. Orr began singing it to himself using words from Psalm 139. These words he jotted down on the back of an envelope while standing in the post office at Ngaruawahia, and they were first published in his book, *All You Need*.

⌒

While this is a wonderful hymn to sing, it is a "dangerous" prayer to offer. We all have sins within us of which we're unaware, for the heart is deceitful above all things. But as we submit ourselves to the searchlight of God's Spirit, we can discover the habits that need to be confessed and the attitudes that need to be changed. As God cleanses us, the result will be . . . revival, one that begins with us.

Wherever He Leads, I'll Go

B. B. McKinney

B. B. McKinney

1. "Take up Thy cross and fol-low Me," I heard my Mas-ter say; "I
2. He drew me clos-er to His side, I sought His will to know, And
3. It may be through the shad-ows dim, Or o'er the storm-y sea, I
4. My heart, my life, my all I bring To Christ who loves me so; He

gave my life to ran-som Thee, Sur-ren-der your all to-day." Wher-
in that will I now a-bide; Wher-ev-er He leads, I'll go.
take my cross and fol-low Him Wher-ev-er He lead-eth me.
is my Mas-ter, Lord, and King, Wher-ev-er He leads I'll go.

ev-er He leads, I'll go, Wher-ev-er He leads, I'll go, I'll

fol-low my Christ who loves me so; Wher-ev-er He leads, I'll go.

Wherever He Leads, I'll Go

1936

Then he said to them all: "If anyone would come after me, he must deny himself and take up his cross daily and follow me." Luke 9:23 (NIV)

The twentieth century produced no greater hymnist than Baylus Benjamin Mc-Kinney, who wrote such classics as: "Breathe on Me," "Have Faith in God," "Send a Great Revival," "Satisfied with Jesus," "Lord, Lay Some Soul Upon My Heart," "Let Others See Jesus in You," and "The Nail-Scarred Hand."

McKinney was born in Heflin, Louisiana during the summer of 1886. He attended Southwestern Baptist Theological Seminary and after further training in music, he returned to the seminary as a member of the music faculty. When the Great Depression sent the seminary into financial crisis, McKinney resigned to serve as assistant pastor of the Travis Avenue Baptist Church in Fort Worth.

In 1935, McKinney was named music editor for the Baptist Sunday School Board of the Southern Baptist Convention. In January of the following year, he traveled to Clanton, Alabama, to participate in the Alabama Sunday School Convention, where he led the music. The featured speaker at the meetings was his good friend, R. S. Jones, missionary to Brazil. Late one afternoon as the two men had supper together, Jones told McKinney that the doctors were forbidding him from returning to Brazil. His health wouldn't allow it.

McKinney's heart went out to his friend, and he asked if Jones had any idea what he'd do now. "I don't know," said Jones, "but wherever He leads I'll go." It was a sentence that lingered in McKinney's mind. Returning to his hotel, McKinney sat down and wrote the words and music of this hymn before leaving for the convention session that night. After Jones had preached, McKinney told the audience of their earlier conversation, and handing a copy of the music to the organist, he sang it as a solo for the first time.

> *Wherever He leads, I'll go,*
> *Wherever He leads I'll go;*
> *I'll follow my Christ who loves me so;*
> *Wherever He leads I'll go.*

For the next several years, McKinney traveled widely among Southern Baptists, promoting the ministry of Christian music and leading singing in churches and conventions. On Sunday, September 7, 1952, McKinney left a conference in Ridgecrest, North Carolina, heading for Gatlinburg, Tennessee. Near Bryson City, North Carolina, he was killed in a car wreck.

He left behind a wife, two sons, several brothers, and a legacy of hundreds of hymns.

It Took a Miracle

John W. Peterson

John W. Peterson

1. My Father is om-nip-o-tent, And that you can't de-ny;
2. Though here His glo-ry has been shown, We still can't ful-ly see
3. The Bi-ble tells us of His pow'r And wis-dom all way through,

A God of might and mir-a-cles; 'Tis writ-ten in the sky.
The won-ders of His might, His throne; 'Twill take e-ter-ni-ty.
And ev-ery lit-tle bird and flow'r Are tes-ti-mo-nies, too.

It took a mir-a-cle to put the stars in place; It took a mir-a-cle to hang the world in space. But when He saved my soul, Cleansed and made me whole, It took a mir-a-cle of love and grace.

It Took a Miracle

1948

He is the Maker of the Bear and Orion, the Pleiades and the constellations of the south. He performs wonders that cannot be fathomed, miracles that cannot be counted. Job 9:9, 10 (NIV)

John W. Peterson's life reads like a novel. He was born in Kansas, where his brothers, Bill and Bob, lived a wild and dangerous life of "boozing, gambling, fast driving, and sheriff-baiting."

Then one night Bill came home, took his mother in his arms, kissed her, and said, "Mother, I have found your Christ as my Savior." The change in him was immediate and dramatic. Soon Bob, too, was saved along with other members of the family. Then John, twelve, gave his heart to Christ as well. The brothers became traveling evangelists, and John often joined them on their trips, singing at the meetings.

When World War II began, John joined the Air Force and became a pilot, who repeatedly risked his life while transporting men and materials over the fabled "China Hump." In his spare time he studied the Bible and wrote gospel songs. When the war ended, John enrolled in the Moody Bible Institute of Chicago.

"I sat in a classroom at Moody one day when the lecturer said something that started me thinking in a concentrated way about the grace and love of God. . . . Soon I lost contact with the lecture, and my mind turned back to my childhood when I had seen the radical change in the lives of my brothers Bob and Bill through the power of the gospel. I relived my own conversion—to me such a miraculous thing. . . .

"My thoughts raced on to the flights over the Himalayas, the spectacular power of God revealed in those electrical storms, the majesty of the mountains themselves, the incredible variety of the jungle, and the star-filled nights of dazzling beauty high in the air.

"As these scenes flashed through my memory, I began to focus on the element of the miraculous in all of God's work, creation, and redemption. The words of a song were forming in my mind, and before the class period was over the chorus was all thought out. I hurried over to the music building, found a vacant studio, and started to write:

> *It took a miracle to put the stars in place;*
> *It took a miracle to hang the world in space;*
> *But when he saved my soul,*
> *Cleansed and made me whole,*
> *It took a miracle of love and grace!*"*

---

*Adapted from *The Miracle Goes On* by John W. Peterson with Richard Engquist (Grand Rapids: Zondervan, 1976), pp. 54–62 and 143–144.

It Is No Secret

Stuart Hamblen

Stuart Hamblen

It is no se-cret what God can do.

What He's done for oth-ers, He'll do for you.

With arms wide o-pen, He'll par-don you,

It is no se-cret what God can do.

WARNER BROS. PUBLICATIONS U.S. INC., Miami FL 33014

It Is No Secret

<u>1949</u>

For whoever calls on the name of the Lord shall be saved. Romans 10:13

Though the 1949 Los Angeles Crusade was to launch Billy Graham to worldwide fame, the meetings appeared to get off to a slow start. Arriving in Los Angeles before the crusade, Mr. Graham gave a news conference, then eagerly waited for the next day to see how the crusade would be publicized. Not a single newspaper carried the story.

But among the supporters Graham *did* have was the influential Presbyterian Bible teacher Henrietta Mears, who invited Billy to her home in Beverly Hills to speak to a group of Hollywood personalities. Present that day was a hard-drinking star of cowboy westerns named Stuart Hamblen who also hosted one of the most popular afternoon radio shows on the West Coast. He was infamous for his gambling and brawling.

The two men took a liking to each other, and Billy longed to win Stuart to Christ. But as the three-week campaign neared its end, there was no sign that the big cowboy was under conviction.

Sensing that momentum for the meetings was building, the local crusade organizers wanted to extend them; but Billy was hesitant, having never done that before. He put out a "fleece," and asked God for a sign. The next morning at 4:30, he was awakened in his room at the Langham Hotel by a phone call. It was Stuart Hamblen, and he was in tears. Billy woke his wife and friends, who gathered in another room to pray while Stuart and his wife, Suzy, drove to the hotel. That night, Stuart gave his heart to the Lord Jesus.

It was the sign Billy needed to extend the meetings.

Meanwhile, Stuart excitedly told the story of his conversion on his radio show, and the local newspapers picked up the story. Soon all of Los Angeles was buzzing about the Billy Graham meetings. The resulting publicity launched a half-century of mass evangelism virtually unparalleled in Christian history.

Shortly afterward, Stuart Hamblen reportedly met movie star John Wayne on a street in Los Angeles. "What's this I hear about you, Stuart?" asked the actor.

"Well, Duke, it's no secret what God can do."

"Sounds like a song," said John. Stuart went home, sat down at his piano and wrote "It Is No Secret." He went on to write 225 other songs before his death in 1989.

His Name Is Wonderful

Audrey Mieir

Audrey Mieir

His name is Won-der-ful, His name is Won-der-ful, His name is Won-der-ful,

Je-sus, my Lord; He is the Might-y King, Mas-ter of ev-'ry-thing;

His name is Won-der-ful, Je-sus, my Lord. He's the Great Shep-herd, The Rock of all

ag - es, Al-might-y God is He. Bow down be - fore Him, Love and a-

dore Him, His name is Won - der - ful, Je - sus my Lord.

His Name Is Wonderful

1959

Therefore God also has highly exalted Him and given Him the name which is above every name. Philippians 2:9

T his song was born in a small church. In an era when bigger is better and success is usually measured by statistics, it's important to remember that small churches can still do great things.

Audrey Mae Mieir born on May 12, 1916, and attended L.I.F.E. Bible College. After marrying Charles B. Mieir in 1936, she was ordained to the Gospel ministry in the International Church of the Foursquare Gospel.

Audrey was a gifted pianist and an inspiring worship leader, song director, and choral clinician. In the 1950s, she was working in her brother-in-law's church, Bethel Union Church in Duarte, California, a suburb of Los Angeles. Christmas fell on Sunday that year, and the church was decorated with pine boughs. The choir loft was now a manger scene, and the young people had worked hard on the performance.

"As the morning service began," Audrey later said, "I was almost overwhelmed with the fragrance, the sounds, and most of all, with the gentle moving of the Spirit in that church. The pastor stood to his feet, opened the Bible, and said, 'His name shall be called Wonderful.' I tell you the truth, that's all it took. I wrote the words and music in the flyleaf of my Bible. In the Sunday evening service, I taught the chorus to a group of young people, and it was sung for the first time."

But Audrey had only written the first part of the song, and though it was well-received, it needed more. A friend told her, "Audrey, it's a good song but there just isn't enough of it. Maybe you could write a bridge for it." Audrey went to lunch that day with her friend's advice ringing in her ears. She ordered a hamburger, opened her Bible, and found a list of names given to Jesus in the Scripture. She jotted some of them down on her napkin. After returning to her office, Audrey went to the piano and began writing: "He's the great Shepherd, the Rock of all ages, Almighty God is He . . . ."

Though it was inspired on Christmas day by a traditional Christmas text, "His Name Is Wonderful" has never been pegged as a Christmas hymn. It's been a favorite of Christians around the world throughout the year.

Heaven Came Down

John W. Peterson   John W. Peterson

1. O what a won-der-ful, won-der-ful day, Day I will nev-er for-
2. Born of the Spir-it with life from a-bove In-to God's fam-ily di-
3. Now I've a hope that will sure-ly en-dure Af-ter the pass-ing of

get;   Af-ter I'd wan-dered in dark-ness a-way, Je-sus, my
vine,   Jus-ti-fied ful-ly thro' Cal-va-ry's love, O what a
time;   I have a fu-ture in heav-en for sure, There in those

Sav-ior I met.   O what a ten-der, com-pas-sion-ate friend,
stand-ing is mine!   And the trans-ac-tion so quick-ly was made,
man-sions sub-lime.   And it's be-cause of that won-der-ful day

He met the need of my heart;   Shad-ows dis-pel-ling, with
When as a sin-ner I came,   Took of the of-fer, of
When at the cross I be-lieved;   Rich-es e-ter-nal and

joy I am tell-ing, He made all the dark-ness de-part!
grace He did prof-fer, He saved me, O praise His dear name!
bless-ings su-per-nal, From His pre-cious hand I re-ceived.

Heaven Came Down

1961

The heavens declare His righteousness, And all the peoples see His glory. Psalm 97:6

As a teenager, John W. Peterson dreamed of being a singer and soloist. He often sang on local radio programs and in churches. "Only in singing did I feel competent and confident," he wrote. "Here was at least one place where I could excel. I knew it, and I made the most of it."

One summer John got a job in a factory, earning fifteen cents an hour at a machine making canvas for wheat binders. The machines were so noisy he sang at the top of his lungs, hours on end, making up melodies and imagining he was on stage.

John realized too late that he was ruining his voice. "I put such a terrific strain on my faltering voice," he wrote, "through overuse and inexperience that I damaged it beyond repair. When I realized fully what had happened, that my voice would never again be beautiful, I suffered such an emotional shock that it took months before I recovered."

Looking back now, John is grateful. "If that had not happened, I might never have developed as a writer," he wrote. "With my voice damaged, I turned more and more to writing and that talent was allowed to emerge and develop. What at first seemed a tragedy was used for good, and the course of my life began to take shape."

Today John W. Peterson is called the "Dean of Modern Hymn Writers." He's the author of such favorites as "So Send I You," "It Took a Miracle," "Surely Goodness and Mercy," "Jesus Led Me All the Way," "No One Understands Like Jesus," and "I Believe in Miracles."

"Heaven Came Down," one of John's most popular compositions, was written during the summer of 1961. He was ministering at Montrose Bible Conference Grounds in Montrose, Pennsylvania. During one of the sessions, an opportunity was given for people to share a word of testimony. A man known as "Old Jim" rose to his feet and told of how he had come to Christ. "It seemed like Heaven came down and glory filled my soul," he said.

"Right away I sensed that it would be a fine title for a song," John wrote, "so I wrote it down and later in the week completed the song. It became a favorite almost immediately."*

CHORUS:

Heaven came down and glory filled my soul (filled my soul),
When at the cross the Savior made me whole (made me whole);
My sins were washed away and my night turned to day,
Heaven came down and glory filled my soul (filled my soul)!

---

*Adapted from *The Miracle Goes On* by John W. Peterson with Richard Engquist (Grand Rapids: Zondervan, 1976), pp. 71–72.

Because He Lives

Gloria Gaither and William J. Gaither

William J. Gaither

1. God sent His Son, they called Him Jesus; He came to love, heal and forgive. He lived and died, to buy my pardon. An empty grave is there to prove my Savior lives!
2. How sweet to hold a new-born baby, And feel the pride, and joy he gives; But greater still the calm assurance, This child can face uncertain days because He lives.
3. And then one day I'll cross that river, I'll fight life's final war with pain; And then as death gives way to victory, I'll see the lights of glory and I'll know He reigns.

Because He lives, I can face tomorrow. Because He lives, all fear is gone; Because I know He holds the future, And life is worth the living, Just because He lives!

Because He Lives

1971

There is hope in your future, says the LORD. Jeremiah 31:17

As I prepared this volume of hymn stories, Gloria Gaither graciously shared with me the background for this beloved song:

When Bill and I started our family in the sixties, racial tensions were tearing the country apart. Civil rights activists had suffered and some had been killed. The Vietnam conflict was claiming thousands of lives, and tensions boiled over on university campuses. Many young people were growing disillustioned and "dropping out."

In this climate, Bill and I sought to write songs with lasting answers to the turmoil of the human spirit. But in the fall of 1969, several things happened to test the reality of our own convictions. We realized we were expecting another baby. Though we had always intended to have another child, we weren't planning on a baby so soon. My body hadn't quite recovered from the last pregnancy. Making matters worse, Bill contracted mononucleosis, which left him exhausted and depressed.

This combination of national turmoil and personal trouble discouraged us, and we occasionally asked each other, "If the world is like this now, what will it be in fifteen or sixteen years for our baby? What will this child face?"

While pondering and praying about these things, we came to realize anew that our courage doesn't come from a stable world, for the world has never been stable. Jesus Himself was born in the cruelest of times. No, we have babies, raise families, and risk living because the Resurrection is true!

Our baby arrived safe and sound, and we named him Benjamin, which means "most beloved son." A few weeks later "Because He Lives" was born in our hearts and poured from our souls:

> *How sweet to hold our newborn baby*
> *And feel the pride and joy he gives;*
> *But greater still, the calm assurance—*
> *This child can face uncertain days because He lives.*

Over the years this song has reassured us that our Lord's Resurrection is the central truth of life. Because He lives, we can face tomorrow. Many times since, as our children grew, our business-life changed, our fortunes shifted, or our direction clouded, our family has found assurance in this very personal song.

It's "our song," but we're grateful others have loved it, too.

The All Sufficient King

Robert J. Morgan

Jerry Carraway

1. We come, O God, in - to your courts, We en - ter through your gate.
2. We step in - to Your Ho - ly Place To walk and live in light.
3. That an - cient tent, O Lord, is You! Our safe a - bid - ing place.

We scan the al - tar where the Lamb Dis - plays Your love so great.
To feed on You and of - fer prayer Like in - cense in Your sight.
A shel - ter in the wil - der - ness Is your sus - tain - ing grace.

We bring our hands and heart and head Where sin - ful dust does cling
O Great High Priest, we sing to You En - throned be - hind the veil.
How might - y does Your Word re - veal The All Suf - fi - cient King

Be - fore the lav - er of your Grace That makes us pure and clean.
Be - tween the an - gels is our Lord Who al - ways does things well.
To You to - day our praise we bring To you our an - thems ring.

The All Sufficient King

<u>2002</u>

Not with the blood of goats and calves, but with His own blood He entered the Most Holy Place once for all, having obtained eternal redemption. Hebrews 9:12

I had long aspired to preach a series of sermons on God's Tent—the Tabernacle. This is the Old Testament's premier "type" of Christ, and fifty chapters in the Bible are devoted to it; but for a long time, I was intimidated by the immensity of the subject. Finally the general outlines of this wonderful topic broke through. I realized that the high white linen curtains surrounding the Tabernacle represent the holiness of God, which separates us from His presence; but there is one entrance, a wide gate, on the Eastern side near the encamped tribe of Judah. That gate represents **Christ our Savior,** our access into God's presence.

Entering, we come to the altar, which represents **Christ our Sacrifice.** Moving east to west, we pass the bronze laver or basin, where the priests wash their hands and feet. This represents **Christ our Sanctifier,** who daily cleanses and purifies us. Proceeding on, we come to the Tabernacle itself. In the first room is the golden candlestick, the table of showbread, and the altar of incense, signifying **Christ our Sufficiency**—the Light of the World, the Bread of Life, and the One who ever lives to intercede for us.

Passing reverently behind the veil into the Most Holy Place, we discover **Christ our Sovereign,** for that room contains the ark of the covenant, the earthly footstool of God's heavenly throne (1 Chronicles 28:2).

One night in the spring of 2002, while attending a conference at the University of Edinburgh, I was unable to sleep. Clicking on the desk lamp in my small room, I visualized myself entering the Tabernacle complex and walking across the courtyard into the Most Holy Place. I was overwhelmed with the awesome privilege of coming boldly right to the throne of the Almighty. The words of this hymn came quickly and easily.

⌒⌒⌒

You, too, can be a hymnist. As you study the Bible, take time to compose your thoughts and devotions into verse form. If you aren't a musician, find a familiar old melody and create new stanzas for it. If no one sings your hymn but you, it will still bless your own soul and please the heart of God. But you might share a copy with your worship leader at church. The world's best hymns, after all, have yet to be written.

Join All the Glorious Names

Isaac Watts, stanzas 2 and 3 Robert J. Morgan

John Darwall

1. Join all the glo-rious names, Of wis-dom, love and pow'r, That ev-er mor-tals knew, That an-gels ev-er bore: All are too mean to speak His worth, Too poor to set my Sav-ior forth.

2. The Babe of Beth-le-hem, the Faith-ful Wit-ness, He Is first and last, was dead, now lives to set us free. He washed our sins. He is the King, the Lord, the Word, to Him we sing.

3. Al-pha, O-me-ga He, One like the Son of Man, Ar-rayed in light, He reigned be-fore the world be-gan. He was, and is, and is to come our Glo-rious Lord, God's on-ly Son.

Join All the Glorious Names
(Revisited)
2004

Thus says the LORD, the King of Israel, And his Redeemer, the LORD of hosts: "I am the First and I am the Last; Besides Me there is no God." Isaiah 44:6

I want to plant an idea in your head, especially if you're a pastor. In researching our great hymns, I noticed that some of the richest were written by pastors for their weekly sermons. John Newton, author of "Amazing Grace" is a great example. He often ended his message with a hymn summarizing the truths he had just preached and it provided us with some of our richest hymnology.

I've occasionally tried this myself. After speaking from a passage, we'll sing a stanza from a well-known hymn, and then add one or two new stanzas I've composed for the occasion. The congregation doesn't know it has just sung a "new" hymn; and though some realize the words seem strangely appropriate to the message, most worshipers don't know their pastor is the culprit. But if my theology, rhyme, and rhythm are reasonably good, the hymn brings the service to an inspiring finish.

Recently I preached on the names of Christ found in the first chapter of Revelation. For the closing hymn, we chose Isaac Watts's great hymn, "Join All the Glorious Names." With apologies to Watts, I added these two stanzas:

> *The Babe of Bethlehem, the Faithful Witness, He*
> *Is first and last, was dead, now lives to set us free.*
> *He washed our sins. He is the King, the Lord, the Word, to Him we sing.*

> *Alpha, Omega He, One like the Son of Man,*
> *Arrayed in light, He reigned before the world began.*
> *He was, and is, and is to come our Glorious Lord, God's only Son.*

On another occasion, I preached a Father's Day sermon from the book of Proverbs. We closed with the moving Irish hymn "Be Thou My Vision," and I wrote a second verse that expressed the truth of the sermon:

> *Bless thou our children that they may believe.*
> *Help us to guide them Thy Son to receive.*
> *Give us righteous garments, wise souls richly dressed,*
> *That our dear children may forever be blessed.*

One couple requested a copy of the words and created an engraving for their child's bedroom. It became their prayer of dedication as parents.

You, too, can write hymns to bless your church. Why not try it soon, before you forget?

INDICES

Alphabetical by Title

Author/Songwriter

First Line of Hymn